Health Care Issues

Bernie Hayes.

Studies in Society

Health Care Issues

Second edition

Erica Bates & Susie Linder-Pelz

ALLEN & UNWIN

First published in 1987
Second edition published 1990
Second impression 1991

Allen & Unwin Pty Ltd
8 Napier Street, North Sydney, NSW 2059 Australia

National Library of Australia
Cataloguing-in-Publication

Bates, Erica M. (Erica Margaret), 1929–1989.
  Health care issues.

  2nd ed.
  Bibliography.
  Includes index.
  ISBN 0 04 442108 7.

  1. Social medicine – Australia.   2. Medical
  policy – Australia.   I. Linder-Pelz, Susie.
  II. Title. (Series: Studies in society
  (Sydney, N.S.W.)).

362.1'042'0994

Set in 10/11pt Times Roman by Best-set Typesetter Ltd.
Printed by Kim Hup Lee, Singapore

Contents

Tables and figures

Dedication

Erica Bates died as the work on this second edition of *Health Care Issues* was coming to an end.

She had been a sociologist of health in the School of Health Administration at the University of New South Wales for nearly twenty years and an associate professor for the last six. She was the author or co-author of 35 published articles and chapters and of six books. In 1977 her first book, *Models of Madness*, was published and this was followed in 1979 by *Mental Disorder or Madness*. She later wrote *Health Systems and Public Scrutiny* (1983) and co-authored *The Health Machine* with Helen Lapsley in 1985. *Health Care Issues* first appeared in 1987. Erica was active and outspoken on a range of social issues including the unanticipated consequences of medical technologies, the need for justice in the allocation of health resources, and the right to die.

Erica was, to an unusual degree, true to her self and her convictions. One of her concerns was the right of ordinary people to have a say in the services and institutions they use. She often quoted the theory of *'exit'* and *'voice'*, which refers to the options consumers have to leave an unsatisfactory situation or to speak up about its shortcomings. Throughout her life Erica raised her voice and then courageously arranged her own exit.

As a colleague and friend, Erica was open and direct, provocative and entertaining, supportive and genuine. She has no substitute.

Susie Linder-Pelz

May 1989

Preface to second edition

In the four years since we prepared the first edition of *Health Care Issues*, new data have become available on many of the issues we addressed. New research findings have been published on such areas as employment injuries, smoking and drug use. The Australian Bureau of Statistics and the Australian Institute of Health have produced a lot of updated national statistics on health status, health service utilisation and the health workforce. Various States have introduced new policies and legislation, for instance regarding the right to refuse life-prolonging medical interventions. Health services have undergone considerable changes too; there is more community based care for the aged, and in general, lengths of stay in hospitals are shorter. In this new edition we document and discuss such changes.

Since this is essentially an update of the earlier *Health Care Issues* we decided it was paramount to preserve the format of the first version. We have therefore kept the four sections, which deal with the *variations* in health status and access to care, the *chronicity* of illhealth, the growth of medical *technology* and the demands for *accountability*. There are still thirteen chapters, covering the same issues. We have even resisted devoting a separate chapter to AIDS even though there were compelling reasons to write one. Instead, we bring AIDS into existing chapters, relating it to chronic disease and illness (ch. 5), the health risks of lifestyle behaviours (ch. 7), the changing delivery of health care (ch. 8) and the ethics of resource allocation (ch. 10). This is typical of how we have introduced new material within the existing structure of *Health Care Issues*. We felt that for this edition only two completely new chapter sections were justified: the one on AIDS in chapter 5 and another on quality assurance in chapter 13.

While we were updating the book, we took the opportunity to improve the sociological discussion that goes with the data. In the previous
edition we distinguished three alternative perspectives on social
structure: *consensus, conflict* and *pluralism*. This approach has apparently been very useful in introducing students to sociological
thinking in the context of health issues. As we anticipated, students are
particularly interested in the complexities and promise of the pluralist
approach. What we have added in this edition is the distinction
between two forms of pluralism. Together with our students, and
following the sociological literature, we decided that it is useful to
distinguish *consensus-oriented* pluralism from *conflict-oriented* pluralism. We have tried, as before, to keep the sociological discussion
simple, clear and approachable.

We wish to acknowledge the financial support of the Faculty of
Professional Studies, at the University of New South Wales. We are
also grateful to our colleagues Colin Grant and Helen Lapsley, in the
School of Health Administration, whose annual publication of *The
Australian Health Care System* has been a key source of information for
this book.

1 Introduction

Themes of this book

Health care has a central place in all societies but health care organisation as a societal task is relatively new. Health care in Western societies such as Australia used to be an unstructured dialogue between one carer and one patient but has now become a complex, scientific and impersonal enterprise in which patients play a role which is much less prominent than that of health professionals.

All advanced societies today share a number of problems in the organisation of their health services. All have populations in which there are more old people than ever before. Those who are sick are treated with new technologies which are not only very expensive but which have changed the nature and quality of health care. The public has come to expect extraordinary achievements from the health care system and from health professionals.

Four features have characterised the health status and health care of Australians in recent years. These are: *variations* among social groups in their health status and access to care, *chronicity* of ill-health, growth of medical *technology*, and demands by the community that there should be more *accountability* of health care providers.

First, health and ill-health are unevenly distributed in different subgroups of Australian society. Furthermore, health care is frequently more available to people with certain social characteristics, rather than being available simply according to 'medical need'.

Second, the major health problems in Australia are mainly chronic conditions. Environmental conditions such as atmospheric pollution, personal choices such as food and drink consumed, and behaviours such as smoking and fast driving play a part in developing these illnesses. The

1

resulting conditions of ill-health such as heart disease, cancer and accidental damage, are characterised by their long-term nature.

Third is the massive use of technology in health care, along with complex economic, legal and ethical consequences. Because many medical technologies are extremely expensive, their increased use has led to very high costs for health services. This cost escalation has caused governments to restrict funds and this in turn affects what care is available and to whom. The escalating cost of hospital care, in particular, has provoked efforts to find alternative forms of and locations for delivery of care.

Fourth is the demand for accountability: governments and citizens now demand that the people who receive financial gains from the delivery of health care must fulfil certain obligations. Governments now exercise more control over all kinds of professional services, lay people have become more informed about health matters, and health services are influenced by the consumer rights movements in other areas.

It should already be clear that these features are interrelated; thus, for example, the need to care for increasing numbers of people with chronic health problems at a time when the health budget is static, contributes to the scarcity of hospital and workforce resources. Each of these four features links a number of issues with which this book deals. They include the ethical and legal problems which have accompanied the introduction of sophisticated technologies to the health field; the ageing population with a high rate of chronic disease and disability; occupational diseases and accidents; stress and damage associated with our technological lifestyle. The interrelationships between diverse health care givers, traditional and new, are also relevant. This book also aims to explain why the dominant influence over health planners, administrators and practitioners has, over the past ten years, been from economics rather than from other social sciences. These issues are the subjects of later chapters. In the first instance, it is necessary to understand that everyone perceives and explains the social world and its issues from a different point of view.

Sociological perspectives on health issues

All the issues discussed here will be interpreted from alternative sociological perspectives, since this book is written for health workers as a supplement to sociological texts. Though such texts deal in detail with sociological theories, they do not generally deal with current issues in health care.

Sociological perspectives are 'different ways of trying to understand the social world'[1] or different ways of explaining how the social world works. One's perspective determines what questions one asks, what facts one notices, how one explains the world and what importance is given to particular events and experiences.

It is often assumed that 'facts' are objective truths, but one's perspective causes one to notice, or be unaware of, particular facts. This principle applies both to human and non-human scenes. For example, a photograph of a particular scene will look quite different when photographed from different angles, that is, from different perspectives. Similarly, it is well known that witnesses to an accident or to an argument will give quite different reports of what happened. Hence it follows that facts can never be absolutely objective; they are subject to the inevitable bias inherent in viewing the social world in one way and not in another. The same 'objective' events can always be explained in more than one way. A certain rate of medical procedures will be seen as evidence of 'overservicing' by people who believe that doctors' main motivation is to make money, but as 'good treatment' by others who believe that doctors know what their patients need and that it is their duty to provide it. If one assumes that society must provide health care for all, the introduction of Medicare in 1984 will be seen as a step towards that goal. If, however, one believes that professionals must be independent of all government controls in order to provide the best service, then Medicare will be seen as interference in the doctor–patient relationship.

The study of sociology has developed relatively recently, that is, over the last 200 years. As societies have become more complex, it has become essential to understand why, in spite of difficulties and conflicts, they still continue to hold together. In order to answer this question, one can focus either on the workings of a society as a whole, which is called a *structural* approach, or on the way in which individuals relate to one another, which is called an *interactionist* approach.[2] The structural approach focuses on society-wide structures or patterns, seeing them as having overriding responsibility for shaping and conditioning individual behaviour, while the interactionist approach focuses on the inter-relations among individuals, seeing those individuals as acting to a large extent independently of social dictates. Although it is clear that the two approaches overlap, an explanation of how society 'works' must be able to link the way in which society as a whole is structured overall, with the way in which people interact in particular situations. When focusing on social structure, for example, a question one would ask might be: what is it about Aboriginal society compared with the rest of Australian society that explains why Aboriginal babies die before the end of their first year much more often than do white babies? If, instead, one focuses on interactions, one would look at the individual Aboriginal pregnant woman and ask why she does not seek prenatal care as often as the white pregnant woman. Both questions are necessary if one is to answer the question of Aboriginal infant deaths.[3] When focusing on the *structure*, one is really looking at those patterns, rules or habits which exist and continue to exist outside and beyond any one individual's life: the Aboriginal perinatal death rate, for example, continues to exist whether any individual baby dies or not. When focusing on the *interaction* between people, on the other hand, one has to examine particular relationships between people and groups, which come to an end when the group disbands or the individual leaves or dies; hence one would look for particular circumstances which will help decide whether a particular Aboriginal baby will live or die.

This book, in looking at Australian health care issues, mostly uses structural perspectives; this is because we are dealing with society-wide patterns of health and health care delivery. Nevertheless, interactionist perspectives on such issues cannot be ignored and we shall refer from time to time to the sort of questions that interactionists would pose in contrast to those posed by people with a structural perspective.

There are three structural perspectives which, while sharing an emphasis on the way society structures human behaviour, differ in their ideas of the basic nature of society. One, which we call the *consensus* perspective, states that common interests and values cause people to cooperate most of the time, while an opposing approach we call the *conflict* perspective. This assumes that the people who own and control economic resources organise social life to their own advantage and to the disadvantage of others. Distinct from these two perspectives is *pluralism*. Here, the assumption is that in Western, technologically sophisticated societies, there is no longer either a single common interest which unites people or a single, economically dominant class of people. Rather, pluralism asserts that power is split among a number of groups and is therefore somewhat fragmented, that pressure groups and individuals are always competing for a share of power, and that existing groups may either retain or lose some of their power and status as new groups emerge.

All members of society have their own beliefs or ideologies, basically along one of these three lines. The writers of this book generally hold a pluralist perspective. However, as sociologists we present all three interpretations when discussing a particular issue. This is done in order that readers will become aware of their own perspective, locate it in relation to other perspectives and consider the validity and limitations that each perspective has in explaining a particular issue.

The *consensus* perspective assumes that the majority of people in a society value similar things, and share beliefs. 'We all know that what is good for the doctors is good for the patients' is one example of a consensus statement. This perspective stresses the regularity and predictability of social life and says that societies work effectively because institutions such as the family and the health system meet individual needs and simultaneously help the overall society to function. Thus, for example, hospitals are seen to be good for patients because they are, by-and-large, smoothly running organisations developed by societies to care for their sick until they either die or can resume their normal, useful lives in the society. They offer full-time care by a team of professionals who have the best facilities and advice at their disposal, and it is efficient and economical to administer all services in the one organisation.

According to the consensus perspective, society is a self-regulating system, stable, cohesive and persisting. All its parts are linked functionally to other parts of the social system; hence the other name for this perspective is *functionalism*. The idea of *system* is central to the consensus perspective; a social system is composed of interacting parts which must work smoothly together so that the whole system can function properly. The health care system is seen as a subsystem which exists in order to carry out specific indispensable tasks. Human interaction in such a system is seen as generally orderly and stable. The emphasis in this perspective is on unity and regularity; like an embroidery, the parts are linked together in a repeated, intricate pattern. Variations among groups are regarded as inevitable and are justified as being necessary for the whole system to function. Words that reflect the consensus view of society are 'common purpose', 'stability' and 'cohesion'; existing social arrangements and variations in opportunity are considered to be 'normal', 'functional' and 'legitimate'. 'We can all agree' is a clear consensus statement.

In contrast, the *conflict* perspective sees discord, dissent and instability in social situations. Rather than seeing common interests among individuals and groups, proponents of this view notice the overriding effects of scarcity of resources and economic inequality. They focus on two classes; the haves and the have-nots, which have opposed interests. In the extreme, the conflict perspective holds that conflict, even revolution, is inevitable because the wealthy keep control over the economic resources while the poor are always kept in want. From this perspective inequalities are seen as unjust and unjustified. The well-off use their wealth to make connections with other advantaged people, and together they then keep control of all the important social institution; thus they create a powerful, united class of people who determinedly ensure that they and their families get access to the best housing, education, jobs and opportunities. Thus, people with a conflict perspective point out, for example, that success in the education system is strongly influenced by the wealth of one's parents, and that the children of professionals such as doctors have a far greater chance of entering universities and having a professional career than do the children of semi-skilled or unskilled workers.[4]

Take once again the example of the hospital. People who begin with a conflict perspective do not see a caring institution where all work together with the common goal of patient welfare. Instead, they see an institution ruled by managers and doctors who are bent on ensuring their own power and financial well-being. Always, from the conflict perspective, the interests of the ruling class of doctors and executives are placed ahead of the interests of the patients and other workers.

Words that express the conflict view are 'power', 'control' 'coercion', 'injustice', 'discrimination' and 'the need for reform'.

The *pluralist perspective* accepts the inevitability of conflict but sees conflict as occuring continuously between groups in society, not merely between the major economic classes. Some pluralists, whom we call *moderate* pluralists, hold a 'balance of power' thesis about social structure. They assume that pressure groups compete, that none dominates absolutely and that groups bargain to achieve their goals. In the moderate pluralist perspective, it is believed that in democratic societies, the opportunity exists for all groups to change their situation. In contrast to the consensus view, moderate pluralists do not believe that everyone values the same things and that all have similar goals and ideals. Moderate pluralists believe that transfers of wealth and power are often made in democratic societies because groups struggle for them, while the conflict view holds that one class will maintain its wealth and power by force if necessary. Moderate pluralists cite as examples the recent increase in the power of Aboriginal groups, women and homosexuals. In the health scene, moderate pluralists would consider that the recent upgrading of nursing education, the implement- ation of Medicare, and the increasing emphasis on community health services, are evidence of changes in the balance of power of interest groups. In trying to explain how hospitals work, moderate pluralists argue that there is continual bargaining among groups as they try to maintain or increase their share of resources and decision-making power. The terms that are commonly used by moderate pluralists are 'competing interest groups' and 'diffusion of power'.[5] Radical plural- ists, on the other hand, are closer to the conflict approach, though there are differences between their views and those of the conflict theorists, which we explain throughout the book. Radical pluralists believe that there are opportunities for interest groups to form and to lobby for changes to be made to their advantage, but they do not accept the 'balance of power' view of the moderate pluralists. Instead, they argue that some groups are much more powerful than others, and that these more powerful groups ally themselves with governments so that govern- ments tend to represent them and will only accept changes that will not damage the interests of the powerful groups. Hence radical pluralists do not believe that all groups can achieve success in obtaining their demands. They also consider that dominant groups deliberately create barriers to changes which would disadvantage them. Examples might be the present situation in maternity hospitals, where radical pluralists emphasise that midwives are prevented from admitting their own patients and referring them to obstetricians if they consider necessary, so that women who want to use the services of a midwife as their primary birth attendants are forced to give birth at home and pay the midwife a full fee which is not reimbursed by Medicare. Thus powerful specialist doctor groups have arranged to achieve their preferred goals, and when a challenge is made to this status quo, the doctors manage to control the media with their own propaganda against that of the midwives. The situation of the midwives is not, however, regarded as hopeless by the radical pluralists who believe that if the midwives made a concerted effort they might eventually get some changes made.

As stated above, consensus, conflict and pluralist perspectives are varieties of *structuralism*, which means that they focus on '. . . how the whole society works, what are its key parts, how they are related and how the social structure might be seen to shape and to delimit individual action'.[6] The language used by people holding each of the structural perspectives is summarised in Figure 1.1. As can be seen in that figure, pluralism is more complicated than either of the other two perspectives. Some pluralists talk of balance of power, while others talk of some elite groups which always have more power than others. Some emphasise the *negotiation* that takes place among interest groups while others see the *coercion* that takes place because some groups are more powerful. In other words, pluralists tend to be either consensus-oriented, and we call this *moderate pluralism*, while others are more conflict-oriented, which we call *radical pluralism*, but both focus on the multiplicity of interests, centres of power, competition, changing alliances and bargaining.

In contrast to the structuralism of the consensus, conflict and pluralist perspectives, *interactionism* is concerned with the way people perceive reality and how this affects their behaviour. The focus of interactionism is limited to interactions among individuals and small groups. These interactions are seen as arising out of people's values and the ways they see themselves, assess their own needs, negotiate with one another and make their own decisions.

The three structural perspectives, called consensus, conflict and pluralism, correspond to three major theories in structural sociology: 'functionalism', 'neo-Marxism' and 'neo-Weberianism' respectively. In

Figure 1.1 **Key words describing the structure of modern society from different perspectives**

CONSENSUS	MODERATE PLURALISM	RADICAL PLURALISM	CONFLICT
Stability	Interest groups	Dominant vs	Ruling class
Agreement	Competition	repressed groups	dominates
Shared values	Negotiation	Elites, monopolies	Economic inequality
Common purpose	Bargaining	are dominant	creates all other
Legitimate authority	Changing power	Control by elites,	inequalities
Variations among	relations	who block change	Discrimination
groups are	Balance of power	Confrontation	Coercion
functional for			Powerlessness
society			

this book, we have used the former terms, which distinguish these theories from each other more simply and clearly. But the reader should be aware that even the terms we have chosen to use are subject to various meanings in the sociological and political science literature, and the particular definitions we have used in this book should be borne in mind throughout. In particular, conflict is the term often given to all sociological theories that are not functionalist, and this includes both Marxist and Weberian analyses. But according to our definitions, both types of 'pluralism' as well as the 'conflict' perspective acknowledge the prevalence of conflicts in society and look for their causes. The fundamental difference is that the neo-Marxist types of conflict perspective see conflict as pervasive and due fundamentally to economic inequality, while pluralists consider that power has various sources, such as information, expertise, charisma and intelligence.

In this book the main focus is not on sociological perspectives as such, but rather on demonstrating how they lead to varying interpretations of health issues. We do not distinguish among the many formulations or theories within each tradition, but rather present sociological explanations as simply as possible in order to show how they can illuminate discussion of health issues. Several texts deal in greater depth with these perspectives.[7]

Major current issues in health policy in Western societies

When health care issues are discussed in modern industrialised societies, it is often assumed that it is experts who should determine what kind of health system is to be installed in a society. But though the carrying out of many health services is a technical matter, the actual organisation of the health system in developed societies today must be a social decision. This is because the new technologies have pushed costs of even basic health care beyond the means of any one individual. Indeed, even before the development of modern technologies, societies had to make arrangements for the delivery of health services to the poor, the mentally disturbed, and the infectious. However, such piecemeal and ad hoc arrangements no longer suffice now that medical care has become highly technological.

In all developed countries today, health services are organised at a social rather than an individual level. With increased knowledge about diseases and their control, as well as a greater understanding of preventive medicine, governments of all political persuasions and at all levels of wealth have found themselves forced to take a major part in organising and financing health services for their population. The aim—and the effect—has been to make more health services available to more people.

Because of the cost of modern medical technology, not even the wealthiest people can pay the true cost of their care for a serious illness or accident, and in all developed countries, governments pay for the bulk of health services from the general tax revenue. Between 60% and 98% of health costs are paid from the public purse.[8] The only exception is the United States and even there, 40% of all health care is paid by government from taxation and 20% is paid by health insurance which is funded mostly by deduction from workers' pay packets. It is therefore obvious that health care organisation is now a totally new enterprise. Only a small part is the doctor–patient relationship, while the bulk of treatment is given by other professional and technical staff, helped by a large number of expensive machines and drugs.

Because Australian governments pay for almost three-quarters of these expensive health services,[9] they are able to demand and obtain a large measure of control over the delivery of health services. The political system is therefore the major determinant of the particular way in which the health system of a country is organised. It is important to be aware, however, that the organisation of the health service does not necessarily reflect the present political system but may be a remnant of the political past.

All Western countries have similar health concerns that will pre-occupy their governments in the next twenty years. These issues are the cost of health care and how to contain it, the financing of health care, the organisation of health delivery services, finding ways to make care equally accessible to the whole population, and the means of ensuring that the quality of health services is maintained at acceptable levels while being kept within financial constraints.

Five causes lie behind the rise in health expenditures everywhere.[10] They are the *ageing* of the population which results in an increase in .chronic diseases and frailty, the increase in the provision and use of *technology* which means that many more tests and treatments are done to each patient, *demands* for more resources by the medical profession and newly vociferous pressure groups such as those at risk of AIDS, the increase in numbers of *staff* necessary to operate the more intensive technology, and the increase in *third-party financing* of health care. This last factor removes from doctors and patients the restraint of cost at the time of illness and indeed, sometimes inspires insured people to demand more services because they have paid for them.

The way in which the health system is financed is a major political issue in all industrialised societies. The system may be financed by taxation or by some form of insurance, which may be a national health insurance system or a system which establishes one or many private insurance companies which obtain their contributions from employers or individuals or both. But in every developed country, the trend has been towards more reliance on government funding, which has brought increased government intervention in and control of health service organisation. Most nations have also experimented with different ways of organising health services, mainly those services over which governments have direct control, but also those over which control is only marginal. This is done by regionalisation and centralisation of services, by changing the way in which doctors are paid, by promoting cooperation or competition among hospitals and doctors, by encouraging or discouraging planning and enforcing or not enforcing the decisions made by planners.

In all countries, the wealthier, the better-educated, the acutely sick, the urban dwellers and the 'interesting' patients obtain relatively good access to care whereas the poor, the old, the minority groups, the chronically ill, rural dwellers, the mentally ill and mentally handicapped and the disabled have greater difficulty in obtaining good care when they need it. Different techniques are used by governments to reduce these imbalances.

In general, it can be said that in a predominantly private-practice health care system, care for the poor is not attended to by the private sector and must be financed by government. In such a system, services purchased by governments can only be equitable, meaning fairly distributed, if the private sector has incentives towards equity. If the public sector is on a restricted budget while the private sector can charge market prices, the poor will not get equal care because the best qualified professionals and the best equipment will be in private hospitals.

Whether a health system is publicly or privately financed, it has become essential for governments to take an interest in the quality of the services that are delivered. The efforts to deal with this need have varied in different countries. The least effort has been made in Britain where there are fiscal controls on doctors but no serious attempt is made to assess the quality of care rendered by the National Health Service. The most determined efforts in this direction have been made by the USA. In that litigious society, the number of malpractice suits rose to unprecedented heights in the 1960s and has not abated, and this has been taken as evidence of some deficiency of quality. In Australia, a number of different attempts have been made to measure the quality of medical care and to ensure that as far as possible, defective care does not occur. Peer review, quality assurance, accreditation of hospitals, tissue audits, limits on length of stay in hospital, are all attempts towards this end, and they are increasingly being required from institutions which want Federal or State financial support.

The changing health profile of Western societies

There are several changes that have occurred in the health status of all developed societies. Many of these new realities are now taken for granted, and it is often forgotten how recent and dramatic the changes of the last 50, 30 and even 10 years have been.

Life expectancy
This has dramatically increased in Western societies during the twentieth century, but the increase is mainly due to the fall in infant and

child deaths. The most significant increases in life expectancy at birth have occurred between about 1881 and 1948. In 1986 life expectancy at birth was 73 years for males and 79 for women, a rise of 5 years for both since 1960.[11] For robust people who survived the dangerous early years, life expectancy has not changed all that much between 1881 and 1982.[12] Reduction in the deaths of infants and young people which were mainly due to infectious diseases, occurred *before* the discovery and widespread use of antibiotics or any other medical intervention, and the improvement was actually due to public health measures such as the provision of clean water, sanitation and sewerage, disposal of waste, and the development of clean methods of food preparation.

Perinatal and infant mortality
Deaths at birth and within the first year of life are generally regarded as sensitive indicators of a country's level of health. Such deaths have been declining in all Western countries, though disadvantaged groups always have the highest infant mortality rates. In Australia they are very much worse for Aboriginal births than for the rest of the population.[13]

Causes of death
Instead of infectious diseases, the most common causes of death in developed countries today are diseases of the circulatory system, heart disease, cancers, respiratory diseases, motor vehicle crashes and other types of accidents. Many of these are referred to as *lifestyle* diseases because they are associated with behaviours such as smoking, inactivity, overeating, and risk-taking in cars. It is, however, essential to remember two facts whenever discussions occur on 'the modern epidemics' and 'lifestyle'. First, we all have to die eventually from *some* cause, so that there will always be some conditions which are the leading causes of death; the people who are lucky, or prudent, will die from the same conditions as their fellow citizens but at a later age. Second, the older people get, the more commonly they have multiple causes of death, so that people may have for example, both a cancer and a heart attack, and to some extent the biases of the attending doctors will determine which cause of death will be put on the death certificate. Indeed, doctors have occasionally commented that there ought to be another category which could be recorded—'body worn out'—when an old person dies with a body which has overall degeneration. Nevertheless, half the cancer deaths in Western societies occur before the age of 65, and so do many of the deaths from heart diseases, so that great efforts are now being made to reduce the rates of these conditions.

Ageing of the population
The reduction in infant deaths, the longer life expectancy and the lowered birth rate have resulted in a change in the population structure to one where there are far more people than ever before who have reached old age. This in itself has created major social changes and health problems, because as people get older they are more likely to get sick and to have not one but a number of conditions.

Chronic illness and disability
All the above factors have resulted in a population which has a great amount of chronic illness and disability. Previously, most people died relatively quickly after accidents, or of infections contracted either because resistance was low or because of an infection during a chronic illness. Now those people are kept alive through such crises by drugs and other technological assistance, and are able to live on for years, eventually to die perhaps of an entirely different cause. But those extra years are not always easy; they are frequently years of pain, incapacity, family disruption and increasing poverty, for which our health and social services are not adapted and for which adequate support systems are not available. Mental illnesses and addictions to drugs and alcohol are also conditions which are increasing in prevalence.

Throughout this book, the discussion of health issues will be supported by Australian data where possible. A large number of studies about the social aspects of health have been carried out in Australia. Many have only been disseminated to limited audiences, although they often contain important information that has been systematically researched. Such research, along with published studies, will be used to illustrate and clarify the issues.

Part I

Variations in health status and health care

2 Social stratification and health

Indicators of social variations

Variations exist in every society and in every social group, but the kind of variation and its extent differ enormously from one society to another, and from one period of time to another.

Socially structured variations occur when some people have more resources than others, and when they have gained this advantage because of their social situation. Put another way, people are located differently in the social system because they have differential access to resources that are scarce and highly valued, such as wealth, power, prestige and health; their access to these resources is largely affected by their age, gender and ethnic origin. A discussion of social variations means a discussion of social *stratification*, the general term for the way in which, in almost all societies, the population divides itself into ranks or strata, one above the other. The people on the top have the most advantageous life chances and the power to change their own and others' destinies, while the people below have fewer resources and less freedom to choose the way they live. Societies differ in the number of strata and the ease with which people can move from one level to another, either up or down.

From a *conflict* point of view, social variations are called inequalities and are about injustice and power relationships; inequality of economic status is a continuous source of conflict and struggle between social classes, with the advantaged fighting to stay in control and the disadvantaged always downtrodden.[1] The *consensus* viewpoint is that society is essentially stable. Variations challenge people to work hard so they can move upwards in the hierarchy and in this way a stable social system will be maintained.[2] The consensus view also holds that by

15

rewarding people unequally, society ensures that tasks will be done by the most suitable individuals who will compete for the most interesting, best paid work. Both perspectives agree that variations are fundamental in every society and since people's health status is an aspect of society, it is inevitable that there will be differences in health. The *pluralist* view is that there are many sources of power and inequality in societies: economic status, genetic factors, education, gender and more. The relationships among these spheres of inequality are complex and so is the distribution of power. Moderate pluralism asserts that in different parts of society there are different pyramids of power; power is thus differentiated and fragmented. The power of each group is held in check and balanced by other competing groups. There is a plurality of interest groups and hence a plurality of bases for conflict. Individuals and groups have some degree of freedom to change the status quo, although that freedom is not unlimited; groups can thus gain or lose power and can move up and down the status ladder.[3] Unlike people with a consensus orientation, moderate pluralists believe that it is possible for groups to change the power arrangements in a society. Compared with moderate pluralists, radical pluralists are not as optimistic about change. They emphasise the unequal status and power that different interest groups have. Those with most status and power, often called elites, are more effective. They influence political agendas, obtain funding for their purposes, and persistently block changes detrimental to their own interests. Changes in the power distribution are, therefore, very slow to come about. In general, however, the pluralist perspective believes that particular efforts can affect social patterns whereas the other two perspectives emphasise the inevitable and overriding effects of social structure.

Whatever one's perspective, it is essential to analyse the health status of a population in order to provide an appropriate and acceptable health service. One must be aware that people in certain subgroups of the population may vary in their experience of accidents, illnesses and disabilities. Health status information is gathered in statistics such as mortality and morbidity rates of the population, which are referred to as *health indicators*. Indicators reflect the state of a population's health and they are variables which help show what changes are occurring in the population's health.

One of the major deficiencies in the health services provided by developed societies is that they were set up to deal with infectious diseases which were the major health problem of 50 years ago. Hospitals were established to deal with acute crises which lasted a short time and ended either in a complete recovery or in death. However, the important health problems of today are those posed by chronic illnesses such as heart disease, cancer and mental illness, by alcohol and drug addiction, by work-related illness and accidents, and by road crashes. These illnesses occasionally result in a quick death, but are more commonly characterised by their long-term nature, by a slow decline, and by remission rather than recovery or cure. In order to be effective, health services must be organised according to the information obtained about relevant and current health indicators.

When health indicators are collected and used, we can discover how the most common illnesses are distributed within a society and which groups are most frequently affected. It is only then that we can attempt to develop appropriate, needed services. It is essential, however, that the statistics that are collected should be valid, objective, sensitive, specific and accurate.[4] The use of such statistics to study health and illness patterns in different populations and social groups is called epidemiology and is an increasingly important field of health and medical research.[5] One problem with statistics, however, is that sometimes the people who decide what information should be collected do not know that some important variations in health exist, because the problems have not come to public attention.

Statistical data should also be collected for various subgroups in the population as well as for the total population. For example, death rates from ischaemic heart disease have declined in Australia over the past 10–15 years. However, it is not enough to point to the declining overall death rate because variations in the heart disease mortality rates of subpopulations are characterised by place of residence, occupation and country of birth.[6] Further, there are variations between groups in the rate of decline of ischaemic heart disease over that period, and in some ethnic groups the condition has even increased. It is only when we have detailed information that we can seek explanations for the trends in disease rates.

Health indicators may seem to be impersonal and objective facts, but the perspectives and biases of the people who collect statistics affect the decisions about which statistics to collect. From the conflict and radical pluralist perspectives, the information collected relates to what is noticed by and interests the more powerful people in society. An extreme example of this is the fact that data on the Aboriginal population was not collected at all until the Referendum in 1967, and it is only since then that the size of the Aboriginal health problem has come to light.

In Australia, no national statistics have been collected by occupation, wealth, or social location, so that the research findings are limited and inadequate. This fact in itself adds weight to the conflict perspective's assertion that inequalities have been deliberately hidden from the community for fear of producing so much indignation that some of the existing power structures would be threatened. The moderate pluralist's view is that society is composed of many different interest groups, each of which has the opportunity to lobby for data pertinent to its interests to be collected.

When conflict writers in Australia refer to inequalities of *social class,*

ethnicity, sex and *age* they are discussing the advantages and disadvantages that certain groups of people have. Those who have more
economic resources are of certain ethnic background such as Anglo-
Saxon and European, and are male, youthful and educated, with
considerable advantage over groups such as the poor, Asians, females
and old people. While social class is a conflict term, referring to the
constant conflict between the upper class (owners of capital) and the
lower class (workers), *socio-economic status* is the consensus term for a
range of economic and social differences among people. The very choice
of term reveals one's perspective. Health variations resulting from social
stratification, ethnicity, gender and old age are the subjects of later
chapters, and the term 'variations' has been chosen to avoid some biases
introduced by the use of the other terms.

Stratification in Australia

For many years there was little dissent from the consensus view that
Australia is a relatively classless, egalitarian society. Only since the
1950s has a conflict view of Australian society been increasingly
articulated. The general conflict view of 'social class', derived from
Marx's views on capitalist society, is that the wealthy people—owners of
capital and the means of production—make constant efforts to maintain
the existing social system which advantages them. The workers
meanwhile are in constant struggle trying to change the status quo and
redress some of the imbalance. Thus there is continuous conflict of
interest between these two classes. 'Social class' is a conflict concept and
emphasises that Western societies are divided along economic lines;[7]
classes are defined as 'segments of the population sharing broadly
similar types and levels of resources, with broadly similar styles of
living'.[8] Consensus theorists do not deny that there can be conflicts of
interest, but their view is that these strains and tensions are not divisive
but are functional in that they keep people motivated to work. Moreover, they believe that tensions are temporary and are constantly being
overcome so that equilibrium is restored in the social system. Their
evidence for this equilibrium is the fact that there has so far been no
revolution, civil war or anarchy in Australian society. Although the
belief that Australian society is egalitarian seems now to have been
invalidated by the prevalence of unemployment and the recognition of
the existence of poverty, we still have no official measure of either
'social class' or 'socio-economic status' that can be applied to the
analysis of various public statistics including health indicators. There
is no agreed-upon definition of either 'social class' or 'socio-economic
status'. The terms are taken to include many different things, such as
income, occupation, educational level or way of life. But unless there is
some measure of where people are located in the social structure, it is
not possible to analyse whether, for example, people have adequate

access to certain health services or whether all people in the population are at equal risk of contracting a certain disease. The perspective chosen will determine whether one talks in terms of 'appropriate', 'adequate' or 'equal' access.

The most useful measure of socio-economic status in Western societies is position in the occupational hierarchy, because this incorporates a number of factors simultaneously.[9] It reflects prestige, range of income, education, type of housing, and potential for status improvement. Occupation can tell us quite a lot about a person's probable state of health. It indicates broadly how strenuous or sedentary the job is, what are the likely working conditions, whether there is exposure to noise, dust, chemicals, or to particular hazards which may affect not only the worker but the worker's family. Miners' exposure to asbestos fibres, for example, affects whole families because wives wash the clothes and children play in the asbestos slag. In other occupations, the family has to relocate to accommodate the worker, and may also be affected by the worker's shiftwork, absence from home, risk of accident and disability and the risk of unemployment.

Occupation is thus a useful indicator of people's socio-economic status and from a practical point of view, it is easier to obtain information about someone's occupation than about their income, education and style of housing. However, the limits of this indicator must be remembered: it omits information about people not in the workforce, such as people who are retired or disabled, and people temporarily or permanently unemployed; it does not include, in the public mind, the fact that women at home with children or elderly dependants are quite definitely working even though no one is paying them for that work. Yet with all these limitations, occupation is still the most useful single indicator of social status that we have, and is therefore generally used by social planners.[10] Although education is not as easily assessed as occupation, many researchers have used people's educational level as an indicator of socioeconomic status.

Another commonly used, indirect measure of people's social status is their area of residence. It is known that the more affluent people live in certain suburbs, while the poorer people live in others, though there are of course some areas which contain people of a wide range of incomes. Voting patterns of particular geographical areas reflect these variations, as do sizes of houses and blocks of land, amenities available, property values and the age structure of the resident population.

There is not a great deal of information in Australia about the relationship between people's health and place in the overall social structure. The consensus theorist would explain this absence of studies of socio-economic status and health in Australia by saying that there is no need for such studies, since there is information available about the death and illness rates of the population as a whole, and this is adequate for planning health services in a relatively egalitarian society. People with a conflict view would point out that there are great differences between Australians in terms of income and ownership of wealth. They would demonstrate this with data showing that the unemployed, particularly the long-term unemployed, are poor while the executives are wealthy; that doctors are richer than nurses; that old-age pensioners living in rented accommodation are poorer than those who have retired with superannuation and own their own homes.[11] Consensus-oriented people would respond that disparities of wealth are smaller in Australia than in Great Britain, the United States, or any Third World country, and that in any case, people will not exert themselves if their exertions do not result in an improvement of their own life chances and those of their children.

Social stratification and health status in Australia: the evidence

The deficiency in Australian research about the health status of particular sub-groups of the population is due to a number of different types of assumptions on the part of the people who decide what kind of health research should be funded. Some of their assumptions are: that more benefit will result from funding research on technical solutions to health problems; that nothing can be done to reduce differences among social groups; that social science research is 'soft' and inaccurate, and that it is more acceptable to research the physical aspects of individual diseases rather than the social factors which result in certain groups being much more severely affected than others by certain diseases. A recent example of this kind of bias occurred with the introduction of the new disease, AIDS, into the community. There was a great deal of publicity with the media spreading public alarm. Research was immediately funded by the National Health and Medical Research Council, to seek a cure for the condition. The male homosexual community was then reported to be the population base for the disease, so community indignation was directed at that group. Initially no social research was funded to examine which particular homosexual groups were at risk, nor how to reduce that risk.

The most common health indicators are *mortality* or death rates, rates of *morbidity* or sickness, and rates of *chronic conditions, disabilities* and *handicaps*. Mortality rates are the easiest to collect and are irrefutable, so that they tend to be the most used when discussing social status as related to health. Clearly, one's life situation is made up of considerably more than one's time and place of death, so that it is important to collect statistics of other kinds as well. But all such statistics incorporate certain biases; for example until recently, studies of occupational disease were generally done on men only, because women have not been grouped by occupation, and the occupational categories themselves suffer from the biases outlined above. Nevertheless, some important information emerges from these studies.

Social stratification and mortality

Evidence associating high rates of infant mortality with economic disadvantage has been available for centuries for a variety of countries around the world. In Australia recent research has confirmed these findings. In Sydney, low birthweight infants are born around twice as frequently to 'socially disadvantaged' women, and low birthweight is the most common cause of infant death and disability.[12] In Western Australia, a study showed that babies born into the family of an unskilled labourer had about twice the chance of perinatal death (being stillborn or dying within first month of life) as the children of professional men and managers.[13] Researchers examined infant mortality rates between 1976 and 1979 in Brisbane, comparing some socioeconomically advantaged with some socioeconomically disadvantaged suburbs. They found that the infant mortality rate increased as the status of the suburb decreased.[14] The causes of this phenomenon are complex, but research in other countries has shown that poorer women are less likely than better-off women to eat well during pregnancy; they are likely to have babies at a very young age or close to the menopause, to have a shorter time between pregnancies, to smoke more and drink more alcohol, and to attend antenatal clinics only late in pregnancy.

It is not only the perinatal and infant mortality rates that vary with social position; it was recently reported that for the last twenty years an average of four babies per thousand have been born with defects of the brain or spine in the western suburbs of Sydney. This is double the State average.[15] This fact was first pointed out in 1971. Various explanations such as poverty and inadequate intake of vitamins among women in these areas have been suggested, but not investigated systematically because funds and facilities have not been available.

McMichael[16] analysed the death rates in the 1970s of Australian males aged between 15–64 by sorting them into social classes according to a standard 4-point occupational prestige scale of social class, Congalton's scale (Figure 2.1). His findings are similar to those of other studies: for each major cause of death, men in the lower social classes died earlier.[17] Table 2.1 shows not only that occupational groups have different overall death rates between the ages of 15 and 64, but that the causes of death differ in each group. It should be noted that the phase 'lower death rates' is somewhat misleading: death rates are always 100% since everyone eventually dies. The phrase always refers to death rates *at certain ages*.

. A number of conclusions can be drawn from the data gathered by McMichael and the figures shown in Table 2.1. For every four male labourers, tradesmen, and process workers who died before the age of 64, only about three men in professional or technical occupations died. And for every professional man who died in an accident before that age, three men in the transport industry died. Every occupational group

Figure 2.1 Mortality gradients by social class, Australia and New Zealand

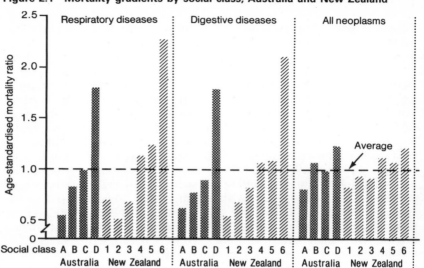

Source: A.J. McMichael 'Social Class (As Estimated by Occupational Prestige) & Mortality in Australian Males in the 1970s' *Community Health Studies* IX, 3, 1985, pp. 220–230

except farmers had more deaths from ischaemic heart disease than expected, but again the professional and administrative occupations come off far better than the other groups, especially workers in transport and communication. For every cause of death, and not only accidents as would be expected, the most dangerous occupations are transport and communication. This means that men in such occupations die considerably earlier than men in other occupational groups. Other studies bring similar evidence. Australian death rates from vascular lesions, ischaemic heart disease and suicide are constantly found to be much higher in the lower socio-economic groups and researchers have demonstrated that this pattern has existed since the 1960s.[18] Similarly, in New Zealand, higher death rates from most disease, but especially for diseases of poverty (infectious and respiratory diseases, and accidents) were found among the lower social classes.[19]

A common misconception, supported by media publicity, is that the responsibilities of executive and professional men cause them to suffer disproportionately from heart attacks and stroke; the reality is that the lower-status workers in lower-paid jobs suffer far more from all these diseases and die earlier than their better-off counterparts. This example supports the arguments generally proposed by conflict theorists, that the groups with more social power and control can manipulate to their own advantage the media (and thereby the beliefs of the public) and that

Table 2.1 Standardised mortality ratios by occupational group for selected causes of death, Australian males 1971 (ages 15–64)

Selected causes of death	Group O Professional Technical etc	Group 1 Administrative Executive etc	Group 2 Clerical	Group 3 Sales	Group 4 Farmers Fishing people etc	Group 6 Transport Communication	Group 7/8 Tradespeople Process Wkrs Labourers	Group 9 Service. Sport Recreation
					Occupational groups			
Malignant neoplasms	97	104	108	110	93	133[a]	121[a]	120[a]
Ischaemic heart disease	107	108	123[a]	114[a]	96	137[a]	115[a]	120[a]
Cerebro-vascular disease	104	108	123	115	85	144[a]	117[a]	135[a]
Arterio-sclerosis	81	69[b]	87	75[b]	88	107	113[a]	114
Motor vehicle accidents	63[b]	76[b]	67[b]	81[b]	188[a]	186[a]	128[a]	106
All other accidents	50[b]	61[b]	42[b]	40[b]	147[a]	149[a]	134[a]	92
All causes	89[b]	93[b]	101	99	98	138[a]	119[a]	122[a]

Notes: SMR for all Australian males = 100.
a Significantly greater than the national average of 100.
b Significantly less than the national average of 100.
SMRs have been approximated to the nearest whole number.
Standard error of each SMR has been omitted to simplify the table.
Group 5 (Miners, Quarry Workers etc) and Group 10 (Armed Forces) were not analysed by selected causes of death because of the small numbers. The SMR for all cause in these groups were: Group 5–163, and Group 10–126.
Source: R. Taylor 'Health and Class in Australia' New Doctor 13, 1979.

they are likely to have easier access to resources such as stress reduction programs, which lower-level people do not have. In addition, higher-status workers have more control over their work and home environment which in itself enables them to make changes to improve their health; they can, for example, afford to take more holidays, buy more expensive and healthy foods, and they are more accepting of health promotion programs to give up smoking and to exercise.

Social stratification and morbidity

In the few studies of morbidity rates and social stratification that have been done in Australia, it has been shown that certain occupational groups have particular health problems. This is evidence that one's health status throughout life has only a partial relationship to biology and a great deal to do with one's current position in the social system.

The findings on the relationship between morbidity and social stratification are more ambiguous than those on mortality.[20] It seems likely that morbidity depends on other factors which, added together, produce some of the illnesses affecting particular social groups. Such information as we do have tends to be somewhat contradictory. It is important to remember that contradictory findings may be real or they may arise partly because researches are carried out in ways that cannot be properly compared. For example, 'social class' might be defined differently by each research team, or different indicators of morbidity may be used by different researchers, some using symptoms reported in a survey while others use subjective health ratings, days of reduced activity, hospitalisation rates or number of doctor visits.

In addition, contradictory findings sometimes emerge in a single study. A health survey in the Gosford–Wyong and Illawarra regions of NSW in 1975 found little evidence of occupational group differences in chronic and recent morbidity as reflected in hospitalisation rates, which implies that the groups were similar in their health status. Yet when the people rated their own health it was found that members of the higher occupational groups rated their health better than did people in lower occupational groups.[21]

Recent analyses of national data found that men in lower status occupations tend to report more illness, chronic conditions and days of reduced activity than men in higher status occupations.[22] For women, however, there is no such clear correspondence between occupational status and health. This may be because occupational status is less easily established for women because many are not in the paid workforce. (However, women who said their major activity was 'home duties' reported consistently higher rates of illness and disability than those in paid employment.[23]) Recent studies have shown that education as well as socioeconomic status is associated with the number of health risk factors that people have; that is, people with lower levels of education live in ways which make them more liable to develop certain diseases than do people with higher levels of education. In 1980 the Australian Heart Foundation did a Heart Risk Factor Prevalence Study, which showed that people with a low level of education tended to have high blood pressure more frequently, to smoke more, to eat more foods rich in cholesterol, to have poorer nutrition generally and to be more over-weight than those with higher education. Women with lower levels of education tended to breast feed their babies for shorter periods of time than did women with higher levels of education, fewer of their children were immunised, and the less educated women had fewer pap smears. Alcohol consumption, however, did not fit in with these findings. Men with lower levels of education did drink more than highly educated men, but in women, the consumption of alcohol went up as educational level rose.[24] Another recent study, in Western Sydney, emphasised the effect of socioeconomic disadvantage on health status. Western Sydney is an area with lower levels of income than the rest of Sydney, and these researchers found that in the western metropolitan suburbs 'premature deaths (that is, before age 65) are significantly higher for four leading causes of death in the Western Metropolitan Health Region compared with the rest of Sydney'.[25] People living in that area were hospitalised more frequently than people in more advantaged suburbs. Further, the researchers reported that even within Western Sydney, 'areas with the greatest socioeconomic disadvantage also suffered the worst health'.[26]

With regard to mental health and social stratification, the findings are similar to those on physical health. Studies have been of two kinds: they have either focused on psychiatric patients or have been community surveys of mental disturbance. Various indicators of social stratification have been used in such studies, and in general it has been found that people of lower social standing had higher rates of mental illnesses.[27] Two explanations have been given for these findings: 'social drift' and 'social inequality'. The former explanation states that people who be-come mentally ill drift down into lower socio-economic groups because their disability affects their work and social relationships. The latter theory holds that people at the bottom of the socio-economic hierarchy have excessive life stresses which cause greater proportions of them than of other socio-economic groups to become mentally ill.[28]

The findings described above can be explained in various ways, depending on one's perspective. The consensus view will emphasise the overall improvement in the population's health over time, and say that those people who look after their health by changing their lifestyle and by being concerned with their health are receiving their due in im-proved health status. Further, since Australians now all have the right of access to health care without paying at the time of need, society has done all it needs to do in looking after the more vulnerable members of the community. From the conflict viewpoint, on the other hand, differences in mortality and morbidity are seen as arising out of the wider issue of social and economic inequality in society as a whole. For example, low-paid workers will, if they reach old age, mostly face that period of their lives in poverty so they have little incentive to give up unhealthy practices. Furthermore, they have access to hospitals only as public patients, which frequently means long waiting times before they get admitted for treatment. Hence the conflict perspective emphasises that the most effective way to improve the health of people in the lower classes is to introduce major social reforms. In that way the poorer people would have more income and be able to increase their control over their lives, which is likely to result in improved health status. Pluralists argue that economic factors are not the only ones accounting for differences in morbidity and mortality; other factors such as genetic disposition, gender, occupation, way of life, health knowledge and general educational level all interact to help produce health differences between groups.

3 Ethnic variations in health status and health care

Culture and structure

In the previous chapter, social variations were discussed in terms of *structural* variations. This means that people's position in society, which is determined by their attributes such as age, sex, socio-economic status and ethnicity, in turn determines their access to resources such as power, prestige and money, which in turn affects what educational, occupational, leisure and health experiences they will have. This is why some people get the best there is available, while others by comparison are not as well off. There are many degrees of relative advantage and disadvantage. In the previous chapter we saw that social stratification has considerable effect on health status. This chapter deals with *ethnicity* as a factor which divides people into relatively advantaged and disadvantaged groups in health matters.[1] Cultural differences are central to the idea of ethnic differences.

Culture refers to the distinctive knowledge, habits, ideas, language and ways of living shared by a group of people. The group might be a family, an organisation or a nation. All have a culture, which provides their members with a world view, an ideology, rules for behaviour, a knowledge of what to believe and how to express their feelings. The adults in a society are generally so accustomed to the rules of their society that they take them for granted—they see what they are expected to see, feel what they are expected to feel and behave as they are expected to behave. But children have not yet learnt those ways of acting and thinking; children's naive questions and unpredictable behaviour reflect personalities that are not yet culturally educated. But it is not only children who have to learn new rules of behaviour. Even adult newcomers to a group, organisation or society need to learn its language, beliefs, attitudes, values and ways of behaving. In fact all human behaviour except the most basic biological processes is part of culture and has to be *learnt*. Thus eating is universal behaviour done as a reaction to hunger contractions in the intestines. But dietary patterns differ from society to society and are learnt: how often one eats and with whom, how food is prepared and by whom, how it is eaten, which food is allowed and which is forbidden, how much food should be eaten, whether being fat or thin is desirable, are patterns that are infinitely varied.

Within Australian society there are distinct culture patterns which are often associated with age, sex and social position. Thus it is possible to distinguish different beliefs, values and lifestyles of men compared with women, of old people compared with other age groups, and of wealthy people compared with less-well-off people. Furthermore, certain more or less homogeneous groups such as patients in a mental institution, nursing students or medical students may have distinctive subcultures. But cultural variations are most visible among different migrant groups, often referred to as people of different *ethnicity*.

'Social structure' refers to lasting patterns of relationships while culture refers to knowledge, beliefs, values and lifestyles. From the *consensus* perspective, the training of children is socialisation which begins at birth and continues throughout life, and which is the means by which people learn the rules of social behaviour. Through socialisa- tion—at home, at school, and through the media, the vast majority are made to conform happily to society's rules and accept its values. The existing order of relationships is seen to be of benefit to the individual and to the society. By contrast, the *conflict* perspective stresses the unequal relations between the people who by virtue of their position in the social structure are dominant and powerful and the people who are subjected to their domination. Instead of beneficent socialisation, the relationships between Australian-born and new Australian, or between husband and wife, boss and worker, are seen to be characterised by constant and inevitable tensions as the dominant groups attempt to shape the attitudes, behaviour and values of the subordinate parties to the relationship, with the latter trying to resist that domination. This conflict perspective highlights the point that social *structure* does not necessarily mean social *order*; 'social structure' means that there are persistent patterns of behaviour but they may be antagonistic ones.[2]

Pluralism accepts neither of these views; from that perspective one can distinguish many different social structures, some complementary and some competing. Since there are now many different cultural groups in Australia, the pluralist view is that these form a multicultural society, competing and cooperating in many ways. The moderate pluralist would argue that multiculturalism allows all ethnic groups the opportunity to obtain benefits for their constituents; the radical pluralist believes that weaker groups will not be able to compete with powerful ones and will therefore be forced to accept many disadvantages.

The meaning of ethnicity in Australian society

There are a number of ways in which a country can become inhabited by more than one cultural or ethnic group. The most frequent method in the past has been through conquest, but the more common modern alternatives are for the host country to invite other nationals to enter or to allow itself to become a refuge for people displaced by political oppression or war in their own country. In the last 200 years, Australia has been in all three of these situations. The white settlers who first came to Australia acted as conquerors towards the Aboriginal inhabitants; later, settlers came from many countries to develop Australia's resources, to occupy the empty spaces and do the work that the established inhabitants did not want to do. Australia has also acted generously as a sanctuary for people evicted from their original homes by war or political opposition. Today Australia is a land with inhabitants from over a hundred cultural backgrounds.

The first use of the word 'ethnicity' was recorded in 1953 in the United States.[3] The term was developed in reaction to the word 'race' which had emphasised the physical characteristics of certain groups; in contrast 'ethnicity' emphasises people's cultural distinctiveness. The distaste which developed for the word 'race' came as a result of the emphasis put on the unchangeability of racial characteristics, and the belief that some of these characteristics were innately superior to others. 'Ethnicity', with its emphasis on culture which is not inborn but learned, and which can be changed if the ethnic group so desires, does not have the offensive overtones of the word 'race'. It must be emphasised that everyone belongs to an ethnic group and the majority Anglo-Celtic population in Australia is as much an ethnic group as each of the minority groups, though the term ethnic is often applied only to the latter.

No one can understand Australia in the 1980s without a knowledge of the changes that occurred when the very British–Australian society of 7.6 million people (in the 1947 Census) doubled in size to 15.2 million by 1982 and changed radically in cultural composition. Half of the population increase in those 35 years was due to the high fertility rates of the 1950s and 1960s, but the growth of the population was doubled by the greatest flow of immigration in Australia's history, with a net gain of about 3 million new settlers between 1947 and 1982[4] plus the children who were born to them after their arrival. It is estimated that directly or indirectly, immigration between 1947 and 1979 was responsible for about 4 million new people in a total growth of about 7 million, or approximately 58.8% of Australia's population growth.[5]

The *origin* of immigrants, as well as the *number* who came, is important here: in the 1947 Census only 9% of the population were born outside Australia and only 2% came from non-English-speaking countries, while in the 1981 Census the comparative figures were 20% and 12%. These 38 years between 1947 and 1985 can be divided into three time periods: the period of assimilation 1947–64, the period of integration 1964–72 and the period of multiculturalism from 1972 onward.[6] The policies of successive Australian governments towards migrants since World War II can best be understood if they are examined from the different theoretical perspectives.

The period of assimilation, between 1947–64, was based on a *consensus* ideology. The aim was that new settlers should acquire as quickly as possible the feelings and attitudes of the established population, so that the two would merge and become indistinguishable. Newcomers were expected to aspire to the existing culture which would, it was assumed, be as British when a third of the population was European as it had been before the migration wave. To this end, migrants were as far as possible chosen from groups which did not look too different from the British; the White Australia Policy was part of this plan, since Asians could not look like the British and assimilation could therefore not occur. The existence of the Aboriginal population with its totally different appearance, language and culture was ignored when this policy was formulated, and was made easier by the fact that they were not counted in the Census nor given Australian citizenship.

The period of integration, between 1964–72, was based on a moderate pluralist ideology. The word 'integration' meant that governments now recognised that it was impossible for migrants to melt unobtrusively into Anglo-Australia; migrants' own national and cultural ties needed to be maintained as a bridge to successful settlement. No certainty was expressed as to the eventual form the society would take but it was becoming clear that there would be changes in the British–Australian society. It was still assumed, however, that these changes would be marginal and that the core institutions of society, such as the system of justice, education, family style, and religion, would be unchanged.

The period of multiculturalism, which began in 1972, was also based on moderate *pluralism* and is still with us. By the 1970s, many ethnic groups had been in Australia long enough to have obtained relative wealth and position, and the larger minority communities had organised themselves as pressure groups which were important to politicians intent on gaining votes. It was accepted by these ethnic leaders that the dominant status groups in society had established positions, money, power and contacts, and that in order to obtain their share of these goods the minorities had to make themselves heard. However, in the 1980s, larger numbers of smaller groups of immigrants settled in Australia. They adopted a radical pluralist approach, and their leaders no longer accepted the government offer to rectify problems gradually by providing interpreters, language teachers, assistance with special health problems and so forth, to enable the immigrant to *earn* a place in society. Instead, these more radical pluralists demand that their constituents be *given* a fair share of society's wealth and power *as of right*; they do not believe they have to earn it. They demanded and

obtained Ethnic Affairs Commissions and anti-discrimination legislation, and their leaders moved to develop relationships on both sides of
the political spectrum.

Immigrant groups have not adopted a conflict ideology in ethnic
relationships in Australia; however, as discussed below, the Aboriginal
community has developed such an ideology. People who hold a conflict
view argue that the talk of multiculturalism and acceptance of diversity
obscure the real issues, which are those of social class rather than
ethnic differences. People with a conflict ideology believe that
multiculturalism ignores the fact that ethnic groups and Aboriginals
are among the poorest groups in the community; that they have the
highest rates of unemployment; they do the most menial and dangerous
tasks; that they live in the least attractive areas; and that they have
almost no representation in our Parliaments, Courts of Law, or in the
top positions of the bureaucracy. From the conflict point of view, it is
futile to say that all ethnic groups are equally respected since there is a
fundamental inequality in economic and political power. Aboriginal
groups have put a conflict ideology into practice, by demanding the
handing over of land and the right to make decisions about its use. It is
hardly surprising to proponents of this ideology to find that the transfer
of power and wealth has drawn strong opposition from the people in
power who want to retain their existing advantages. We will now look at
the periods of assimilation, integration and multiculturalism in more
detail.

The period of assimilation—1947–64
During World War II, Australians began to fear that they would be
overrun by Asian people and the slogan 'populate or perish' became
accepted by the government and the population. The government
promotion of the European immigration program was based on this fear
and was therefore widely welcomed. Immigrants were also needed to
manufacture the goods that were in chronic undersupply at the time,
and to perform the jobs that established Australians did not want in
an era of over-full employment. The original aim was to bring out
ten British migrants for every non-British, but in spite of assisted
passages, there were not enough British wanting to come. Australia
therefore began a search for non-British migrants. At first, northern
Europeans such as Germans, Dutch and Scandinavians were preferred,
but as that source was also insufficient, the majority had to be recruited
from the southern European countries, mainly Italy and Greece. They
came mostly from the lower socio-economic groups in their own
countries who wanted to improve their lives and were therefore
prepared to take the low-paid, low-status, unskilled jobs in mining,
manufacturing and building in which employers needed their labour.

The general belief at the time was that when migrants learned English
and entered the workforce their assimilation would naturally follow. It

did not occur to the government that any particular effort should be made to assist migrants to achieve this desired assimilation; mainstream Australian institutions were considered adequate and it was accepted that it was the migrants' job to find them and use them. Any failure on the part of migrants and their children to 'fit in' was attributed to lack of motivation and it was believed that unmotivated people deserved to sink to the bottom of the social pile. This is in keeping with consensus ideology.

At the time, this idea was easy to promote, since the newcomers were at the bottom of the workforce. It was therefore easy to believe that British ways were the best. 'Wogs' were regarded as stupid because they knew no English and had strange habits and customs which should be abandoned as rapidly as possible. At the same time, wider societal debates about inequality in society had not yet surfaced in the media and were confined to a few University departments. The position of women, Aborigines, migrants and the aged, was not a matter that entered the general public consciousness. Consensus ideology was dominant and pervasive.

In the 1960s there was a gradual change in Australian attitudes to 'intellectuals'. People became aware that education was the key to increasing our competitiveness internationally, and that education can lead to better jobs and thereby to a higher standard of living. Consumerism and anti-authoritarianism became part of the public consciousness, and during these years the ideology of assimilation also began to change. The women's movement, the hippie drop-out generation of students, the Aboriginal rights movement, the widespread resistance to the Vietnam war, all appeared in the mid-1960s. An increasing proportion of the population began to develop a new perspective. They began to believe that the disadvantaged position of certain groups was not the fault of individual members of those groups, but resulted from the structures of power in the society itself. Thus a conflict view of the country's state of affairs was gradually entering the debate. Inequality began to be seen as evidence of oppression, of the determination of people who had control of political power, economic power, the Courts of Law and the public service, to maintain their advantage and ensure that the people with few resources did not catch up to the establishment.

The period of integration 1964–72
The events described above forced the government and the bureaucracies into a new phase by the mid-1960s. Large numbers of migrants, living together in poverty in the inner suburbs of the cities, had now become visible. Charitable groups began to draw public attention to migrants' problems. Migrants themselves took a part in this change by showing their dissatisfaction in a number of ways. There were riots: in 1952 a riot by unemployed Italians in Bonegilla, and by British hostel migrants in Melbourne and Adelaide. In 1964 there were strikes at General Motors and Mt Isa; in 1966 a riot by Yugoslavs in NSW. Com-

plaints were made at diplomatic levels by the British and Italian governments about treatment of their nationals in Australia. As their numbers increased, ethnic groups formed their own organisations and newspapers, and these grew as more migrants became established and prosperous. Public consciousness was further raised by publicity about the number of migrants who were leaving Australia because they felt unwelcome. Together with a developing awareness of the importance of immigrants in Australia, came a consciousness of Australia as a non-British, independent nation. In the 1960 Census, there was no opportunity to describe oneself as Australian: we were British. But after that Census there were so many protests that the forms were amended for the next one. Similarly, for the first time in 1972, Australian citizens were issued with Australian passports. The very strong ties to Britain were weakened during the 1960s with the decline of the British Empire, and with the increase in numbers of Australian citizens who had no emotional ties with it.

The recognition of a changing public consciousness forced government and bureaucracies into a process of adaptation. By the mid-1960s there were more migrants in opinion leadership roles, and a number of ethnic organisations were formed: in 1964 the Department of Immigration changed the name of its 'Assimilation Section' to 'Integration Section'.[7]

Implicit in this change was an admission at government level that new arrivals were disadvantaged, and that it was an obligation of the government to do something to help them. Nothing much was actually done, but a number of inquiries were set up in the 1960s which brought about change during the 1970s.[8] One indicator of things to come during this period was the signing of an agreement with Turkey in 1968, which was the first agreement signed with a non-European country. It therefore marked the end of the White Australia Policy, although this fact was disguised by redrawing the map of Europe to include Turkey. The agreement also marked a major change in defining government responsibilities to migrants, by accepting the right of Turkish children to learn Turkish, by guaranteeing English classes for assisted migrants and accepting in writing that Turkish citizens in Australia had the same rights as Australians to social services.

It is clear that by the end of the 1960s the power relationships in Australia had changed and, aware of this change, ethnic communities were one constituency to which the Whitlam-led Labor Party appealed during the election campaign in 1972. By then, it was accepted that disadvantaged groups such as ethnic groups, women, Aboriginals, and the disabled had a right to organise to improve their position. These groups were involved in raising the consciousness of their members to a recognition that their low social status was not their fault, nor due to inferiority of ability or effort on their part, but the result of discrimination against them by other social groups. The pluralist view was gradually becoming more radical.

Multiculturalism—1972 and onwards

With the election of the Labor Government the first aim of the ethnic organisations was achieved. The new government was committed to intervention at government level to reduce inequality in Australian society. Funds were given to telephone interpreter services, to community development, to the employment of multilingual staff members in community health centres, and there was insistence on ethnic representation on all bodies that served migrant populations.

The establishment in 1974 of the Federal Office of Community Relations was a major shift in government activity, as was the signing by Australia in 1975 of the International Convention on the Elimination of all Forms of Racial Discrimination. This committed the government to promote tolerance, friendship and understanding across all groups in the society. During this period, as European migration sources dried up, increasing numbers came from Turkey, Lebanon and Latin America. During the 1970s, the White Australia Policy was completely abandoned, and the Indo-Chinese refugees started to enter in larger numbers. As the various immigrant groups developed a voice, the multicultural philosophy became inevitable.

Although the Labor Government was dismissed in 1975 and replaced by the Liberal–Country Party, there was not much change in the composition of immigrants during the 1970s. It was by now impossible to return to a White Australia policy without antagonising our major trading partners, and equally impossible to send away the boatloads of desperate refugees who began to arrive from Indo-China. This acceptance, however, did not mean that adequate provision was made for services to immigrants, even in the second generation, in order to make them as well off as the average Australian. Compared to most Australians, immigrants and their children are still in the lower income groups, receive fewer years of education, and have higher rates of unemployment than those who have been here for longer.

It is important, however, to distinguish between different ethnic groups. The main distinction is not between those who speak, or do not speak, English; the crucial element is that of the social level to which the immigrants belonged in their own countries, as indicated by their level of education and occupation. It is very difficult, as an adult, to learn a second language if one does not understand the grammatical structure of one's native tongue; it is impossible to improve one's occupational level unless one has a basic education on which to build. In every Western developed country the less-skilled jobs are disappearing and the educational level needed for the remaining jobs is far higher than it used to be. So migrants from Turkey, Lebanon and southern Europe are doubly disadvantaged, because they have mostly come from the less educated strata in their own society.[9] Southern European migrants have mostly come from a rural background and are transported to an industrialised, urbanised, sophisticated society with a very different structure of occupations. Instead of requiring only a willingness to work on the land, most urban jobs require a relatively high level of literacy and a capacity for abstract thinking. It is hard to acquire these skills quickly.

It has also been said that the people who have migrated here from southern and eastern Europe have been the less successful in their own society; they are 'economic fugitives from their own country' where conditions were economically depressed.[10] They therefore have to take the most menial jobs in Australia, and they are eventually turned into an underclass—doing the dirtiest tasks in extremely difficult physical conditions. On the other hand the Indo-Chinese, who have more frequently come as destitute refugees and who also speak no English, are generally successful members of the urban middle class in their own society. They have at least ten years' education, they learn to speak English relatively easily, they obtain jobs and their children complete high school and also frequently obtain a tertiary education.

Figures from the 1986 Census indicate that those born overseas now make up 21% of the population. Those from the UK and Ireland are the largest group—36% of the foreign-born. The second largest group consists of those from southern Europe. Those from Italy, Greece, Yugoslavia and Malta make up a total of 20% of the foreign-born. Asians constitute approximately 12% of migrants.

In the 1980s, Asian migrants have increased relative to British and European migrants. This was due partly to the need to assist Indo-Chinese refugees. As the economy was in recession, the unemployment problem influenced the government to reduce the number of skilled immigrants allowed to enter. These had come mainly from Britain and Europe, but are admitted now only in a small number of categories where shortages exist in Australia. The main category of entry for migrants in recent years has been 'family reunion', with the Asian Australians sponsoring more family members than migrants who came from Europe. Hence the number of Asian refugees coming here since 1979, plus the recently extended family reunion program, has added to the proportion of Asian migrants admitted to Australia.

The continuing uneasiness of the Federal Government with regard to immigration policy was shown when the Fitzgerald Committee was set up in 1987 to advise on Australia's immigration policy. The report, published in 1988[11] became the subject of heated debate among people with different perspectives, because, as the Report stated 'tolerance of ethnic diversity does not entail majority support for multiculturalism'.[12] From the conservative consensus corner there were cheers of approval, but from the conflict side it was considered that the ruling class was once more attempting to dominate the debate. From the pluralists there were protests that the virtues of multiculturalism had been disregarded. The fact is that the report seriously questioned the basis of the immigration policy of the 1970s and 1980s, although the Prime Minister later emphasised his Government's continuing support for multiculturalism, a moderate pluralist approach, while the Leader of the Opposition argued from the consensus perspective for a united Australia.

The health of migrants

For a long time it has been obvious that migrants have different illness patterns from Australian-born residents; for some health conditions the migrants are worse off and for other conditions migrants are better off.[13] Australian-born men die earlier and report more acute and chronic symptoms than do migrant men from European and English-speaking countries. The pattern for women is similar to that for men: Australian-born women die earlier and have more chronic symptoms than women born overseas. However, migrants from Southern Europe have more mental health problems than any other group.

Moderate pluralists would say that the data on the health status of migrants shows how any interest group can achieve the changes that it wants. The community as a whole now wrongly believes that migrants' health is worse than that of Australian-born people. This is because ethnic interest groups and migrant health workers have successfully used the media to influence public opinion and obtain more resources.

Early studies of health problems among migrants in the 1960s found that Anglo-Saxon patients tended to have more chronic and degenerative diseases whilst non-British migrants were more often admitted to hospital with infectious diseases.[14] The most common 'imported' disease was tuberculosis, which had been almost eliminated among native Australians. In the 1960s, new arrivals were reported as having infection rates between twice and four times as high as Australians.[15]

It is however, facile to assume that only new settlers bring tuberculosis into the country. Over 60% of overseas-born people who develop tuberculosis have been in Australia for over 10 years, and obviously developed the disease in this country.[16] This then raises questions not about diseases imported from overseas but about the conditions under which migrants live in Australia. Research by the Poverty Commission in the early 1970s found that 'considerable numbers of migrants live in very poor conditions with inadequate, overcrowded housing and tend to be employed in occupations requiring heavy physical exertion, and the combination of these two factors provides a particularly favourable milieu for the development of tuberculosis'.[17] The pluralist view is that the problem should not be considered as being located solely within migrants nor as only due to economic disadvantage. Rather, it should be seen as an interactive situation, with the host society bearing at least an equal share of the responsibility for developing, and solving, such problems. Indeed, when examining Australian research on migrant health, one can classify the discussion in terms similar to the theoretical approaches outlined.

From the consensus perspective, one can regard the problems as being located within the migrants themselves or, from the moderate pluralist perspective, as social problems resulting from the dislocation caused by immigration. Most researchers on migrant health have adopted a consensus perspective, explaining variations in mental health among ethnic groups in terms of the cultural, economic and genetic factors in the migrant's background and the stresses experienced in the process of migrating. Thus they consider that the problems originate within the particular migrants themselves, and that migrants should be responsible for solving their own problems. Alternatively, the conflict perspective locates the full responsibility for the health disadvantages of migrants in the societies from which they come and to which they go. The conflict perspective emphasises the fact that the occupations which most migrants from southern Europe and Asia enter are the least desirable: unskilled, heavy work in manufacturing, repetitive process work in the most difficult conditions. These are also, of course, the occupations of the native-born lower socio-economic groups in Australia. No statistics are kept on the representation of migrants in occupational accidents, though pejorative comments such as 'Mediterranean back' are commonplace. It is likely that back injury is more common among migrants because in many factories and much heavy industry migrant workers predominate, and the injury could really be described as 'factory back'. The word 'Mediterranean' merely describes the fact that some groups are restricted to these occupations. When recently arrived migrants are injured, they are often more anxious than other Australians because they have no stopgap resources, are often unaware of their compensation rights, are managed without proper understanding of their language restrictions, and lack the family and social support they had in their own country. In the conflict view it is hardly surprising that migrants are over-represented in occupational accident litigation, and it is doubly offensive to migrants to have such problems referred to as 'neurosis'.[18] Follow-up studies have demonstrated that the pain of the injured is 'real', in that the crippling pain remained after the financial settlement was completed.[19] The host society, which invited the migrants for its own economic and strategic advantage, is regarded as responsible for developing services fully acceptable to migrant groups as well as restructuring its economy to enable new settlers to have opportunities equal to those who have lived there all their lives. When economic recession came in the 1980s, government grants for research became increasingly difficult to obtain. Epidemiological research into migrant health was therefore not updated, although considerable publicity was given to conflict-oriented statements describing Australia as a divided society with a growing gap between the rich and the poor, with the majority of recent migrants being poor.

Studies done in Australia, as well as overseas, generally show that the longer the period of residence in the new country, the more the

migrants' illness and death patterns resemble those of the host population.[20] Socio-cultural factors such as the changed diet and lifestyle of
the new settlers are the probable causes.[21]

The mental health of immigrants has been more systematically
studied than their physical health. This is obviously a difficult field to
study, because different cultural patterns affect even the definition of
mental illness. In addition, problems of language misunderstandings are
greater in psychiatric than physical illness. Hence the fact that certain
migrant groups have particularly high rates of psychiatric diagnosis
should not be taken as definite indication that they have higher rates of
psychiatric illness. However, there is evidence that some migrant groups
have higher rates of psychiatric breakdown than native-born Australians.[22] For example, it was noted in 1961 that non-British migrants had
more psychiatric disorders, especially schizophrenia, than British and
Australian-born people.[23] The reasons were assumed to be the greater
stresses of eastern-European migration: they were involuntary migrants, with language problems, disadvantaged educationally and economically in their home countries, experiencing hardship and uncertainty
in the early years here. Women in some groups have particularly high
rates of mental illness and this is thought to be due to language, work
and family stresses which migrant women experience in a new and
foreign society.

Health services for minority ethnic groups

In the previous section, different perspectives on the issue of migrant
health status were outlined. These different approaches can also help us
understand the responses of different ethnic groups to their illness and
to the health services available; they can also help us understand the
governments' responses to migrant health needs.

The history of health services to ethnic groups is an excellent case
study of the change in community perspectives from consensus to
moderate pluralism. For the first 25 years of the post-war immigration
program, the delivery of health and social services was made on a totally
monocultural model. Not until 1973 did the Department of Social
Security start translating its welfare forms into languages other than
English.[24]

Since that time, however, changes have been relatively rapid.
Moderate pluralists would say that this is a result of the ethnic groups'
organisation and consequent political influence. Invisible until the more
articulate and longer-resident members began to make governments
aware of their importance, ethnic groups have now become an
important political consistuency. They have forced governments to
adapt the delivery of services to the wishes of their clientele, rather than

expecting the clients to accept without complaint what was offered. The changed climate can be demonstrated by the guidelines issued in 1983–84 by the then Minister for Health and the Health Department in NSW, where the Minister's Preface states 'Improvement in the quality of health services available to ethnic groups within our community is a matter of great importance to this Government',[25] and the guidelines stated that the aim is 'to provide acceptable as well as clinically appropriate services for people of different linguistic and cultural backgrounds'.[26] To this end, migrant health units have been set up in many States. These changes follow a decade of increasingly vociferous complaints, first from the Poverty Commission and then from health professionals of ethnic background who were able to put their groups' case forcibly to the NSW Government.

The major complaints fell into four main groups: communication breakdown, ethnic groups' lack of information on how to use the health services and consequent inadequate access to services, prejudice on the part of staff and culturally inappropriate services, and inadequate involvement of ethnic groups in improving services.

Communication breakdown was inevitable when no interpreter services were provided for non-English speaking people. It was common for young children to be expected to interpret for their parents and hospital staff, mainly low-level domestic workers who were frequently recent migrants, used also to be regarded as adequate interpreters.

The obvious unsuitability of such people for this role was not regarded as a sufficiently good reason to spend public money on competent interpreter services, and stories were frequent of parents having to be told by their children that they had a terminal illness, or of patients having to explain their emotional problems to the cleaner; and in reverse, instructions about medication and after-care were not interpreted correctly and were consequently misunderstood. A study of satisfaction with health services in the inner suburbs of Melbourne found that the biggest problem was the shortage of trained interpreters and bilingual personnel at all levels of health and social services.[27] Non-compliance was a common experience, with the resultant stereotyping of the migrant as 'stupid'. This reflects a consensus view of the client-practitioner relationship, which assumes that practitioners are well-meaning and doing their best, and that ignorance of English is due to patients' laziness or stupidity and inability to learn. The contrasting conflict view calls this 'victim blaming' because the migrants are held responsible for their own misfortune.[28]

Lack of information and inadequate access. It was obvious that people who could not understand the language of the country could not manage to understand how to use the rather complex Australian health system;

they did not know what services were available, what they cost, nor where to obtain them. Large numbers had no health insurance at the time when it was still essential.[29] They did not properly understand the difference between a general practitioner and a specialist, the difference between outpatient and casualty departments, nor about the existence of such services as social work, family planning and mental health services.

Prejudice against migrants by the high-status health workers was frequently reported, and is demonstrated by such common terms as 'Mediterranean back', and by the fact that, for example, a much higher proportion of overseas-born applicants for rehabilitation was rejected than Australian-born.[30]

Ethnic groups expressed frustration and dissatisfaction with the attitudes of staff in institutions and migrants stayed away unless desperate. The Poverty Report describes how migrants' cultural differences were ignored: their food preferences not taken into account, their anxieties unmet, their requests for the continual presence of their families rejected. They had expectations of a patient–doctor relationship which differed from the deferential Anglo-Saxon mode; they expected more attention from everyone when ill than Anglo-Saxon norms permit. Very little modification was attempted until the 1980s.

It is important to bear in mind that while these problems were widespread, there were subtle but important differences in the knowledge, attitudes and practices of the various ethnic groups. The cultural patterns relating to health have been better documented for some groups than for others.[31] It is now accepted that cultural factors explain the difficulties experienced by many migrants in the Australian health care system.[32]

Inadequate involvement of ethnic groups in service improvement. In response to instructions by politicians, health departments in several States have begun to develop guidelines to improve migrant access to the health system. In NSW these guidelines deal with communication problems, with the use of the professional interpreter service which must now be used preoperatively, postoperatively, on discharge and during psychiatric assessment.[33] With a policy of equal employment opportunity, more bilingual and multilingual staff have been recruited. New guidelines have instructed administrators to modify hospital services to provide for dietary preferences and to change regulations about visitors to take different cultures into account. Hospital routines have also been modified to provide for cultural and religious differences in dealing with birth, death, and worship. Migrant health workers have been appointed at the regional level, as have ethnic health workers in community health centres to 'provide information, counselling and prevention services in culturally and linguistically appropriate ways'.[34] Staff in public contact positions are receiving in-service training in migrant health. Ethnic Services Committees have been established, with representation of medical, nursing, administrative and paramedical staff and with members from the Health Care Interpreter Service and Ethnic Community organisations. Progress in the implementation of guidelines must be reported each year to the Minister for Health.

Clearly, although it would be too much to expect an instant change of style in the delivery of health services, there is a very serious attempt by governments to make health services more responsive to the needs and wishes of the whole population rather than only one segment. The NSW Government, at least, has made its position very clear. 'It is the unequivocal policy of the NSW Government that all ethnic groups within the community should have equality of access to services and that these services should be appropriate to our multicultural society... adaptations must occur to ensure that members of ethnic groups have access to the services the Government provides'.[35]

Pluralists point out that all these changes are an example of the effectiveness of pressure group politics. Only when groups become visible, articulate and powerful are their wishes recognised.

Aboriginals and ethnicity

The cultural patterns and structural differences which affect the health status and health care of ethnic minorities apply also to the Aboriginals although Aboriginals present a special case. Unlike the immigrants, the Aboriginals had been the victims of conquest, which decimated their population, their culture, their lifestyle and their health.

Until the 1960s, the hopes of governments were that the problem would quietly go away, that Aboriginals would die out, or at least be assimilated, and it was not until the era of protests in the mid-1960s that these goals were redefined. Not until the 1967 Referendum, when the Commonwealth was given the power to legislate for them, were Aboriginals given the right to vote, or to be admitted as Australian citizens; not until the 1971 Census were they counted as part of the population. Until then no one knew how many there were, nor their rates of birth, sickness and death. In that first Census, a population of almost 116 000 was counted, or less than 1% of the population; but due to a redefinition of the term 'Aboriginal' which now asks people to define themselves as Aboriginal or Torres Strait Islander, the next two Censuses counted about 160 000, 1.1% of the total Census population.

Relationships between Aboriginals and other Australians moved through the same phases as with other ethnic groups, governed by the dominant ideology in each period. Early in the twentieth century, total assimilation was the aim. After depriving the Aboriginals of their land and making them dependent on handouts, governments created reserves for them and put white officials in charge. From the white point of view, the reserves were a generous way of providing a lazy life for a backward, coloured, stupid minority. From the Aboriginals' viewpoint the effect was to deprive them of their freedom and make them withdraw into a state of complete apathy, thus reinforcing white ideas about their stupidity. The extent of the determination to obliterate Aboriginals as an identifiable group can be gauged by the fact that in NSW between 1883 and 1969, the NSW Aborigines' Protection Board removed more than 5000 Aboriginal children from their families and placed them into white institutions such as schools. The destiny of the Aboriginals in 1937 'lay in their cultural absorption by the people of the Commonwealth'.[36]

A moderate pluralist approach began to be accepted in the 1950s and 1960s by the white Australian population. While a consensus ideology was dominant in 1965 when assimilation was redefined as meaning integration, moderate pluralism was the philosophy of the Referendum of 1967 which authorised the separate counting of Aboriginals in the Census and gave recognition to the fact that they had not been assimilated and were still a culturally separate group. The moderate pluralist ideology in the 1970s propounded that Aboriginals were part of Australian multicultural society and had social positions similar to other ethnic groups. The Aboriginal activists themselves rejected moderate pluralist approaches; their demands were in accordance with a conflict ideology. They began a Black Power movement and demanded land rights, which are now being granted in rather a piecemeal fashion. As one of their leaders has said, 'I believe that aboriginal society needs to state clearly that we have not given up the struggle for our historical heritage and to force the white system to accept, by whatever means we can, to recognise that this is our land and we mean to get it back'.[37]

Aboriginal health

The great difference between Aboriginal health and the health of the rest of Australian society has been pointed out in a number of reports since Aboriginals were first counted in 1971.[38]

Conflict assumptions underlie the most recent reports. The fundamental causes of Aboriginal ill-health are seen to rest in their poverty, their disorganised society and their lack of meaningful social role. Evidence supports the view that the most effective way of improving the health status of a disadvantaged group is to improve their whole social situation. The Report from the House of Representatives stated: 'the provision of health services alone, whatever their form of organisation will not be sufficient to have a marked effect on Aboriginal health. Any new Aboriginal health initiative must be based on a recognition that health and ill-health are multifactorial and are the result of the interaction of such factors as lack of water, poor housing, an unhygienic environment, insecure tenure in land whether for physical or spiritual sustenance, domicile or economic self-sufficiency, personal stress, cultural and social disintegration, and so on'.[39] Since that Parliamentary Report in 1979, which described activity from the 1960s, the position has not markedly improved. The conflict view emphasises that more than a decade of special Aboriginal health programs has failed to make an appreciable difference, and that the social inequality of Aboriginals is still as great as it was in the 1970s. While from a conflict perspective, poverty and powerlessness are still at the root of the problem, the consensus perspective would stress the inability of Aboriginal society and culture to cope with modernisation.

Assessment of current Aboriginal health is severely limited by the lack of comprehensive data, even on birth and infant death statistics.[40] But on every indicator available, Aboriginal health is very much worse than that of other Australians. Infant mortality is three times as high; there are almost three times as many babies born with low birthweight; their life expectancy is about 20 years below that of white Australians. Infectious diseases such as diarrhoea, leprosy, tuberculosis, pneumonia and venereal diseases are between four and nine times higher than in whites. Blindness is three times more common in Aboriginals than in whites, mainly caused by the infection of trachoma. But it is not only the infectious diseases that are so common: the Aboriginals have combined a susceptibility to infections with the development of the lifestyle diseases of Western civilisations. Hypertension, renal problems and diabetes are more prevalent than among the white population; these are associated with obesity and a poor diet necessitated by poverty. Alcoholism and injuries are a major problem in almost all Aboriginal communities. The rate of hospitalisation for Aboriginals is two to three times higher than for other Australians, and five times higher for children less than five years of age.[41]

Health services for Aboriginals

While Aboriginal health is an extreme example of structured differences according to membership of a cultural group, the way in which health services have been provided to Aboriginals is not really different in kind from the way in which health services have been provided to other minority ethnic groups in Australia. The typical pattern, as described from the conflict perspective, has been that the health service is organised by male members of the Anglo-Celtic middle class who do not know the language of the people for whom the service is organised, nor their attitudes to male–female relationships. They generally lack awareness of relevant cultural beliefs about illness and death, and focus on the clinical and individual aspects of health. When the ethnic group complains that services are inadequate, or stays away from them altogether, the organisers express hurt indignation. Their attitude is that the patient must fit the program; that the program is good and should not be affected by patients' complaints. Proper evaluation of the service is rarely done because funds are not given for that purpose, though the need for evaluation is always emphasised.

Only when the complaints become so vociferous that public attention is drawn to the situation, are changes made. The organisation of Aboriginal health services is an excellent case history of the above description. It was not until 1973 that some changes were made which take into account that Aborigines have attitudes to their health that are very different from those of most Western societies.

The main innovation since 1973 has been the development of about 30 Aboriginal-controlled Aboriginal Medical Services, which have been established in all mainland States and in the Northern Territory. There are also some 40 Aboriginal-controlled alcohol rehabilitation units. They are mainly staffed by community health nurses and community health workers, with only a few doctors conducting periodic clinics. The bulk of the work is clinical, but all aim also at prevention. Staff work in the community through clinics and home visits, giving advice on diet, hygiene and home management, teaching people how to deal with problems such as diabetes and skin infections. Most staff are Aboriginal and the services are controlled by Aboriginal communities, but the higher grades of nursing and medical staff are still almost wholly white.

For several reasons, hospital services for Aboriginals are not delivered as appropriately as the community-based Aboriginal medical services. The number of Aboriginals employed in hospitals is very small, even when the majority of patients are Aboriginals. When Aboriginals are employed it is mainly in unskilled areas.[42] Nor are there many Aboriginals appointed as Board members in such hospitals so that it is not surprising to observers with a radical pluralist or conflict perspective that Aboriginals fear and avoid hospitals.

Pluralists point out that it is hard for white Australians to understand the health problems of Aboriginals without some information about Aboriginals' beliefs relating to life and death. Aboriginals do not value each individual life as being above the welfare of the social group. Health is not viewed as being one of the inalienable rights of life. They feel sadness and grief when someone dies, but they view this as an inevitable result of the spiritual forces outside them, and are more accepting of the inevitability of death. This interpretation of meanings and values that people attach to illness and death is done from the interactionist perspective. This point of view emphasises that Western-style hospitals present particular problems when they are expected to service Aboriginal needs. Aboriginals believe that it is essential for people to die in their place of birth in order to ensure continuity of Aboriginal law and knowledge. When old people die in the right place, their life force goes back to the earth and is regenerated when others are born. When an aged person dies in hospital, this continuity is lost for ever and the tribal law and knowledge which gives meaning to the whole community is weakened. It is therefore extremely important to the whole community that dying patients should be able to go home before death, even if this means that death occurs somewhat earlier than would have happened had they remained in hospital. It is for this reason that it is relatively common for Aboriginals to 'abscond' from hospital: more than their death, they fear that they will die far from their home. Hospitals are seen as alien and lonely, because people's illnesses in their own environment attended by the healer, the family and the whole group, are usually experiences that draw the community together. Illness in hospital cannot fulfil this function and the suffering caused by the illness itself is made far worse by the lack of social supports in the hospital.

The fundamental difference between Western and Aboriginal attitudes is that in Western society, when an individual is ill, the primary task is getting the person well; discomforts, unhappiness and pain are seen as less important than the attempt at cure. This is not the case in Aboriginal society, where an individual illness is seen as a social problem, and the most important task is holding the community together and keeping its spiritual life intact, even if the individual life is thereby shortened or put at risk. Pluralist and interactionist perspectives stress that, since Australian society now accepts the right of ethnic groups to determine their own lifestyles, Aboriginals will certainly have to be given every assistance to deal with their health problems; however, they should be allowed to do this according to their own value systems.

4 Health variations according to gender

Sex and gender distinguished

It is well known in Western societies that women experience more illness and visit doctors more frequently than do men, although men die younger. This chapter will examine the extent to which that view is supported by evidence with respect to Australian women and men. We begin, however, as we did the preceding chapters on social variations in health, with a clarification of the terminologies used in the literature.

There is a significant difference in meaning between 'sex' and 'gender'. There is no doubt that women differ biologically from men, but biology is not the main reason why sex variations create so much interest. Being female or male implies a great deal more than mere biology; the sexes differ in the way in which they are socialised and educated, in their psychology and in their whole life experiences. *Gender* is the term used to express these divergences and male and female gender refers to the *social* meaning of being a man or a woman. It is gender which interests behavioural scientists when attempting to understand the different ways men and women behave in relation to their health, as well as the variations in their health status.[1]

In all societies, gender dissimilarities are used as a basis for separating activities; for example, the division of labour is partly based on gender. The commonly accepted, consensus view of male and female roles is that the sexes have functions which are complementary to one another; for example, females are responsible for child-care and domestic work while men must earn the money and do the outside work. This view asserts that since men and women are different, they should be treated differently, but that their contribution is equally valued. Men's career role is valued and it is their duty to provide for their wives and children.

Women's reproductive role is equally valued and society shows this by creating special services to protect this role. From a conflict perspective, the division of roles between the sexes is not seen in terms of complementarity but rather in terms of inequality and exploitation. The evidence cited is that women's domestic labour is unpaid and under-valued, and that in the paid labour force women receive less money for their work than do men; that women are not represented in positions of power; and that one of the consequences is that their health is worse than that of men. The pluralist explanation is that gender inequalities are not only—or even primarily—due to economic subordination, but are due to several other factors such as the historical lack of political representation, value differences between women and men, biology and lifestyle.

It is obvious that at particular times in their lives, women have greater contact with health services than do men: menstrual problems, contraception, pregnancy and birth are all specific to women, and in Western society these are the domain of the health system. In addition, because of their role as the main carers of children and old people, women more often than men take children and old people for medical consultations.

When considering differences in health status according to gender, the first task is to disentangle a number of issues which have become intertwined. To do this, one must look separately at statistics of mortality, rates of disability and handicap, the amount of illness reported, hospitalisation rates and rates of attendance at doctors' surgeries.

Mortality differentials

The most clearcut information about gender differences comes from death rates; here it is clear that men are the ones who are disadvantaged. In every country where statistics are kept, men have a shorter life expectancy than women. Moreover, the difference in life expectancy between men and women has been increasing since the beginning of this century. A baby girl born in Australia in 1986 can expect to live to 79 years, while a boy can expect to live only until 73; a woman who was 60 in 1986 could expect to live till the age of 83, while a man of the same age could expect to live only until the age of 78 and 79.[2]

The causes of death also differ between men and women.[3] The principal causes of death of the whole population are diseases of the circulatory system which account for 45% of deaths, and cancers which account for about 24% of deaths. There is little difference between the sexes here. However, those are diseases which occur mostly in later life and which are the main causes of death of the people who have reached middle or old age; they do not generally deprive people of many years of life. The deaths that occur at *younger* ages show a considerable

difference according to sex: the most significant difference being in
deaths due to accidents. At every age up to 44 years, men die in far
greater numbers from that cause, both as a result of motor vehicle
crashes and all other accidents. In addition, males between 15 and 44
commit suicide relatively frequently; in deaths of men between 25 and
44, suicide is the second main cause of death. It must be remembered
that these are mostly untimely deaths of healthy people in the younger
age groups, are often preventable, and deprive the young people and
society of many productive years.

Table 4.1   Number dead at specific ages by cause, per 100 000

	Males		Females
Died between 1 & 14 years			
Total deaths	35		24
Percentage of deaths due to violence	51%		50%
Female deaths as percentage of male deaths		67%	
Died between 15 & 24 years			
Total deaths	129		48
Percentage of deaths due to violence	78%		62%
Female deaths as percentage of male deaths		35%	
Died between 25 & 44 years			
Total deaths	150		77
Percentage of deaths due to violence	49%		26%
Female deaths as percentage of male deaths		48%	
Total deaths	314		149
Total female deaths as percentage of male deaths		47%	

Source: Based on *Australia's Health*, Australian Institute of Health, 1988, pp 43–48, which in turn
used *Deaths Australia 1986*, ABS, Cat. No. 3302.0 and *Causes of Death Australia, 1986*, ABS Cat.
No, 3303.0

These statistics can be most easily understood by imagining a group
of 100 000 one-year-old males and 100 000 one-year-old females born
between 1942 and 1985 (see Table 4.1). Of the boys, 164 will be dead
before they are 24 years old; most of them will have died a violent
death. More than half will have died in motor vehicle crashes, the rest in
some other accident, or will have committed suicide. For the remainder,
cancer is the most likely cause of death. By the age of 44, another 150
will be dead, again from motor vehicle crashes, some other accident and
suicide, while others will probably have died from diseases of the
circulatory system or from cancers. Again, more than half will have died
violent deaths. The fate of the females will have been rather better. By

the age of 24, only 72 of the females will be dead. This is 44% the number of males who will have died. The most likely cause of death will also be accidents, while suicide takes far fewer. By the age of 44, another 77 will have died, most likely from cancer. The better life chances of the females are very obvious: by the age of 44 only 149 will have died while 314 males are dead. An important point is that those females who died between the ages of 25 and 44 were mostly ill people, while more than half the males dying between these ages were presumably healthy people who were either involved in an accident or felt so strongly that they did not want to go on living that they suicided.

Although the proportion of deaths occurring in the younger age groups is now low, they are unusual and in our society are regarded as untimely. Hence some attention is now being given to causal factors, in particular since a large proportion of these factors are behavioural and hence considered avoidable. From their early years, males are encouraged to explore, be active and take risks. Analysis of the tendency of young males to take unreasonable risks in sports such as sailing, diving, surfing, and climbing, is only beginning; it is already clear that young men, much more commonly than young women, drive while drunk. The analysis of male and female suicide rates is also important; whereas successful suicides are more frequent in males, the reverse is true for attempted suicide rates, which are higher in females. Studies are now being made about predisposing factors in young suicides, but no information has yet emerged to explain the difference in successful suicides between the sexes.[4]

There has so far been no real analysis of the reasons why young men are still so predisposed to violent behaviour that they kill themselves by accident or on purpose three times as often as young women. A consensus view of this fact is that this behaviour is part of natural male aggression which, while regrettable, does make a functional contribution to society since aggression assists men in their role as protectors and defenders of their families and society. Aggression is also said to help drive men to great achievements, while for young women such aggression is said to be dysfunctional for their role as nurturant mothers. The conflict perspective would point out that it is disproportionately young men from the lower class who die. Partly because of their frustration at their powerlessness, partly because they cannot afford to keep their motor vehicles safe, and partly because they have to work at the most dangerous jobs, many young men who do not want to take risks feel forced to accept them because they would lose status by seeming to be afraid. Pluralists and interactionists, when considering male aggression, tend to focus on the multiplicity of influences such as peer group pressures that affect behaviour; while pluralists would also be interested in the society-wide patterns of male aggression, interactionists would primarily be interested in interpreting particular instances of suicidal or aggressive behaviour.

The huge difference between the sexes in the rate of untimely deaths is now being exacerbated by the deaths due to AIDS. It is estimated that the death rate from AIDS will continue to double until the end of the century, and about 95% of the victims are men between the ages of 20 and 40 (see ch. 5).

Disability and handicap: differences between men and women

Morbidity is much harder to study than is mortality because it is much harder to define precisely.[5] Comparisons between studies are not accurate, since the studies may have used different indicators of morbidity.

In Australia, statistics about illness, disability and handicap are collected by the Australian Bureau of Statistics by community surveys. This means that representative samples of the population are asked a number of questions about their health status, but inherent in this method of information gathering are a number of factors which result in biases. For example, people vary in their perception of an illness and its seriousness. In Western societies it is widely believed that women find it more acceptable to say they are ill than do men. This may increase the amount of illness and disability reported by females. However, the evidence that there are gender differences in reporting illnesses is not clearcut.[6] The social acceptability of an illness is also variable; less acceptable illnesses are likely to be under-reported. Heart disease, for example, is more socially acceptable than, say, mental illness or sexually transmitted disease. In particular, women are more likely to report mental or emotional illness than are men, since in our society it is more acceptable for women than men to admit to emotional problems.[7] Measures of severity, of chronicity and of limitation in activity cannot be standardised easily and will therefore vary between respondents and from one survey to another. The method of collecting information may also bias the result. Most information is gathered by women who make up most of the interviewers; hence it is likely that some embarrassment will occur in men, which may result in under reporting of certain conditions such as urinary problems, sexual dysfunctions or sexually transmitted diseases. Women may, of course, also be embarrassed to report certain conditions, which again may add to the bias of the surveys.

The survey of handicap in 1981[8] found that the rates of disability and handicap were similar for both sexes in the middle years, although males are at a considerable disadvantage between the ages of 5 and 14 years and 45 and 64 years, while it is only after the age of 65 years that women are worse off. More disabilities come from physical rather than mental disorders, and more men than women suffer from physical disabilities in the ratio of 126 per 1000 men to 115 per 1000 women. In mental disability, exclusive of alcoholism, the ratios are reversed, with 24 per 1000 males compared to 31 per 1000 females reporting a mental disability.[9]

The most common disabling physical conditions for both sexes were musculoskeletal diseases (arthritis and low back pain) and the second most common was hearing loss. Overall, males and females hardly differed in their reports of moderate or severe handicaps in self-care, mobility and communication.[10]

Gender patterns of illness behaviour and health service utilisation

There is evidence that in Australia, as elsewhere, women consult doctors and other health workers, both conventional and alternative, more than do men;[11] they take more medicines of every kind, they spend more days in bed and more time in hospital.[12] Even when obstetrics is screened out, women's hospitalisation rates between ages 15 and 64 are still higher than men's, but are slightly lower in the later years.[13] In contrast to a common misconception, men's and women's admission rates for psychiatric reasons are almost equal if one combines admissions to psychiatric hospitals with admissions to the psychiatric wards of general hospitals.[14]

Men and women enter hospital for different reasons. The most common reason for male admissions is accidental injury, followed by digestive and respiratory trace diseases which are frequently related to smoking. For females, the most common reason is obstetrics, followed by conditions of the genito-urinary system.[15] In psychiatric admissions, men are most commonly admitted for alcoholism and its consequent psychoses, while women are most commonly admitted for depression and psychosomatic disorders.[16] More women than men are treated for schizophrenia, senile brain disorders, depressive psychoses and psychoneurosis, while more men than women are treated for mental retardation, alcoholism, and personality disorders.

Differing gender patterns of physical and mental illnesses

When reporting illness conditions, women report many more than do men; this holds true for both physical and mental conditions.[17] Australian women report experiencing roughly 13% more illness conditions than do Australian men.[18] It should also be remembered, however, that there are many conditions which are experienced more by men, such as gout, hangover, tinea, ulcer, loss of hearing and arteriosclerosis.[19] Three major morbidity surveys done in Australia have shown women reporting significantly more chronic and psychosocial symptoms than do men; only on acute symptoms is there little difference between the sexes.[20]

During their fertile years, from about 11 to 50, most women visit the doctor regularly, in particular for gynaecological and obstetric reasons, so that health risks are likely to be discovered and treated at an early stage. For example, blood pressure is usually taken, a urine sample collected, a pap smear done and a breast examination made at an annual visit to obtain a contraceptive prescription. Men do not routinely attend doctors when feeling well, so that their health problems are likely to be discovered and treatment begun at a more advanced stage. Hence it is not surprising that women report more physical symptoms and illnesses but less physical disability and handicap when compared with men. However, with respect to mental health, women report more disability and handicap as well as symptoms. But the rate of alcoholism among men—although men do not always report it—is as prevalent as depression among women, so that the overall incidence of mental disorder is similar in both sexes.

In summary, the Australian data suggest that men are somewhat disadvantaged in physical disability, women experience much more depression, and men have a much higher rate of alcoholism and alcohol-related disorders.

For at least a decade there has been much debate as to why women experience more depression than men and report more symptoms of ill-health in general. Originally, three explanations were suggested:[21] women report more illness than men because it is culturally more acceptable for them to be ill; the sick role is more compatible with women's other role responsibilities; women have more illness than men because their social roles are more stressful. Another possible explanation, as mentioned above, might be that since women attend doctors in health, enabling their diseases to be discovered earlier than men's, the possibly false impression is given that women actually have more illness.

All explanations have centred around the social role of women, which is saying that socio-cultural factors are more important than biological factors.[22] The Australian Health Survey of 1977–78 found that women who gave 'home duties' as their usual major activity reported consistently higher rates of recent and chronic illness, mental ill-health and days of reduced activity than women in paid employment.[23] A number of explanations can be suggested. Women might be more likely to become depressed because they have been expected to be passive and to depend on men, without having ways to express their aggression; alternatively, women have low self-esteem because their domestic roles are socially undervalued. In the same vein, it is suggested that marriage often limits women to domestic and maternal roles, which in our society are uninteresting and have low prestige. Housewives' lives have little externally imposed structure, so that they need more self-motivation to do their work; further, as labour-saving devices increase, housewives may have more time to worry about their problems. The housewife tends to be isolated from the community and yet has constant demands made on her by family members of all ages; she has little privacy and opportunity to develop her leisure interests. These socio-cultural theories, posed from pluralist perspectives, would help explain not only why women experience more emotional distress than men, but why married women in particular report worse health than never-married ones.[24]

Women's health care

The present emphasis on women's health problems and women's health care has not developed simply because women seek health care more frequently. Since the early 1970s, women have persistently complained about their experiences in health care. They have not complained so much about the results of treatment as about the way the services are delivered. It is well established that people's satisfaction with health services is related more the attitudes shown by the professionals than to what is actually done.[25] Women's resentment has come about because of the way in which women have been treated by a male-dominated health system in a male-dominated society, and this feeling has roused women to express their dissatisfaction in terms sufficiently forceful to persuade governments in almost every State to set up task forces to examine women's health, and to fund special health services for women.

In the consensus view of women's health, the involvement of medicine in women's sexual and reproductive lives has been a great help to women and therefore both the medical profession and the community— including women themselves—have encouraged it. Since women must keep healthy in order to fulfil their roles as wives and mothers, the authority of doctors is seen as functional and helpful. By contrast, men's reproductive role is not their main social role; therefore there is no need to develop medical expertise and technologies to protect male reproductive organs. According to this perspective, the care of all ill-health should be entrusted to the legitimate experts, who act in the best interests of individual patients and the society as a whole. The consensus view is that women are doing themselves and their babies a grave disservice if they reject the benefits of modern medical science. A moderate pluralist perspective adds to the consensus view a belief in the possibility of change. Moderate pluralism is expressed, for example in the language used in the report 'National Policy on Women's Health: A Framework for Change'.[26] It talks of influencing policy, not of radical change, and these strategies include negotiation and choices. Moderate strategies for change build on existing policies, programs and services, and include coordination, negotiation, liaison, education and equal opportunity. In sum, the existing structure of health services is considered to be basically sound because it emphasises the safety of the woman and her child. However, the structure should perhaps be more flexible and open so that it can more effectively meet the range of women's wishes and needs.

From the radical pluralist point of view it is considered that medical elites have developed power in order to force women to behave in a way which suits male preferences and which serves male advantages. It is still mostly male doctors who give women orders, which enables men to control women's lives by controlling their reproductive roles; women are told that they are weak and frail and therefore unable to compete for the more difficult social roles which also hold greater rewards. Hence men can keep the more advantageous roles without facing competition from women.[27] This perspective accepts that women have special health needs connected to their reproductive role, but it is pointed out that women's health is seen as a sub-speciality while men's health is part of the mainstream of health services. Instead of being accepted as normal, women's reproductive system has been regarded as a source of emotional instability; the Greek word for uterus is 'hyster' which developed into the word 'hysteria' or irrational behaviour which is often regarded as typical of women. Recently, women have expressed considerable resentment at the fact that all their health care, and indeed their general social position, are controlled by medical considerations ostensibly to protect and enhance women's reproductive functions. It is claimed that this works to women's social and economic disadvantage.

Women with a radical pluralist perspective believe that they should organise themselves so as to control reproductive and sexual events themselves, and wish to use doctors only as consultants and advisers. It is the desire to learn to understand their own bodies and to control their own care which is at the base of women's demands for change in health care delivery, though women differ on how these changes in health care should be brought about. Some of the most radical criticism of health services has been of standard obstetric and gynaecological care. Women have been treated as passive recipients of male advice and orders; they have been deprived, by male physicians, of control over their fertility, pregnancies and birth experiences. Proponents of the conflict perspective argue that women are disproportionately located in the oppressed and exploited working class, where poverty and deprivation prevent them from obtaining adequate and appropriate care.

The vocal critics of the established health care system began to articulate their criticisms in the 1970s, with complaints about the male domination of medicine, particularly of the specialty of obstetrics and gynaecology where about 90% of Australian practitioners are male. Resentment has been expressed about the way in which women have been portrayed in medical textbooks, where they are often assumed to be irrational and in need of tranquillisers. As a result of these complaints, the Australian Department of Health, in conjunction with the National Advisory Committee for International Women's Year, in 1975 sponsored the world's first national conference concerned exclusively with women's health, called 'Women's Health in a Changing Society'. The aims were to reassess and change those attitudes to women which are harmful and limited, to identify and find ways to overcome areas of discrimination against women and to emphasise the creative and positive in women.[28] At the conference, a large number of women complained about their treatment by doctors and the medical establishment could not ignore the implications. The *Medical Journal of Australia* published an editorial, acknowledging '. . .the dissatisfaction expressed by a number of delegates with the treatment they had received from their own doctors. . .if our patients have so clearly demonstrated their dissatisfaction, then something has gone wrong either with our intent or with our practice'.[29]

In the decade after this conference, the women's health movement gathered strength and influence, although it is not yet clear whether any major change has occurred in health service delivery. Another National Conference on Women's Health, a decade after the first one, was held in September 1985, so there is no doubt that women's health, like migrant health, has been placed on the political agenda. At least two State governments have established Women's Health Units[30] and articles on women's health services now regularly appear in the media.

Summarising the issue of gender variations in health, men and women suffer different disadvantages in their health status; men's disadvantages are fewer but more serious, and women's complaints have recently been the louder. The same is found in the U.S.[31] This is probably due to the increased assertiveness of women and the general change in women's roles over the last twenty years.

Demands for changes in women's health care should not however obscure the fact that worldwide, women 'have benefited much more than men from the health advance possible with capitalism, while men have suffered more from the rise of stress-induced and other risk factors'.[32] A case can be made to balance some of the attention which has recently been given to women's complaints: men's poorer health *outcomes* need to be addressed, while the *process* of giving health care remains women's main health issue.

Part II

Chronicity

5   Chronicity of ill-health

Chronic disability and handicap

Disease patterns in all industralised nations changed between the beginning of this century and the 1950s and then again worldwide in the 1980s. Throughout history, the most common diseases had been fevers and acute infections: they came on suddenly and lasted for only a short time. No matter what treatment was given, the patient either recovered completely or died. Only a few diseases, like tuberculosis, had a different pattern. These diseases had a slow onset and a long course, which is more like the pattern of the most prevalent conditions from the 1950s to the 1980s.

Such chronic conditions are diseases which are slow and insidious in onset, long-term in duration, and handicapping in their effects. Patients mostly retain the disease for the rest of their lives. These chronic diseases are of many kinds. Cancers, heart disease, arthritis, diabetes and mental illness are examples. They may flare up and then settle down, they may slowly and relentless worsen, or they may produce one acute episode and never recur and the patient may die of a totally unrelated cause many years later.

To avoid confusion, it is important to explain the terminology used in this book. *A chronic disease* means some observable disturbance or abnormality lasting more than six months. *Illness* refers to the experience of being unwell, whether or not an objective cause can be found. *Handicap or disability*, which are here used interchangeably, refer to the limitation on activity which may result from illness or disease. *Handicap* therefore includes chronic diseases and illnesses as well as the consequences of accidents and congenital impairments (see Figure 5.1).

The importance of the problem of chronic conditions may be gauged

Figure 5.1 Chronic conditions (diseases, illnesses, accidents and other impairments) of which some are handicapping.

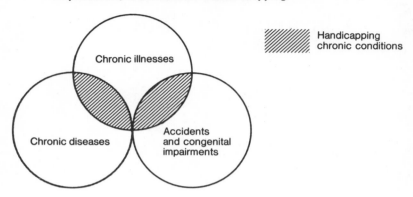

by the fact that one set of figures shows that about 14% of Australians suffer from a chronic mental or physical condition of varying severity.[1] In another estimate about 45% of Australians reported a chronic condition.[2] These two very different estimates are an example of the difficulty of quoting accurate figures on illness and handicap surveys. The ten most frequently reported conditions were arthritis, hay fever, hypertensive disease, eczema and dermatitis, migraine, bronchitis, asthma, deafness, varicose veins and heart disease, though it is clear that some of these conditions are far more serious than others.

Since chronic conditions are now increasing in importance as public health problems, it is clear that the emphasis must be on morbidity rather than mortality data when describing the population's health. There is now almost an epidemic of conditions from which people do not die, though the condition is present for a long time and may have far-reaching effects on people's lives. In 1988 nearly 16% of the Australian population were disabled, compared with 13% in 1981.[3] According to 1981 data, shown in Figure 5.2, an average of about one in 10 Australians had a handicap, which the Bureau of Statistics distinguishes from disability, but as would be expected, comparatively few young people were handicapped. It is after about the age of 45 that the proportion of handicapped people rises steeply. The proportion of people with chronic conditions who were handicapped by those condition was also about 10%, and this rises rapidly at middle age.

AIDS: acute and chronic

Chronic diseases were the most prevalent conditions from the middle of the twentieth century until the 1980s. At that time, the whole picture was changed by the development of AIDS which, worldwide, has become the most significant health problem of this century. In 1988 a new case of AIDS was diagnosed on average every fourteen minutes in the United States.[4] AIDS is a true epidemic not only in the sense of its causing much loss of life but also because its spread is still out of control.

AIDS does not fit into the standard description of communicable, acute or chronic diseases: it is all three. It is *communicable* in that it is caused by a virus, transmitted by particular types of human contact; it is *chronic* because it lies inactive in the body for many years before symptoms appear. There are *acute* episodes of AIDS–related diseases and remissions in between these episodes.

The precurser of AIDS is HIV—the Human Immunodeficiency Virus. Even if HIV does not progress to full-blown AIDS, it causes the development of a number of AIDs–related conditions, such as various types of cancer and neurological problems. The AIDS antibody test has been developed to detect the presence in a person's blood of a specific marker of HIV, so that the presence of the virus can now be detected during the long dormant period which precedes the full development of the disease. During this long period of asymptomatic infection, the person can infect others, and it is because of this possibility that considerable controversy has erupted as to whether people should be compelled to have the test.

AIDS mainly affects people of ages different to those affected by most other acute or chronic diseases. The main AIDS risk groups are sexually active homosexual and bisexual men, and intravenous drug users who share infected needles. Because both these groups have sexual contacts with many partners the infection rate has begun to spread throughout the heterosexual population. The most commonly affected people are aged between 20 and 40 years. Less commonly affected are other groups such as babies of women with AIDS, and some recipients of blood transfusions in the early 1980s, who were transfused before the Red Cross successfully instituted measures to check blood.

The first Australian case was notified in 1982. There was only a tiny number of cases in the first years, because although cases were increasing exponentially, such a small beginning still resulted in only very few cases. In 1983 there were six new cases, 1984—42 cases, 1985—113, 1986—223, 1987—360, 1988—447.[5] By 1987 it was plain that even if the number of cases only doubles every year, and this was the scenario still forecast in 1988, the situation may be out of control.[6] Indeed it was said in 1988, 'If no further infections occurred from today, the prevalence in our communities of those with the full symptoms of the disease would continue to increase for about another ten years'.[7]

As of early 1989, it seems that there is a slight levelling off of the epidemic. It is estimated that there will be no more than 600 new cases altogether in 1989, and certainly no doubling of numbers of new cases.[8] Although estimates change almost daily, governments, epidemiologists, clinicians and health educators all hope an exponential growth will not occur. They fear not only the suffering and loss of life but the enormous costs to society. These include the cost of setting up and running services, as well as carrying out research, educational and screening programs. In addition, there are the costs of each patient which include the cost of treatment, care, lost productivity and social benefits. In 1988 it was estimated that each case costs about $½ million.[9]

Since the aim of this book is to examine the sociological perspectives from which people view health issues, an elaboration of these perspectives relating to AIDS is our main concern here. The most straightforward perspective is that articulated by the conservatives, who believe that this disease is God's punishment for those who have sinned. In this view, deviant people have carried out active homosexual practices, or injected themselves with illegal drugs. Individual behaviour is responsible for illhealth and this view is reflected in the statement 'You don't catch AIDS—you let someone give it to you'.[10] This view reflects a consensus perspective, which considers that there is only one set of moral standards and practices which is functional for the health of individuals and society. Other behaviours are considered deviant and should be punished accordingly. People with a consensus perspective support HIV testing among the high risk groups, compulsory notification of infection, and restrictive measures such as refusing admission of AIDS-infected people to certain treatments or jobs.

Equally straightforward is the basic conflict perspective, which regards drug addicts and homosexuals as victims, exploited by the rich and powerful, who owe it to the disadvantaged to try to compensate for their exploitation. From the conflict perspective, the efforts of the ruling class to control AIDS by compulsory testing are paternalistic and coercive. In this view it would be disastrous for AIDS sufferers if a vaccine against the virus were developed before a cure, since this 'would lead to funds being spent on mass immunisation programs at the cost of research into an effective treatment. At a macro level this may make sense, but we are talking about human beings'.[11] In the conflict perspective the oppressed include Aborigines and their supporters, who fear an epidemic of AIDS because of the high proportion of Aborigines in poverty and in jails.

Pluralists draw attention to the many groups which have an interest in AIDS issues. There are the health worker groups, fearful of becoming infected, some of whom are demanding that patients should be tested for HIV before major surgery so that doctors and nurses can take extra precautions.[12] Funeral workers are another group of people who are afraid of being infected because they have contact with AIDS-infected bodies.

Other interest groups include researchers, who are finding jobs because of this new epidemic, and while deploring the problem, would lose their jobs if the problem were solved rapidly. Also benefiting are public health specialists concerned with improving the public health status, and who are receiving Government funds which are flowing with unprecedented rapidity to AIDS projects. There are the unions, who are lobbying for the protection of workers in various industries. They want to protect their members from infection and they also want to ensure that their members are not forced to be tested for HIV because that would be an invasion of privacy. Employer groups want to ensure that they have a healthy workforce and not one which is already infected with an inevitably fatal condition; nor do they want to be burdened with people who are going to need all their sick leave provisions, who will perhaps be unable to continue full-time work, and who may have to be shifted to light duties.

Life insurance companies want to make sure that they do not insure people with poor life expectancy; civil libertarians want to protect civil liberties. Governments are facing an enormous problem, because the cost of AIDS treatment could clearly wreck the entire health budget. Other groups which pluralists consider in their analysis are those who see AIDS as an opportunity of making money: the condom manufacturers and distributors, the drug companies who are hoping to develop a new drug and various groups who market 'cures' of various kinds, whether demonstrably effective or not.[13]

There are significant differences among pluralists in their perception of whether and how the interests of all these different groups are met. Moderate pluralists draw attention to the negotiation that takes place, for example, between employers, insurers and unions; they claim that the majority of interest groups manage to obtain their goals through processes of lobbying and negotiation. Radical pluralists emphasise the imbalance of power among the different groups. They argue that employers begin from a position of much greater power than do the unions, and that the employers are able to ally themselves with other powerful groups such as insurers in order to block workplace regulations favoured by the unions.

There are also different pluralist views of the position taken by the gay community. Moderate pluralists applaud the way the gay community has responded to AIDS by working with the health professionals, participating in educational efforts, changing dangerous practices and caring for victims through various voluntary arrangements. Radical pluralists, by contrast, note the ways in which the gay community has amassed unprecedented power and, as a result, has pitted itself against the powerful medical establishment. From this perspective there has been an ongoing confrontation between the two power blocs. On the one side is the gay community and its allies in the social services who push for a community education approach to preventing and thereby controlling the epidemic. On the other side is the medical scientific elite which is appalled at the 'demedicalisation' of the disease. They believe that more money should be spent on studying

the virological and immunological aspects of AIDS, as well as the
precise mechanisms of transmission and the clinical management of the
syndrome.[14] To radical pluralists, one of the most significant aspects of
the AIDS issue is that the medical model has been challenged quite
successfully by the community education model.

Researchers, and public health people often talk from a pluralist
perspective. They want to protect civil liberties yet act in a socially
responsible way to protect the public's health. They advocate a campaign for voluntary testing, allowing people to chose whether or not
they give their names. They are against attempting to control AIDS
through legislation because there is evidence it does not work.[15]

Living with a chronic condition

Chronic diseases, handicaps and illnesses cannot be considered separately, since chronic conditions are multiple conditions. Linking handicap to medically diagnosed illnesses, diseases and impairments is a
relatively new way of defining handicap. In the past, people have
thought of handicap as a limitation in daily living, being more of a
problem when the condition is very visible and when it seriously limits
acitivity. Doctors' definitions were used only for the purposes of pension
assessment. Now, however, doctors are regarded as the people who
decide whether someone has disease, an illness or an impairment, and
whether this is accepted as being genuine: this new role is often referred
to from the radical pluralist perspective as part of the *medicalisation* of
society by the medical elite.

Chronic conditions tend to begin with one condition which gradually
leads to a number of others. The gradual breakdown of one organ or
physiological system leads in turn to the involvement of others. The
long-term loss of resistance associated with many chronic diseases
makes people more susceptible to additional illnesses and diseases.
Furthermore, the use of extremely powerful chemotherapeutic agents
and radical surgical procedures as treatments for one chronic disease
such as cancer often lead to disabling side-effects. Thus, a series of
relatively minor conditions often interlock with one another to create
considerable disability.

The burden of chronic conditions is made greater by the changing age
structure of the population, as well as by the continuing advance of
medical technology which often has the paradoxical effect of converting
formerly terminal medical conditions into debilitating chronic ones. The
patients who would once have died of fever at relatively early age now
live on to develop cancer or heart disease. There is no reason to suppose
that both these trends will not continue for decades. Chronic conditions,
therefore, are rapidly becoming the major class of medical problems
faced jointly by patients and health care workers.[16]

Figure 5.2 Handicapped persons as a percentage of the total population in each age group

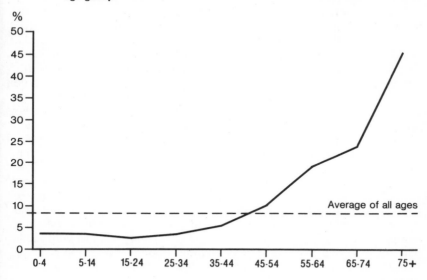

Source: Australian Bureau of Statistics *Handicapped Persons Survey, 1981* Catalogue No.4343.0, AGPS, 1982, p.5.

Social rejection of illness and handicap: the idea of deviance

The extent to which a condition is handicapping is affected by social and psychological factors. Limitations on or changes in a person's behaviour may occur not only because of an actual impairment but also as a result of the person's reaction to it or the reaction of others. At the broadest level these reactions are socially determined: they are related to how handicap is regarded in a particular society or community, the behaviour that is expected from people with a disability and the opportunities which are open to them. At the individual level, reactions to handicap are also affected by personal experiences, expectations and interpretations; people with an *interactionist* perspective regard these individual responses as the most important aspect of the analysis and study of handicap in society.

Physical illness differs from all other types of deviance in that it is always unwelcome both to sick people and to the people with whom they mix.[17] All societies, in varying degrees, value and reward health, strength and beauty. In Western societies like Australia there are contradictory and competing values in this regard. First, there is an extremely high, and quite unrealistic, expectation that everybody ought to have youth, health and physical beauty. Yet the reality is that most people are not rich, everyone dies either before or after becoming old, and with age come illnesses and consequent problems.

The image created by the media is of a healthy population, but, as has been discussed above, the changes in disease patterns in industrial societies over the past seventy years or so have resulted in a high level of chronic disease. Long-term illness often brings with it a reduction of income and the poor tend to be more seriously ill than the well-off.[18] The reality is that illness, poverty and ageing are endemic[19] and in order that those who at any time are well can escape from this realisation, the ill, poor and old tend to be pitied but avoided. As far as possible, they are put aside into institutions like hospitals and hostels, retirement villages and sheltered workshops.

Interactionists have demonstrated that rejection of the ill, poor and old occurs in both major and minor ways. People are given labels: 'he's a cripple'; impatient and intolerant remarks are made: 'can't you walk faster?' 'are you deaf?' There are ever-present reminders to the handicapped in onlookers' expressions of pain, embarrassment and fear. Perceiving pain, discomfort and bodily damage in others inevitably brings to all healthy people the reminder that they too are vulnerable. The result is that avoidance of the handicapped is a common reaction. People tend to avoid what they fear, hoping that by ignoring the unpleasant, it will go away.

The degree of stigma[20] associated with different physical illnesses varies as the result of a number of factors, such as the visibility of the condition (deformity, loss of an eye or a limb), the effect of the illness on the person's lifestyle, and the dangerousness of the disease. The relationship between the degree of stigma and some of these factors is readily apparent. For example, a person with an invisible, mild, curable and non-communicable disease, such as fibrositis, will hardly be stigmatised or rejected, while a person with a severe, disabling, obvious and chronic condition, such as paraplegia, will be.

When people with a visible physical handicap are avoided, they react as most people do when they are stigmatised; they hide the condition which others reject. For this reason, diseases are concealed in our society. This occurs at both a social and individual level. On the social level we hide the sick in hospitals and nursing homes. On an individual level, disease also tends to be hidden as far as possible because the rewards for doing so are high. Anyone who has had a mental breakdown will be unlikely to admit this to a new employer, or to a new acquaintance.

The social rejection of illness and handicap happened in Western societies as the medical profession got more authority in defining what was sickness and what was health. Doctors were given the role of deciding when people needed medical treatment and what behaviours could be expected of sick people. In the doctor–patient relationship the doctor was the authoritative expert and the patient was the passive recipient of treatment and instructions. According to classical medical sociology, the people who sought medical advice were entering the *sick role*[21] This meant that they regarded themselves as ill, and behaved as they had learned sick people behave; they expected their lives to change in a number of temporary or permanent ways. The *sick role* in Western society still involves two *exemptions* and two *obligations*. Sick people are exempt from normal role obligations so that they no longer have to work or attend to normal household and social duties. Second, they do not have to feel guilty when they do not fulfil these duties. Their obligations are that they do have to 'try' to get well, and are obliged to put themselves in the hands of those experts who society decides are competent to cure and care for sick people: in our society those experts are the doctors, and sick people are expected to obey those experts.

Focusing on the role behaviour of patients and practitioners reflects a consensus perspective on the health care system. In this view, society is an ordered system with all its institutions such as hospitals, schools and the police force working towards the maintenance of that order. The aim is to have a stable society: one where all the members are well, happy and working to help themselves and society as a whole. Ill-health causes individuals to deviate from their normal, social functioning. Therefore ill health is considered to be more than simply a biological breakdown; it is motivated deviance from socially acceptable, 'normal' roles. Non-fulfilment of social roles is seen as threatening to the smooth functioning of society; the danger is that people who are ill may enjoy their illness as an excuse to opt out of work, so that it is not good for society to permit them to be too comfortable when they are ill. For this reason, illness behaviour needs to be controlled by authority figures like doctors, whose job it is to return sick (deviant) people to good health and (normal) social functioning.

This traditional, functionalist or consensus view of the doctor–patient relationship has been challenged on two main points: it does not fit the most common modern illnesses, which are chronic, and it ignores elements of power and conflict in all human relationships.[22] The consensus model of the doctor–patient relationship makes a good deal of sense when patients are acutely ill *or* in extreme cases when patients are incapable of acting or thinking for themselves. However, that model does not apply when the patient is chronically ill. In such conditions, the active cooperation of the patient is often necessary. Examples of such conditions are hypertension, heart disease and diabetes where, in order to improve their health, people may have to change their behaviour by doing more exercise, stopping smoking and regulating food intake. Also, chronic conditions are not generally curable by following the doctor's advice, so that no matter how compliant the patient is, health will not return, and the person may never be able to resume previous work or social roles.

Many conditions reach a certain point of stability where the person is neither fully healthy nor very ill, but can function reasonably adequately as an ordinary member of society. A number of permanent disabilities come into this category—for example visual handicap, deafness, mild cerebral palsy and limblessness. The task, then, of dealing with patients with chronic conditions is very different from the brief, episodic treatment of acute patients. What is needed is management of the condition, by patient and professional—not treatment by the professional and compliance by the patient. Doctors and nurses also now deal not only with chronic diseases but more commonly than in the past with mental illness, congenital handicaps, permanent physical and mental impairments, and with the whole area of prevention and health promotion. Such illnesses require longer and more complex treatment, and a prolonged relationship develops between a patient and a team of professionals. And most importantly, the role of the patient in the treatment and rehabilitation process is very often an active one. Such patients are helped not only by health workers but by their own efforts and by support and therapy groups.[23]

The radical pluralist view of the doctor–patient relationship emphasises the imbalance in that relationship. Rather than assuming that the authority of the doctor and passivity of the patient is acceptable to both sides, the conflicts resulting from that unequal relationship are highlighted. It is seen as essentially as being about the use of power, where doctors have—by virtue of their knowledge and authority—a large measure of control over patients' lives and this may not suit the patient. Moreover, in this perspective of the doctor–patient relationship, it is not assumed that the patients' return to health is the single, agreed-upon goal of both doctor and patient, but rather that each party has additional and conflicting goals. For example, the doctors may also want to maximise the medical interest and income derived from their work, whereas patients may want simple and trouble-free treatments. As a result the doctor and the patient will have different expectations of the roles each is to play. In the radical pluralist view, medical professionals enjoy having far-reaching control over people's behaviour and lifestyles. They have the power to decide whether someone is given exemption from work, is entitled to workers' compensation or is admitted to hospital. Even in the doctor's office, the doctor is in control and is the one who can decide how the interview will run, for how long, and what information will be given to patients.

Although people with a moderate pluralist perspective have suggested that there are now major changes in doctor-patient relationships, recent studies in Australia have found that the traditional doctor–patient interaction is deeply rooted: patients were surprisingly passive, in that they did not ask some questions even though they wanted to[24] and doctors still have negative views of patients who deviate from the traditional sick role.[25] While from all perspectives it has been accepted that the view of illness as deviance[26] and the traditional authoritarian doctor–patient relationship is inappropriate in cases of chronic illness, professional training has only recently begun to address the management of chronic conditions. Many patients are still forced into an ambiguous role in which they are not really sure what kind of behaviour is expected of them, and their families and friends find it difficult to work out their relationships with the patient and the doctor.

Rehabilitation

It is clear that rehabilitation has become increasingly important in the delivery of health services. To understand its effect, it is necessary first to decide what the term means. To say that it means retraining people to enable them to become employed is too narrow, since many rehabilitation programs are aimed at old people who have retired and at younger people who will never be fit to work. Indeed, it has been said that many rehabilitation programs are far too ambitious, aiming to make people into something to which they had never aspired.

The problem is greatest when the patient suffers from a long-term chronic and fluctuating illness since the particular times when rehabilitation is required cannot be clearly established. If the patient sees a series of doctors in private practice there is frequently a fragmentation of responsibility and no one is sure who is in charge of coordinating the treatment. Doctors dealing with the technical aspects of care are often unsure of what aids are available to make daily life easier, and it may be quite difficult for the patient to find out what help exists or which professional is the relevant expert. The idea of rehabilitation implies that if the treatment is successful, the patient should return to a previous level of capacity, including perhaps a return to work. This notion fits that of disability as deviance. It can therefore be seen that the emphasis on rehabilitiation derives from the consensus view that the first priority is to return disabled people to useful activities. This is seen as being for the good of the individual as well as society. An important aspect of this functionalist perspective of rehabilitation, which is 'to increase their comfort and functional capacity, and to help them cope with continuing illness and disability',[27] is that the medical professional is seen as the key initiator and implementer of the rehabilitation program.

Moderate pluralists argue that the disabled have formed pressure groups and have supporters among welfare and health professionals. As a result, the disabled now have a voice and are being heard. Disabled people already have more responsibility for coping with their condition, learning self-management and becoming experts in their own disability. In this view, health professionals and institutions are ceasing to take a dominant role, but become consultants to the patient who makes the major decisions.

Moderate pluralists would point out that rehabilitation agencies have flourished because they have become pressure groups in demanding funds and services for their particular clientele. However, in order to justify their demand for public money, they have to show how useful is the task they perform. At a time of financial restrictions, one of the major criteria of success used by agencies is an economic one: if, as result of the agencies' efforts, the rehabilitated person is able to work, the government saves an invalid pension. This means that agencies have to try to get their clients to support themselves and it is widely believed that the ability to be economically independent is of major importance ot the welfare of the disabled. The moderate pluralist viewpoint emphasises that people who need rehabilitation services are not a homogeneous group; there is a need for alternative types of service to meet people's varied needs and this is already happening. In the radical pluralist view, disabled and handicapped people are a powerless group whose interests are not being adequately met: they are handicapped in money, mobility and in health and welfare service provision the voice of the disabled is not heard and changes are too slow. Rarely do disabled people take part in the decisions being made for their benefit. Legislation has traditionally been handed down to the disadvantaged as a charity and not as a right; the disadvantaged have not themselves had access to power. The disadvantaged, including the handicapped, have generally accepted the dependency taught them. This view also emphasises that chronic illness brings to the fore the inherent conflicts of interest between the physicians who seek to control the nature and quality of their work, the patients who seek to control their bodies and what happens to them, and the funding agencies who seek to control the flow of funds. Ultimately, according to the radical pluralist model, these three interests are not reconcilable; the relative gain of one interest group comes at the expense of one or both of the others. From this perspective, then, '. . . the history of provision for the handicapped in most industrialized societies shows the interaction of two not always compatible social movements: humanitarian concern for the most visibly and "innocently" disabled (crippled children, or the blind) and economic pressures towards the rehabilitation of potential wage-earners'.[28]

People with a conflict perspective do not pay attention to the complex power play among government, professional and consumer groups. Instead, they consider that disabled people inevitably slip into, or remain in, a situation of low income and powerlessness because politicians, professionals employers, housing and health care industries benefit from maintaining the *status quo*.

The changing nature of services for chronic conditions

From any perspective it would seem that the long-term character of chronic conditions requires new types of organisation. Arrangements have to be suitable for repeated interaction between patients and health workers over months and years. There are as yet few facilities oriented towards such care. On the one hand, most hospital inpatient depart-ments are set up for acute care and are oriented almost exclusively toward the care of people for relatively short periods because acute inpatient care is very expensive. On the other hand, outpatient clinics tend to focus on the occasional monitoring of patient signs and symptoms rather than on the provision of ongoing comprehensive care. Continuity of care is further jeopardised by the high turnover of profes-sional workers. The result is that patients and staff are often relative strangers to one another in a medical situation which requires trust and detailed knowledge.

Moderate pluralists would argue that community services are being steadily increased and the needs of all special groups are being ad-dressed. Radical pluralists, however, consider that only cosmetic changes are taking place because the decision-makers (mainly politicians) re-spond to the elite groups allied to the medical professions. These groups lobby effectively for money to be spent on acute facilities. Thus the needs of chronically ill and disabled patients for continuous care are poorly satisfied.

The conception of illness as a short, acute experience with a clear outcome is now gradually being changed into one of a slow, insidious process where no one can be sure what will happen next. In the same way the concept of handicap now needs to be changed. A handicap used to be easily defined; it could be seen. Today the concept has broadened: a handicap may come and go, may get better or worse, may be visible or invisible, and the patient may need rehabilitation at particular times and not at others. And in any case, handicapped people cannot be handled by the health system alone: the available finance, the domestic accom-modation, the family support structure, and employment and activity needs all need to be taken into account when planning a rehabilitation or management program. Hence many agencies need to become in-volved. It is here that the state's health services have to interact with other agencies, and this may lead to the patient's being lost between agencies. It is often necessary for patients themselves to search out the agencies they can use, because there is no real coordination between agencies, nor between the government health and welfare systems and the voluntary sector. It is also important to remember that some handi-capped people are financially far better off than others. This is because in our adversarial system of justice, people are given compensation if they can blame someone else for their condition and hence they are much better off than if they are disabled merely through misfortune.

Chronic conditions are expensive. Even where extremely elaborate and expensive technologies are not normally used in the care of a parti-cular illness, the need for routine monitoring, the occurrence of crises, the use of drugs over long periods of time, and the extensive interaction among professionals, patients, and families and friends, all make the care of chronic conditions expensive. In addition, the complex and multiple nature of many chronic illnesses and the need for a variety of ancillary services substantially increase the direct costs of chronic illness care. Furthermore, the opportunity costs of chronic conditions are very high in comparison to acute illnesses; lost work alone requires many patients to become welfare recipients.

Chronic conditions require a wide variety of ancillary services if the patients are to be properly cared for. Social workers or psychologists are usually needed in order to cope effectively with the disease-induced stress. Patients also need educational services to inform them about their condition, its medical and social consequences, and alternative strategies for its management. Usually professionals are too busy to provide adequate detailed information, and explanatory and supportive services are intermittent and poorly organised. Services such as physiotherapy and occupational therapy may be needed but are not always available.

It is agreed from all perspectives that the current medical system continues to invest the major part of its time, fiscal resources and intervention strategies in the treatment of the acute phases of the disease process. From the consensus perspective this has obvious benefits: physical discomfort is reduced, pathological effects are lessened and life is prolonged. But people who take either a radical pluralist or a conflict view emphasise that the problems of the devastating changes in lifestyle which result from chronic conditions are not being adequately addressed. Long-term care has low status among health professionals. High status and high income which give the medical elite its power derive from dramatic interventions such as organ transplants, rather than from a great deal of effort which produces only a slight improvement.[29] From the radical pluralist point of view, therefore, the proponents of high tech, acute care have a vested interest in not changing existing services.

A moderate pluralist perspective is more optimistic. Few services have been available in the past for the chronically ill, but this is gradually changing as it is becoming more widely understood just how common chronic conditions are in Australia, and as the handicapped themselves begin to form interest groups, and complain of their treatment.[30] Regulations for new buildings now require facilities for access by the handicapped, and public sector employment for the handicapped is encouraged. Health departments are beginning to develop systems for coordinating care in the community, and although the facilities are still very inadequate, their efforts are making some changes. There is more emphasis on coordination of services, on home support for patients by community workers and on helping community groups to assist handicapped people with physical aids, transport and housing.

6   The shadow of illness on an ageing population

Old age as a social status

Old age is both a physical and a social status which is evaluated differently at different times and in different societies. Old people used to be a relatively rare phenomenon since in earlier times, in traditional societies, the proportion of people who lived on into old age was very much smaller than it is today. Until the early part of the twentieth century, six siblings and their spouses might have had one or perhaps two living aged relatives, whereas now one couple might have four or more aged relatives to worry about. There is no doubt that old people have been much more revered in societies other than ours, but those differ from modern Western societies in a number of important ways. Industralised societies are societies in a condition of rapid change, and the aged are not generally respected in a rapidly changing society because their experience and ideas belong to an earlier period. It should be noted, however, that recent researchers have challenged the accuracy of the belief that old people used to be highly respected in Western societies. Apparently this is a greatly romanticised reading of the past. Three-generation households, or extended families, were not a common feature in England, western Europe, the United States or Australia before industrialisation.[1] Nowadays, people in industrial societies have fewer children, younger people are very mobile, most women are working outside the home and cities are large. One consequence is that old people frequently have no relatives living close by or even in the same city. When problems arise, therefore, the people who often give help are neighbours and friends. Mostly, if the problem persists, some kind of welfare or health service has to step in.

It should, however, be remembered that the increase in the proportion of people aged 65 or more is not something that has occurred very recently; rather, it has been so much talked about recently that everyone is aware of it as a 'problem'. But in fact it was between 1921 and 1947 that the aged proportion of the population in Australia increased significantly (Table 6.1). Between these years, the proportion of people older than 65 almost doubled and since then their number has only increased by a further 20%.

Table 6.1   Proportion of the Australian population aged 65 and over

Census of:	1921	1933	1947	1954	1966	1976	1980	1983	1984	1986
	4.4	6.5	8.0	8.3	8.5	8.9	9.6	10.0	10.1	10.5

Sources: W.D. Borrie *Population and Australia. Recent Demographic Trends and their implications* Supplementary Report of the National Population Enquiry. Canberra. AGPS, Australian Bureau of Statistics. *Estimated Resident Population of Australia by Age and Sex* 30.6.83., ABS Catalogue No. 3201.0, 1983; *Australian Demographic Trends 1986* ABS Catalogue No. 3102.0, Canberra, 1986, Table 2.2, p. 24.

Both the average age and the proportion of older people relative to younger groups have increased and are still increasing. At present 10% of Australians are over 65 but it is predicted that by the year 2001 this percentage will rise to about 12%.[2] Of particular concern is the expected rise in the proportion of people aged 85 or more, known as the frail aged. While the population aged 75–84 will increase by 87%, the proportion aged 85 and over will increase by 151%.[3] In addition to their increased numbers, these people will live to a greater age. At birth, men today have a life expectancy of 73 years and women of nearly 79 years, but if a man has reached 65 years he can expect an additional 14 years of life, taking him to over 79 years, while a woman who has reached the same age of 65 can expect over 18 years more, so that her life expectancy then becomes 83 years. Thus many people will survive for additional years during the period in which they will be at the greatest risk of frailty and handicap. This increase in the number of frail aged will have significant economic and social consequences.

Chronic conditions increase with age

The older age groups are of concern to health professionals for several reasons. The proportion of young people in the Australian population has decreased since the 1950s and the priority which was then given to education and to housing for young couples has started to give way to the provision of services for people over 65. As people age, they are increasingly susceptible to diseases and disabilities, many of them part of the natural process of ageing. Psychological and social factors may worsen the effects of chronic illness. People often become anxious and depressed; if they live alone and lack family support, have inadequate income or poor accommodation, living a normal life may become impossible.[4]

Among Australians aged 65 and over, there is a steep rise both in the proportion of people with disabilities and the number of disabilities each person gets. For example, a person aged 60 suffering from arthritis is likely to develop additional chronic conditions such as hypertension and deafness. The proportion of all people in an age group who are handicapped rises steeply after age 65 (see Figure 5.2).

The proportion of people with severe handicap (in terms of self-care, mobility or communication) in the age group 75 and over is an increase of about 50% over that of the age group 65–74; this is a bigger jump than between any other two age groups. On the other hand, the proportion of people aged 75 and over reporting mild and moderate handicap declined by 50%[5], presumably because others have either become worse or died.

In 1975, a survey in Sydney's eastern and inner city suburbs found that 45% of persons over 60 had at least one disability affecting their functional capacity.[6] A more recent report showed that rates of disability increase with age so that almost half the people over 74 years have a limiting physical disability which requires professional attention.[7] A day census in NSW in 1980 showed that while 3% of people aged 65–74 were in a hospital or nursing home, this proportion increased to 14% of people over the age of 75.[8] Another indicator of the health status of the elderly is that half the people aged 65–74 use aids such as walking sticks, wheel chairs, and hearing aids, while 70% aged over 75 do so.[9] It is, however, important to note the other implication of these figures. While it is clear that institutionalisation does rise with age, the overwhelming majority of old people are in fact living in the community. Indeed, only about 4% of aged people ever enter a nursing home, and clearly most elderly people still manage to live independently even if they need aids to do so.

It should be evident from this listing of numerous disabilities and handicapping conditions that the health status of older people in our society is a matter of serious concern, which will become even more of a problem as the number and proportion of old people increases. Further, the health status of old people in a society is related to the health status of the population in general. Nutritional intake, physical activity, alcohol consumption and smoking patterns during earlier phases of life influence the patterns of biological ageing and consequently the kinds of diseases and level of disability among old people.[10]

Some models of old age

The way in which old people are viewed by a society or its subgroups depends upon the theories of ageing which are current at the time. These theories fall into two groups, broadly reflecting either a consensus or a conflict perspective.

Consensus models of ageing essentially assert that old people should adapt themselves to society, for their own benefit as well as for the benefit of others. This adaptation can, however, be managed in a number of ways. Early consensus theorists subscribed to a 'biological decline' model, which states that a gradual reduction in physical and mental capacity is an inevitable part of ageing. This belief leads logically to 'disengagement theory' which was first proposed in 1961[11] and stated that as people age, they gradually lose interest in the world's affairs and in society, thus preparing for their inevitable departure. They wish to retire from work, they reduce their activities and are replaced by others. By the time they die, they have been replaced and so their deaths are not disruptive to social functioning. Successful ageing would therefore mean a decrease in physical and social involvement and activity. 'Activity theory' developed in the 1970s.[12] This theory states that a successful old age is one in which the older person adapts to a new set of roles which are, however, of lesser importance than the roles occupied by the middle-aged and the young. Health professionals today generally accept activity theory.

'Inequality theory' is based on a conflict perspective. Here it is emphasised that the inequality which characterises all of society continues in old age. A large proportion of elderly people are poor, some because they were always poor[13] and some because they cannot manage on the pension they receive, although they used to manage on their earnings. For people who are now old, superannuation tended to be restricted to males who were white-collar workers, and it has been argued that the situation of people who were always poor is made worse because the old age pension is only about 25% of average weekly earnings.[14] For those old people who have been unable to buy a house during their working lives, and who must therefore rent accommodation, the pension is not adequate to provide a basic degree of comfort. As a result of these factors, middle-class old people are healthier, warmer, better fed and able to choose either to participate actively or to retreat, while the lower-class old person can make no such choices.

For 75% of the aged, the pension is the sole or major source of income and the ways in which they can use their free time in retirement is therefore restricted; at the same time as their income is diminished, their needs for comfort and assistance increase. The conflict approach therefore argues that the aged are low in economic power which is reflected in their low political power, which in turn results in the aged not receiving a just allocation of resources. However, the aged are now joining together to achieve a political lobby with considerable voting power.

In contrast to the structural theories of ageing discussed above, an example of the interactionist approach to ageing is *labelling* theory. It argues that people are not old until they are so considered and the timing of this labelling can vary greatly both within and between societies. Often in our society, women of 60 and men of 65 are so labelled, though frequently they are as active as much younger people. Labelling people as old has a number of consequences, mostly undesired by the people so labelled. The labelling process treats the elderly as if they were deviant, by stigmatising them and keeping them powerless. A high proportion of older people show that they dislike the label by saying that they feel young, by dyeing their hair, using make-up and talking about their 'young' outlook. According to labelling theory, old people are avoided; they have reduced opportunities for social interaction at work and in family life, they become isolated and often lonely and depressed, and all these factors increase the likelihood of mental and physical deterioration.

Old age in Australian society today

Old people today represent the first generation in which almost everyone has a good chance of reaching at least 65 years, so that advanced age no longer represents an extraordinary condition. One of the most striking characteristics of this age group is the preponderance of women. This is partly because women live longer than men as shown by the figures on p.74. Of the people 75 years and older, there are almost twice as many women as men. In addition to these extra years women can expect to live, women in Australia have generally married men older than themselves, so that on average they can expect to be widows for about twelve years. The consequence is that most aged men are married and most aged women are widows and this trend is exacerbated in the oldest groups where 75% of women aged 80 and over are widows but only 42% of men aged 80 and over are widowers.[16] By 85 years and over, 92% of women and 60% of men have no spouse, but as there are very many more women than men alive at the age of 85, this means that most people aged 85 and over are widowed women.

Because of the large number of people surviving into old age, the term 'aged' needs to be refined: the 'young' old are 65–75; the 'middle' group are 75–84 years and the 'old old' are 85 years or more. The young old are generally active, fit, living at home with a spouse and quite independent; as they grow older they need more support, especially after they lose their spouse and become handicapped in a number of ways.

The first restriction tends to be a gradual loss of mobility: it becomes more difficult to get about in daily life. People give up their car either because it is too expensive to keep repaired or because of physical impairments which prevent driving. Public transport in many areas is not satisfactory and even if it exists, it is often not easy to use because it is not designed for access by slow or handicapped people: high steps on buses and sudden stops and starts do not make for security in travelling. Difficulty occurs also in walking and particularly if shopping has to be carried, if indeed the shops are within walking distance. Taxis of course are not affordable on a pension, yet this would frequently be the only practical way in which old people could stay living independently in their own homes.

Loss of mobility is due to conditions such as diabetes, peripheral vascular disease and bunions, all of which cause difficulty in walking. Podiatry is an essential service which is underfunded and lacks recognition of its importance. An old person can have a leg amputated at no cost, but has to pay cash from the pension for foot care from a private podiatrist since there are almost no podiatrists employed in hospitals or by community health centres. Public health provision of podiatry would be one of the most cost effective services if it were made widely available.

Most people who are poor—whatever age they are—are women, and their poverty is worse as they grow older. Most of the old people with disabilities which limit their activity and mobility are women. A 'Triple Jeopardy State' has been described as being one in which the aged person is disabled, on a low income and living alone—and these are predominantly women.[17]

The carers for old people are also predominantly women. Over-whelmingly they are female members of families caring for their elderly relatives.[18] Women over the age of 60 make a huge contribution to the support of older men and adult children, as well as to aged and disabled parents.[19] Most voluntary workers in the community are women, and the paid health and welfare workforces are also dominated by women. From a radical pluralist perspective this contrasts with the fact that mostly it is men who, as doctors and administrators in the top positions, exert power over these unpaid or poorly-paid women workers.

According to the moderate pluralist perspective, considerable changes are likely in this scenario in the future. Women are no longer as avail-able as they used to be to dispense help for no paid return, since they have opted in overwhelming numbers to return to the paid workforce. They no longer expect to spend their lives in caring first for children and then for old people. This means that governments will have to pay more for community support workers, that more unemployed young people of both sexes will perhaps spend a period of pre-employment time in doing such work, and that more of the 'young old', the recently retired people of both sexes, will have to be attracted to this kind of activity, whether paid or unpaid. Radical pluralists are less optimistic about the likelihood of such changes, because they consider that the power of male leaders in government and the public service is firmly entrenched.

Health care for the aged: progress or stalemate?

Interactionists point out that what people most fear about growing old is the possibility—indeed the probability—of a period of ill-health, disability and dependency before death. Ill-health cuts across all social, political and economic lines but disability is more common, more severe and occurs earlier at the lower socio-economic levels of society. A large proportion of the health industry is geared to meeting the needs of sick, ailing, frail and dying old people, since a quiet death in one's sleep is the fate of only a lucky few; most people face an uncomfortable pre-death period of limited activity.

Because the onset of most disabilities is slow, people generally learn to cope and continue to live in their own homes even if they live alone. Eventually, though, problems with shopping and transport, and lack of support services may prevent people from coping at home alone. A common fear is the possibility of developing Alzheimer's disease or senile dementia, the likelihood of which increases with age. A quarter of the very old (over 85) are incapacitated by it and 40% of nursing home beds are used by people with this disease. This is perhaps the most feared condition of all, because it is totally destructive of dignity and autonomy. Radical pluralists say that it is clear evidence of the low status of the elderly in our society that 'no disorder has been less studied, or treated with more contempt by the health professions, than dementia, although it is one of the most prevalent and demanding problems affecting old people'.[20]

Health care for the aged, like health care for the chronically ill, is affected by the fact that a large part of Australian medicine is carried out in teaching hospitals. The teaching hospital's expensive bed is not allowed to be 'wasted' on problems it cannot alleviate, so that old people with chronic problems are not admitted unless they have an acute episode of illness. This means that continuing disability is hardly seen at all by young doctors and nurses in training, yet it is continuing diseases that are the greatest problem in old age, especially multi-system diseases or reductions in function. The psychological reaction of an old person to the threat of pain, helplessness and death is very significant and can be the most important single determinant of outcome.[21] Yet interactionists emphasise that professionals are not taught techniques for helping people cope with these fears, and psychological and social factors are given far less attention than the physical, which may be the least predictive of the life-chances of the person affected.

Despite the increase in limiting disabilities and handicaps as people age, only 6% of persons aged 65 or more in 1981 were long-term residents of institutions.[22] Table 6.2 shows how few of the older handicapped people are in institutions. The Macleay Report[23] demonstrated that $848 million was spent in direct subsidies for aged institutional care while only $77 million was spent on home care—a 1:11 ratio. Yet only 4%–5% of aged people need institutional care, while the rest need domestic help, support and occasional palliation. Yet although many aged Australians are handicapped and only a small proportion of them are in institutions, only 3% of aged Australians were in 1981 receiving visits from a domiciliary nurse.[24] The Committee on Care of the Aged and Infirm found in 1977 that despite large and increasing expenditures, there remained a lack of domiciliary care, long waiting lists for nursing homes, and gaps between the fees for nursing homes and the benefits retrievable by the old people.[25] The main reasons for the many problems in the area of services for the aged were lack of long-term planning, lack of coordination between the various levels of government, and between government and non-government sections, and the past emphasis on institutional care rather than domiciliary services. This picture is now undergoing rapid change, although it is not known which forces pushed to the forefront the new ideas about the management of frail and handicapped old people. Clearly, economic factors have played a major role since there are now so many more old people in Australia as compared to, say, the 1950s, and their numbers are expected to increase markedly over the next 30 years. As a consequence of increased awareness of those problems, some coordinated geriatric services are now beginning to be developed, with a multidisciplinary team of salaried staff responsible for delivering all services in a specific area.

In addition, from all perspectives, nursing home care has lost its appeal as compared to the more modern goal of keeping people in the community as long as possible. A series of reports between 1981 and 1987 came to similar conclusions.[26] The means to this end are twofold: a doubling in funds for the Home and Community Care Program, which includes the Home Nursing Service, from $30 million in 1986 to over $60m. in 1987[27] and the establishment and funding of a number of multidisciplinary geriatric assessment teams. Their task is to coordinate the care arrangements for the aged people whom they see with the goal of keeping them in their own homes or in minimum care situations for as long as possible.

If one holds a consensus or moderate pluralist perspective, one will argue that the Australian health care system has responded to the growing number of old people by providing needed services. In this view, the system is adapting well considering the increasing number of elderly people. Morbidity and mortality data are collected as key indicators of need. It is said that the system has responded by training health professionals in techniques of caring for aged and by encouraging teamwork to coordinate and optimise services. This not only meets the needs of the individuals but also those of society: new jobs are created, financing of health care is rationalised, efficient care delivery improves job satisfaction of doctors and nurses, and progress is made.

People holding a radical pluralist perspective emphasise a very different set of facts: despite the formulation of policies to coordinate services for the aged, not much actual coordination has taken place because fragmentary legislation and administrative complexity persist. Services are still fragmented, 'there are still few rehabilitation programs, and nursing homes are too often the beginning of permanent institutionalisation for the patient.'[28] There are a number of interest

Table 6.2 Percentages of aged Australians handicapped and institutionalised, 1981

Age	Percentage of age group handicapped		Percentage of handicapped in institutions	
	M	F	M	F
65–69	22.2	21.3	6.8	5.9
70–74	27.5	26.9	8.3	11.1
75–79	32.7	40.9	11.6	17.7
80–84	42.4	52.6	22.3	29.0
85+	54.5	67.5	33.0	52.0
Total aged population	28.6	33.9	12.3	21.6

Source: From D.M. Gibson and D.T. Rowland 'Community vs Institutional Care: The Case of the Australian Aged' *Social Science and Medicine* 18, 11, 1984, pp.997–1004, Table 1. Gibson and Rowland used ABS unpublished tables from the Survey of Handicapped Persons 1981.

groups such as associations of nursing home proprietors which exert considerable power and are slowing changes. In this view the fragmentation of services for the elderly is inevitable because the mixture of public funding and private enterprise is fraught with many conflicts of interest.

In the conflict view, the powerful medical profession and private nursing home proprietors who belong to the capitalist ruling class have succeeded in keeping down the voices of the aged and their advocates who are lower-status professionals such as social workers and clergy. In that view, fee-for-service medical care prevents essential government intervention in the planning and delivery of services for the aged; only salaried physicians and nurses can give appropriate and equitable services.

The social organisation of death and dying

Every known culture has reflected on the fact that all human life ends in death. In myth and legend, folk and fairytale, religion and philosophy, people have analysed their feelings about their inevitable earthly end. But simultaneously, human beings have always longed for eternal life and many myths and religions record an ideal time when people were immortal, or at least had the possibility of immortality. The Old Testament, for example, tells that Adam and Eve lost their chance of immortality when they transgressed against the command of God. There are, however, opposing myths which tell how people wearied of immortality and welcomed the advent of death as a relief from disease, old age, the boredom of routine and the threat of overpopulation. The myths of all societies emphasise that death is a necessary part of human life. When a Moslem baby is born, for example, it is required that a doctor or other important man must whisper in the child's ear within the first few hours: 'You are born now; one day you will die; live for God'. Relatives are expected to whisper similar words to a dying adult. Of course this does not mean that any society has passively accepted individual deaths; rather, in every viable society of which we know, efforts to postpone death have been important. In each society, a basic part of the medical task has been the prolongation of life.

However, the postponement of death has not in any society been the foremost aim of the medical worker. There has always been a distinction between deaths which are unreasonable and undesirable, and those which are not. In order to understand what constitutes a 'reasonable' death, we must consider what that society regards as a reasonable life. Deaths of sick people who cannot recover, who are severely crippled and handicapped, and deaths of older people who are no longer able to enjoy life or contribute to the society are generally regarded as natural, even desirable. However, Western societies have become quite unusual in that they have laws which enshrine the belief that human life of all ages and with considerable handicaps is sacred and should be preserved with enormous effort, time and cost.

In the consensus view, it is assumed that life should be extended as long as possible; that living, except for isolated cases, is better than dying; that death in hospital is easier than death in the home; that people generally prefer not to know that they are dying. Because overall life expectancy has increased, death is thought of as the business of the old and the death of a child or young person is regarded as worse than the death of an old person. Death is also increasingly an experience that has grown apart from the mainstream of everyday life and therefore is less expected by each of us as our own fate. Until about a hundred years ago every child that survived to adulthood would have experienced the deaths of siblings, cousins and adult relatives and seen their dead bodies, while now such an experience is rare and indeed, for many people, the death of someone in their own family does not come until middle age.

Pluralists and interactionists study the decisions *who* will die, and *where*, *when* and *how* they will die; these decisions are part of the dying process of each individual as well as of the social structuring of death and dying. Although many deaths are unpredictable, in others such decisions can frequently be made and indeed, health professionals are often forced to make them. They decide where death will occur, how and when death comes about, who is to be with the dying patient, and whether and how the patient and relatives are to learn that death is close.

In terminal care, the technical aspects of managing death tend to get more attention than the psychological and emotional aspects. It has been noted that Australian journals of psychiatry and sociology are remarkably silent on matters of death and dying.[29] Separating out the care of the body from the care of the mind depersonalises death, and prevents people from participating in the management of their own death as they used to do in earlier times. Indeed, in the Middle Ages and the Renaissance, death was seen as an exceptional opportunity to give one's individuality its definitive form; nowadays, the behaviour of doctors and nurses towards dying patients is regarded as being outside their professional activities. Doctors' conduct towards the dying is based on commonsense assumptions, 'essentially untouched by professional considerations or by current knowledge from the behavioural sciences'.[30] The technological aspects of care are planned, clearly described, carried out as ordered, reported in writing or orally and assessed by peers and superiors. This technical approach is an off-shoot of the functionalist—consensus belief in modern science, which assumes that the important functions are those of maintaining life and avoiding death. In complete contrast, the non-technical activities of professionals toward dying patients—of concern to interactionists—are non-accountable and are not evaluated as part of the assessment of the quality of care.

People now rarely die at home. Increasingly since about 1930, deaths occur in institutions: in hospitals, nursing homes or hospices. This is partly because death and its management are unfamiliar to most people today, and partly because most modern deaths are often slow and painful, in contrast to deaths in earlier times when rapidly overwhelming infections were the main cause of death. Families are frequently barred from the final death scene, partly because attempts at rescue are still being made but most importantly because families make a fuss, disrupt the work of the ward and upset other patients and the staff. In our society, a solitary death at home is seen as being particularly sad. Most people who live alone cannot manage when they become ill, so they have to go to an institution even if they do so reluctantly. Since it is expected that more people will survive into old age and widowhood, and more families will have all younger members in the workforce, it seems unlikely that the number of institutional deaths will decrease. Nursing home managers dislike a large proportion of high-dependency patients because this involves a lot of heavy nursing care, and staff are not selected for their interest in palliative care or the dying process. Hence nursing homes are not ideal places for dying. For these reasons more community based services are being made available to help those families who are willing to care for a dying person at home. They need domestic help, medical and nursing service, advice, equipment loans and help with transport, availability of pain relief and the opportunity for admission of the patient to hospice, nursing home or hospital, either short-time or long-term, whenever the family feels it can no longer cope.

Recent developments in palliative care reflect, like the national childbirth movement, pluralist and conflict criticisms of the way birth and death have been managed in our society. These views challenge the functionalist or consensus belief that death is a medical issue best dealt with by medical experts, that this medical decision-making is good for patients and their families as well as for society, and that medical teams should decide when, where and how patients will die. Moderate pluralists point to the need to consider the range of people's wishes and responses to dying and to provide alternative ways of dying: they argue that while some people may indeed wish to trust in the doctor's decision-making and may not even want to know if they are dying, others may wish not only to know but to actively decide when they will die and which medical and technological measures are to be taken. Radical pluralists put it in terms of the need for interest groups such as the Voluntary Euthanasia Society and the Medical Consumers' Association to raise public awareness of the issues in order to take some power away from the medical elite.

Most American states now have passed legislation giving people the 'Right to Die'. This legislation prevents doctors and hospitals from giving people extraordinary treatment once they have stated in writing their wish to die naturally from their terminal illness. In South Australia, a similar law was enacted in 1983, in Tasmania in 1984 and in Victoria in 1987. These laws enable an adult to make a direction that extraordinary measures are not to be used to keep him or her alive. 'Extraordinary measures' are very broadly defined in the laws, as being 'medical or surgical measures that prolong life by supplanting or maintaining the operation of bodily functions that are temporarily or permanently incapable of independent operation'. But this definition does not, for example, prevent the forced administration of antibiotics which may be administered to cure a terminal pneumonia which would result in a quicker, less painful death than the cancer from which the patient also suffers. The development of medical technology, which frequently delays death beyond the wish of the patient, has been instrumental in the formation of voluntary euthanasia societies, which now exist in all developed countries, including Australia. They aim to change the laws so that people will have the right to choose to live and when to die.

The conflict perspective focuses on the control that medical professionals and organisations have over the process of dying. In this perspective it is alleged that death and dying have been exploited for profit by the dominant class, of which the medical profession and private medical institutions are representatives. Proponents of the conflict view point out that people are often given no choice, but have to become consumers of a technology that will decide when and how they will die. This conflict view emphasises, on the one hand, the limited success that medicine and technology have had in controlling pain and improving the quality of life of terminally ill people, and advocates, on the other hand, stronger emphasis on the role of the patients–consumers in deciding when, where and how they will die.

It has been commonly said that ours is a death-denying society.[31] Yet every society develops a standardised way of dealing with dying, death, the disposal of bodies, mourning rituals and the passing on of property and responsibilities; hence it really cannot be said that of any society that it is 'death-denying'. But in our society, individual death is infrequently discussed, it is uncommon for people to die or be laid out at home, it is rare that dead bodies are actually viewed, and the deaths of younger people are regarded as tragic and premature because most deaths occur after the age of 50. This picture is quite a recent one, as before the beginning of this century deaths occurred commonly at all ages. The population as a whole had familiarity with death, which most frequently occurred at home. Dying, like being born, was part of normal life, and ordinary people were used to seeing and handling dead bodies. Death in Australian society is not part of the common experience, and is therefore more frightening than it used to be. In order to keep the inevitable away from the timid, dying and dead people are kept out of sight so that their very invisibility makes the reality even more frightening. One of the most important boasts of science and technology is that, with their aid, events can be predicted and controlled. Death shatters this illusion and forces everyone to realise that no matter how much technology there is, we will always have to live with the unpredictable.

7   Health disregarded: drugs and chronic conditions

Seeing the issue of drugs from different perspectives

In recent years there has been increasing emphasis on the social and health effects of drugs of addiction in industrialised societies. The focus has been mainly on two legal drugs, tobacco and alcohol, and on three illegal drugs: marijuana, heroin and, more recently, cocaine. All these drugs have social ramifications far wider than their health effects. The illegal drugs are intertwined with crime both violent and victimless, and with the corruption of politicians, police and lawyers. A confounding factor in the community concern with drug problems is the recently discovered danger of contracting AIDS as a result of sharing needles. The legal drugs provide a major source of income to governments through excise and the taxation system, as well as stimulating employment, building construction, the advertising industry, and international trade. But the common health feature of all these drugs, whether legal or illegal, is their addictive nature and the fact that their use may cause a number of serious, chronic, and frequently disabling diseases. Hence the generic word 'drug', when used in this chapter, includes both the licit and illicit drugs of addiction: tobacco as well as heroin, alcohol as well as marijuana and cocaine.

We do not discuss here most of the drugs used in medicine for therapeutic purposes. It should be emphasised at the beginning of this chapter that it has been well known for many years that various drugs have damaging effects on the human body. However, health professionals who try to motivate governments to take effective action to prevent abuse have generally been unsuccessful, since a number of disparate interest-groups combine to oppose any serious government action. Thus civil libertarians believe that people have the right to choose whether or not to injure themselves (a consensus perspective); manufacturers, advertisers and the mass media agree with this view. Similarily, unions point out that drug industries provide employment for many thousands. Seen from the radical pluralist perspective, these groups merely want to maintain their profitable industries.

In almost every known human society, some mood-altering addictive drugs have been in common use. The god Bacchus was created by the ancient Romans to describe their relationship with alcohol, the tribal Indians of the Americas chewed cocaine and smoked tobacco in pipes of peace; opiates were freely used in Australia in the nineteenth century.[1] Because politicians see no votes to be won in restricting access, it is unlikely that modern governments could, or would wish to, create new rules which would completely prevent the general use of pleasurable drugs which are also addictive. However, in today's society there are strong pressures on governments to tackle the health and social problems posed by drugs of addiction. Illegal drugs provide the media with sensational stories of corruption, needle sharing can spread HIV infection, and interest groups have begun to pressure governments to reduce the damage to health that is caused by tobacco and alcohol. Since heart disease, cancer and accidents, which are major causes of death, are all linked to the consumption of tobacco and alcohol, there is a prima facie case for governments to seek ways of reducing the damage these drugs cause.

The consensus case here tends to focus on two contradictory aims: to maintain the flourishing and legal business associated with the production and sale of tobacco and alcohol, while simultaneously telling governments that it is their responsibility to prevent the consequent damage to health. The conflict-oriented case rests on two different contradictory beliefs: that it is the capitalist desire to create wealth that brings about the production of products that damage people's health, but that the poor are entitled to use such products as give them pleasure, without being victimised for indulging in activities which are available to the well-off.

Illegal drugs

As a result of increasing public concern, there have recently been a number of government reports and discussions of the use of illegal drugs in Australia.[2] Some of these give excellent accounts of the issues but it must be recognised that all these reports are written from a consensus viewpoint, and make the basic assumption that 'drug programs must be coordinated with programs which are designed to alleviate the social problems'.[3] The conflict perspective, on the other hand, argues that both legal and illegal drugs are abused far more by the higher status, wealthy class than by the poor, that it is the poor who are selected out and punished as a result of police prejudice; that the rich can avoid arrest and fines because they can afford representation by barristers while the poor cannot; and that the consumers of illegal drugs are not criminals but the victims of the drug producers.[4] Because the true criminals are wealthy and have links with the capitalist class, they are able to escape punishment, while the small-time drug addicts and peddlers are pursued. The conflict perspective holds that since the chain of promotion, criminal activity and abuse of illegal drugs is tightly interlinked, little has been, or can be, achieved in piecemeal efforts of well-intentioned people who try to assist drug addicts and 'cure' them: these efforts are not much use when the chain of production and availability continues unchecked. The odd 'success' story which is told to encourage health workers and addicts is very much a way of justifying useless activity and maintaining the status quo of wealth and power, conflict theorists would say. Such isolated 'success' stories ignore the reality of the pressures which exist to continue the total chain of drug availability. It is easy for governments to call addiction a health issue and to set up within a health department a chronically underfunded drug addiction program; it has so far proved impossible to attack the problem at its criminal and economic source.

Recent reports, written from a radical pluralist perspective, have generally concluded that until the sources of supply of such drugs as heroin and cocaine are blocked, and the authorities follow the money trail to prevent the laundering of profits which enables the suppliers to reinvest their wealth in legitimate industries, health programs can have only a cosmetic effect. The Royal Commissions cited above and especially the 1987–88 Fitzgerald Commission into corruption in Queensland, have shown that the illegal drug chain ties up massively with crime, as well as with damage to people who take the drugs. The criminal and economic dimensions of drugs are the focus of the conflict and radical pluralist views, which contrast with the consensus view of addiction to illegal drugs as being mainly a personal health problem.

In 1988 significant changes occurred in the thinking of governments and health professionals. Because of the danger of spreading AIDS by needle sharing among addicts of heroin, in particular, governments began a more determined program of public education. The aim was to gain community acceptance for health departments' decision to begin a needle exchange program, in which clean needles are issued to addicts in an attempt to prevent needle sharing. These programs were soon in place, although the media reported that needle sharing still continued, though possibly less widespread. Of course, accurate evidence is hard to obtain.[5]

Tobacco: a legal drug of addiction

Although the use of tobacco and alcohol has been high in Australia since the first years of settlement, these uses have only recently been considered a 'problem'. While the main causes of death and illness were infections which moved rapidly through their course, there was no need—and no opportunity—to study conditions which took many years to take their toll. Thus it was not until the infections were eliminated as the main causes of death and were replaced by chronic diseases, like heart disease and cancer which killed people more slowly, that the opportunity came to study the effect of a substance such as tobacco. The use of tobacco is reported not only in modern but in many ancient societies. Some evidence of its use has been found in Egyptian mummies, and it has been commonly used in primitive as well as developed societies without being regarded as a drug to be proscribed, because it does not cause the user to behave in an anti-social way or to be perceived as anti-social. Indeed, tobacco has been used for centuries as a social lubricant; pipes of peace have sealed treaties of friendship, governments have issued it to soldiers in the battlefield as a stress relieving agent, and it is in many ways rather similar to other substances such as chewing gum, sweets and dummies for babies which are used for oral gratification.

In almost all its social characteristics, tobacco is quite different from alcohol, with which it is often grouped. Rather, tobacco is similar to various analgesic substances which are also taken for the relief of tension. Public condemnation of tobacco smoking and analgesic use is of quite recent origin; it began among the medical profession which focused not on social consequences but on unfavourable health consequences for individual users. It is only recently that people with a radical pluralist or conflict perspective have begun to claim that tobacco manufacturers have been trying to conceal the health consequences of their products. While continuing to advertise and promote their products under the guise of 'freedom of choice' and 'unproven ill-effects', manufacturers have continued to try to win new adherents by targeting their advertisements, with considerable success, to previously low-smoking groups such as women and teenagers. Both these groups have taken up smoking in increasing numbers, while the previously heavy-smoking group of middle-aged men has begun increasingly to give up the habit as a result of publicity about the likely consequences such as heart disease and lung cancer.

Epidemiologists have conducted surveys of smoking patterns in Australia since the early 1970s; before that, only the tobacco companies did market surveys since the health consequences had not been established. The first official evidence of damage caused by smoking came in 1962, when the Royal College of Physicians in London issued the first of three major reports confirming the health dangers of smoking,[6] and in 1964 the US Surgeon-General issued his famous report.[7] Since then, regular surveys of smoking habits have been done in many countries and there are many detailed research reports describing smoking patterns and the illness patterns which are be associated with them.

Several trends are emerging from such surveys. First, between 10% and 40% of the Australian population now smokes cigarettes. There are, however, considerable differences in the age and social class distribution of smokers. The most recent authoritative surveys, reported in the *Medical Journal of Australia*, deal with data collected in 1986. This shows that 'the habit of smoking has become highly stratified socially'.[8] Forty-two percent of men from blue-collar households smoked, compared with 23% of men from upper white-collar households. Similar differences were reported among women (36% of women from blue-collar households smoked, as compared with 17% of women from upper white-collar households. Between 1983 and 1986 the percentage of men smoking fell from 40% to 33%, and while the percentage of women smokers fell from 31% to 29%, women in their twenties continued to smoke.[9]

The health consequences of smoking have been illustrated in a number of ways. It has been suggested, for example, that the difference between male and female life expectancy in terms of improvements in longevity since the 1920s has been largely due to the fact that smoking used to be mainly a part of the male lifestyle, being socially disapproved for women.[10] With women's liberation and changes in role came the targeting by advertisers of women as cigarette consumers. This targeting has been successful, and has already contributed to a considerable increase in lung cancer among women, so much so that this cancer is now rivalling breast cancer as a major cause of women's cancer deaths.[11] The relationship between lung cancer and cigarette smoking has now been well established.[12] The rate of increase in lung cancer has been quite startling: it takes 20–30 years for such a cancer to develop, so that statistics need to be examined over a long period of time. Since in one recent Australian survey, 41% of females between 20 and 24 were reported as smoking cigarettes, an upsurge in smoking-related diseases, both now and over the next 20–30 years should not be surprising.[13]

As smoking increases in a population, so do lung cancer numbers. And as men are beginning to give up smoking, their lung cancer rates are declining while the rates for women are increasing. But lung cancer is only one of the health consequences of smoking. Some of the other illnesses associated with smoking include various diseases of the respiratory system, (such as cancer of the bronchus, chronic bronchitis and emphysema), cancer of the pancreas, ischaemic heart disease, arteriosclerosis, hypertension, and various other diseases of the circulatory system. The ill-effects of nicotine also pass through the placenta of the pregnant woman, if the woman smokes, damaging the foetus. In the years since 1984, exposure to the smoke of others (passive smoking,) has also become targeted as a health hazard. It is difficult to state accurately the years of life lost as a result of smoking, but the tables created by the Royal College of Physicians state, for example, that a man of 30 who smokes an average of 10–19 cigarettes per day could expect a loss of 5.5 years of life expectancy; that is, about 13% of his life.[14]

It is also not really possible to calculate the costs smoking causes to the community in health service utilisation. This is because everyone eventually has to die from some cause, and treatment of all terminal illness will be expensive. Further, there is not a direct causal relationship between smoking and illness, especially expensive illness; some smokers die instantaneously of a heart attack or an accident, costing little or nothing in health expenses. Also, smoking is commonly not the only health-denying practice in which people indulge; it is often associated with other practices such as a sedentary lifestyle and excessive indulgence in food and alcohol. Nevertheless, in spite of the impossibility of estimating the exact costs of tobacco-related illness, there is no longer any doubt that smoking and a number of illnesses are significantly related, and the human costs of this are sufficiently unpleasant to make anti-smoking campaigns a high priority for health professionals and governments. Tobacco-smoking differs from alcohol and other drug consumption in another very significant way, as the Royal College of Physicians pointed out over 20 years ago: it is not an occasional habit, practised in moderation, which can be taken up and dropped at will. The majority of smokers are so addicted that they need a constant level of nicotine in their bloodstream and can rarely go more than a few hours without a cigarette. On the other hand, the vast majority of drinkers of alcohol, and even users of barbiturates, can tolerate quite long periods of abstention. It is this fact which makes tobacco promotion so different from the promotion of alcohol: the tobacco manufacturers can rely upon a vast, addicted population once the new generation has passed the first resistance; the stakes are therefore very high.

In recent years there has been increased activity on both sides of the smoking issue: those supporting the freedom to smoke and to promote cigarettes against those who want to abolish the use of tobacco. Governments of all nations have found themselves simultaneously on both sides of the debate. All governments gain as well as lose by the existence of the tobacco industry. It was reliably reported in 1984 that the Australian Federal Government received about $800m per year in tobacco excise duty.[15] In addition, a large number of jobs is dependent on the existence of the tobacco industry—these jobs being in the manufacture, distribution and sale of the products, in the advertisting industry, and in the publishing industry in newspapers and magazines, some of which are kept viable by their tobacco advertisements. Some arts and sports sponsorship is also taken up by the tobacco companies, though an increasing number of organisers of such events now refuse to accept this sponsorship. The taxes paid by workers in the industry, and the fact that these people do not depend on unemployment benefits, add considerable weight to governments' argument that the tobacco industry is an important one in the country's economy. Ironically, as a result of the illnesses caused by smoking, there are many jobs in the health sector which would not be there but for the tobacco industry. These include the jobs of health promoters dedicated to wiping out the industry altogether.

Equally strong are the arguments of the anti-smoking lobby, which is also supported by government. There, the emphasis is laid on the illnesses caused by smoking, though the cost estimates of these illnesses vary widely, from the NH & MRC's estimate of $650 million per annum[16] to $2500 m per annum quoted in 1988 by the Anti-cancer Council of Victoria. But, as discussed above, there is no accurate way of costing the health effects of tobacco, and the important anti-smoking argument must rest on social grounds, on the suffering, the disabilities, and the early deaths caused by smoking. The loss to families, the painful suffering of people who contract lung cancer and circulatory diseases, the premature and low-weight births and reduced brain size of smoking-affected foetuses, are not fully quantifiable but represent serious social damage. It is these which have given impetus to the anti-smoking lobby and have forced the tobacco industry ever further into a defensive stance That industry now argues mainly on the basis of people's civil liberty to smoke, presented as an individual right in an increasingly programmed society. The anti-smoking lobby counters by citing the many millions of dollars spent annually on tobacco advertising, the addictive nature of tobacco which takes away people's freedom *not* to smoke, and the right of non-smokers and children to breathe unpolluted air. The language of rights and freedoms is increasingly taking over from the language of dollar costs on both sides of the debate.

The worldwide problem of alcohol

Socially, tobacco and alcohol are drugs of very different kinds and the difference between them is greater than the difference between tobacco and heroin or alcohol and heroin. Unlike tobacco, which is now used only by a minority, alcohol is used at some time by 80–90% of the Australian population.[17] However the amount consumed and the frequency of its use vary enormously. Alcohol, unlike tobacco, can cause seriously disruptive behaviour in many people when drunk in large quantities, because it reduces inhibitions. Alcohol is, for example, associated with over 70% of major violent crimes[18] and with half the motor vehicle crash deaths in Australia.[19]

The drinking of alcohol has been an essential part of the social behaviour of almost all known societies, ancient and modern. Alcohol is often used in ritual and ceremony (Jesus turned water into wine at the wedding at Cana, for example) and occasional drunkenness at times of feasting has been part of these social rituals. But in modern societies, there is a crucial change in general consumption patterns and social attitudes to alcohol. Drinking is no longer confined to special occasions or religious ritual, but is part of the daily life of most of the population. This goes back to the beginnings of Australian society. The Senate Standing Committee Report puts into perspective the agonising of moralists about our 'modern scourge':

> Alcoholism, drunkenness and the basic problems associated with them—such as personal misery, economic ruin and crime—have been features of Australian society since the very first days of the white man's settlement on the continent. . .
>
> . . . Various writers who described the early days of the colony drew attention to the fact that 'many poor settlers were ruined by the craving for liquor', that church services were rendered impossible because of the number of drunken soldiers and convicts surrounding the outside of the place of public worship, and that the colony's first murder, in January 1794, was probably directly related to the theft of money to buy liquor.[20]

The conflict perspective points to the way in which alcohol consumption patterns are structured into industrialised societies, largely due to the massive population increases of the twentieth century. A major part of this change is due to the commercialisation of the production of alcohol in order to make it accessible to the larger populations. Like the tobacco industry, the liquor industry has become a large and important industry, producing large-scale employment, profits for invested capital and considerable revenue for governments, both in the form of excise on the product and in taxes paid by the manufacturing companies and the workers individually.

It is evident, from the Senate Committee's Report quoted above, that conservative authorities have been concerned for many years at the damage caused by excessive alcohol consumption in Australia. However in recent years that concern has escalated, as some adverse consequences have shown up of the liquor industry's successful campaign to increase alcohol consumption. These consequences have included social disruption, traffic crashes, crime and damage to individual health. In addition to the commercial push to increase consumption throughout the population, it is obvious when reading the histories quoted above that there have been in Australia since the first settlement, extremely permissive social attitudes towards heavy drinking. At that time, the dominant, consensus view of society assumed that alcoholics are quite different from controlled drinkers. This is in keeping with the consensus view that the majority of society conforms and is normal, while the minority who act differently are deviant. The evidence is now growing, however, that alcohol abusers, alcoholics and heavy drinkers are not completely different from ordinary drinkers. When the consumption of alcohol rises in any community, there is an increase in the proportion who are drinking to excess,[21] that is, 'any increase in the overall consumption produces a corresponding increase in the incidence of abuse'.[22] Hence, the most important predictor of the level of alcoholic problems is the extent to which alcohol use is integrated in day-to-day living.

The 'alcohol problem' can be encapsulated if one examines the figures on overall consumption in Australia. Three comparisons are useful here: first, the international figures, comparing the amount of alcohol consumed in different countries; second, an examination of the amount of alcohol consumed in one country such as Australia at different periods in its history; third, an examination of the amount of alcohol drunk by different subgroups in Australia at different times. It must be emphasised, however, that surveys on the use of alcohol come up with different results, depending on the agency doing the study, the sampling method, the exact questions asked, the respondents' truthfulness and their ability to recollect their exact consumption, and the researchers' perspective which influences their interpretation of the results.

Because there are clearly no 'correct' or 'accurate' figures of alcohol consumption per country (or consequently within countries) we shall examine the reported trends that emerge from a number of studies of alcohol consumption, done over a period of several years. First, in the various lists of total consumption per country, Australia occupies a position about one-third of the way down. The consumption of alcohol in Australia is always below most of Continental Europe and above Britain, the USA, Ireland and the Scandinavian countries. Second, in the twentieth century there has been a general international trend towards increased alcohol consumption. It was reported by the World Health Organisation[23] that alcohol consumption is increasing even in Moslem countries where traditionally alcohol was proscribed. It is therefore not surprising that total consumption in Australia also increased.

Every Australian report states that overall, alcohol consumption per head increased considerably till 1975 but since then there has been a decrease in the per capita amount of alcohol consumed. 'The major change in the consumption of alcohol in Australia has been in the form in which it is consumed. Since the mid-1970s beer consumption has decreased by 20%...At the same time, however, table wine consumption has increased by approximately 180%.'[24] Particular subgroups vary in their consumption levels, and different researchers report different results for particular subgroups. All surveys, however, show that the middle-aged drink more than the young, that Catholics drink more than Protestants or Jews, and that a high level of alcohol consumption occurs in particular social groups such as seasonal workers, shift workers, and workers in transport, mining or the waterfront.[25] Men drink more than women, though surveys show that over the last decade younger women are drinking more.[26] In the nineteenth century in Australia, the main body of drinkers was male adults, while during the twentieth century, women and adolescents in large numbers have become occasional or frequent drinkers.

The prevalence of alcoholism and the damaging effects of alcohol go together with the highest number of drinkers: it is highest among the Australian-born, especially those of Irish-Catholic origin, and lowest among the migrant groups of Italian, Greek and Jewish origin. It is also related to social position, and is 'at least 3 times more common in the lowest socio-economic groups' than in the highest.[27] It has been argued from the conflict point of view that this is related to the ability of people from the upper classes to hide their problems by being admitted to private clinics rather than to public mental hospitals, to be able to drink in clubs or privately at home rather than to appear drunk in public in the streets, and to employ barristers to enable them to escape drink-driving charges or gaol.[28]

Surveys now show a large number of young people, adolescents under 20, who are drinking more than 8 drinks per day, which is the accepted danger level to health. It has been reported that in Sydney as many as 10% of school children between the ages of 12 and 17 get 'very drunk' at least once a month, and that half of all school children are regular users of alcohol.[29] There is a feeling among many health and education workers that the proportion of teenagers who drink heavily has escalated significantly in recent years.[30] These findings give social planners cause for concern; if these young people continue to drink at such levels, there will be a continuing increase in the prevalence of chronic illnesses such as some mental disorders, liver and heart disease that are associated with excessive use of alcohol.

It seems that the only way in which the social damage caused by alcohol can be reduced is to continue to reduce its overall consumption in the society—and that is an extremely difficult task, given the inter-relationships between the liquor industry, the country's affluence, and most people's desire to enjoy the benefits of alcohol. To radical pluralists it is therefore not surprising that governments have not acted upon the recommendations of reports which have recommended all sorts of restrictions on alcohol production, advertising and sales, as well as countries face the consequences of this drug in similar fashion: by retaining the industry and maintaining the freedom of the majority to drink it, while simultaneously introducing a series of piecemeal programs aimed at patching up the damage that a certain proportion of drinkers do to themselves, their families, and the wider society. Below, we look at that damage in more detail.

Alcohol and chronic conditions

In recent years, the spotlight has been increasingly turned on alcohol as constituting 'the major drug of abuse in Australia, (which)...now constitutes a problem of epidemic proportions...(and is)...a potential national disaster'.[31] There are consequences of excessive alcohol consumption in terms of the effects on personal health, the disruption of family life, absenteeism in industry, industrial accidents, incompetence, and work-group disruption. There is also damage to life and property caused by car crashes; alcohol plays a part in about 40% of fatal crashes.[32] Alcohol is also often associated with violent crimes such as rape. Excess alcohol consumption is a risk factor for a large number of illnesses, including cancers of the digestive system, motor vehicle accidents, other accidents, poisoning and violence, foetal alcohol syndrome, permanent brain damage and cirrhosis of the liver.[33]

It should be obvious from the above discussion that it makes no sense to try to apportion the 'health costs of alcohol' as is so frequently attempted by writers on the subject. There are enormous and unattributable social costs as a consequence of the existence and consumption of alcohol; there are also enormous economic benefits. The general areas where costs are incurred have been described; the social and economic benefits are far wider than is usually mentioned by writers who refer mainly to the excise gained by governments. As does tobacco, alcohol spawns major industries. As an example, the wine industry alone has in the last twenty years become an important part of the Australian economy, affecting rural development and involving the existence of whole towns. It has also created a significant level of overseas exports. The industry employs people in beverage manufacturing, liquor outlets, licensed clubs, the restaurant and entertainment industries, advertising, wine writing and relevant book production. In addition, such industries have strong side-effects; for example, when NSW decided to reduce the permissible alcohol blood-level for drivers from 0.08 to 0.05, the-tow-truck industry protested, panel beaters laid off staff and hospital bed occupancy fell. However, recruitment to the police traffic control unit increased so that more random breath tests could be carried out, and breath-testing kit production rose markedly.

The pluralist perspective emphasises that modern society is so intertwined that even small changes can have a wide impact, so that, rather than trying to assess 'costs to the health system which alcohol causes' or 'economic benefits that alcohol brings', it is more fruitful to consider what might be the wider social goals related to alcohol. Moderate pluralists would value reasonable freedom to drink, a low level of abuse, and a low level of social disruption; having decided on these goals, they would plan a multi-faceted program to achieve them. When discussing the health effects of drugs such as alcohol, it is important to bear in mind the comparison of health damage done by the various drugs (Fig 7.1). Tobacco causes by far the greatest damage, being associated with 81% of drug-related deaths in 1987. Alcohol was associated with 16% of deaths linked to drug use and 3% were due to illicit drugs.[34] However, it is also important to note that from 1977 to 1986, death rates due to illicit drugs decreased by 9%; alcohol deaths were down by 20% and even tobacco deaths have decreased by 6%.[35]

Mood-changing pills

The medical prescription rates of various drugs are also a part of the whole drug issue, since tranquillisers and antidepressants are often used instead of alcohol to achieve an altered mood. The prescription rates of these drugs have increased by a factor of two to three in the years since 1970. For example, tranquilliser prescriptions between 1970 and 1981 increased from 1.17 million prescriptions to 3.69 million; analgesics from 5.25 million to 12.21 million, and antidepressants from 0.68 million to 3.32 million.

Alcohol, as stated above, is used in excess more frequently by men than women. The reverse is true of the over-the-counter and prescription drugs, which are more commonly bought by women and prescribed by doctors for women.

People take drugs for two main reasons: either to restore themselves to what they regard as a 'good' condition without pain and discomfort, or to release themselves from a poor condition they do not enjoy, and to feel happier or calmer. Alcohol as well as a number of pills and powders, such as analgesics, barbiturates, and tranquillisers are taken for these reasons; they are all essentially depressants, slowing down the activity of the central nervous system. Since their functional effect is similar, one has to seek social, not functional, explanations of the fact that men more frequently choose to depress their nervous system with alcohol, while women more often choose pills and powders to achieve the same effect. These explanations are related to social norms and social pressures. Men have the opportunity—and are frequently strongly pressured—to join drinking groups for business or 'mateship', and this allows them to change their mood with a group, in public. By contrast, women, particularly when middle-aged and older, are often very isolated. Hence, when they feel need for a change of mood, they are more likely to resort to taking a pill.

Some of the pills commonly used can be bought over the counter, such as analgesics like aspirin, and antihistamines which have the effect of causing sleepiness; others like barbiturates and tranquillisers are available only on prescription. Surveys report that women take such drugs two to three times as frequently as men.[36] Nevertheless, the total size of the group taking such drugs is relatively small: between 2% and 10% of the population report themselves as taking some pill or powder every day, and many of these people take only one.[37] Renal failure is the major chronic illness resulting from the frequent taking of compound analgesic powders, but no correlation has been found between end stage renal failure and the sales of these powders.[38] Further, when one examines drug-related deaths in Australia, as shown in Table 7.1, it is clear that pills taken, whether doctor-prescribed or self-prescribed, are few in quantity compared to the tobacco and alcohol consumed, especially as the drugs included in the 'drug' category also include all

Table 7.1   Drug-related deaths in Australia, 1986

Tobacco	17,230	81%
Alcohol	3,403	16%
Opiates	213	1%
All other drugs	425	2%
Total deaths caused by drug use	21,271	100%

Source: Commonwealth Department of Community Services and Health. Statistics on Drug Abuse in Australia, 1988. An information document for use in association with the National Campaign Against Drug Abuse. AGPS, Canberra, 1988, p. 33

illegal drugs. The important aspect of 'pill-popping' is not that it contributes to deaths, but that such drugs affect the user's psychological functioning. Hence the questions asked about why people choose to take these drugs and why they are prescribed so frequently by doctors are different from the questions that are raised by alcohol consumption. These questions and answers will differ according to the questioner's theoretical perspective.

Summarising the different explanations of drug-taking

Since the desire to change one's perception or one's mood is so universal, how can one account for the frequent attempts by governments and other social agencies to reduce or abolish the use of the various drugs? From the consensus viewpoint, one would consider the issue to be one of social order. People who hold a consensus perspective are essentially concerned with the need for regulation in human affairs, since regulation holds society together. If people are able to escape from reality by some kind of intoxication, one consequence is that they will abandon or delay fulfilling their responsibilities, which means that some of society's work will not get done as planned. Hence some agency has to be appointed to prevent people from opting out, to punish people who do not perform as they should, and to decide when such punishment is appropriate. In our society there are two main agencies for these purposes: the police and the health professions. These agencies can test people to see if they have taken excessive quantities of the substance (by breathalyser tests, or blood tests for various drugs) and punish them according to rules laid down by the agencies of control. These agencies can also refuse to allow people to purchase the drug; doctors can prescribe tranquillisers or refuse to do so; governments can set minimum ages at which tobacco and alcohol may be purchased. Agents of control such as health agencies can also develop educational programs to try to turn people against ever consuming the drug or wean them if they have started; the consensus perspective endorses this approach.

FREEPOST 393
TIME AUSTRALIA MAGAZINE PTY LTD
(Incorporated in Victoria)
G.P.O. Box 3873
SYDNEY NSW 2001

Social control agents can also punish suppliers and users who try to break the rules.

Essentially the holders of a consensus perspective want to ensure that society's activities continue without serious disruption and therefore people must be, as far as possible, maintained in a sober, active and healthy condition without being allowed to opt out of their social roles. In its extreme form, the consensus perspective becomes highly abstemious, and is epitomised by a puritan approach, which rejects pleasure-seeking and actively promotes discomfort in order to develop physical and mental hardiness. Lord Baden-Powell, the founder of the Boy Scout movement, is a typical example of a believer in this philosophy and wrote in the first edition of 'Scouting for Boys' in 1907, that scouts should in their daily lives train themselves to do without water, by holding a pebble in their mouths to produce extra saliva; he believed the intake of all substances including water should be reduced to the minimum in order to improve the character.

The consensus perspective focuses on the duty of society to minimise deviance. Hence, help is offered to people who fail to meet the standards of sobriety set by the authorities; these people are defined as 'sick'.[39] It is from the consensus perspective that research is sponsored to seek a 'genetic marker' which might predispose some people to alcoholism,[40] and it is from the consensus perspective that drug addiction is called a 'disease' and handed over to health professionals to 'treat'. It is from the consensus perspective that it is argued that people have the right to smoke or drink provided they do not opt out of their social obligations. From this perspective it is also argued that these industries are economically important to our society and produce a product that many people want to buy and that most people use responsibly. It is also from that perspective that it is said that people 'deserve' a reward after doing their day's work, and that others are entitled to produce the drugs at a profit.

Moderate pluralism also acknowledges a diversity of interests and goals. Society is not seen as having a unitary goal of peace and achievement, nor as being a system of oppressors and oppressed. Inequalities are seen as being unavoidable but able to be minimised by the application of principles of justice and equity. From this perspective, addictive drugs should be available and people should be able to choose whether or not to use them except when this use involves harm to others who are innocent. It is regarded that each social group is free to decide which drugs are useful and which should be avoided in its own interests. Women may, for example, choose to join a women's network or to stay home and take tranquillisers, or to go to a hotel and drink alcohol; Aboriginals can, as the Pitjantjatjara have done, ban alcohol from their tribal land or maintain their right to drink with white people.

The radical pluralist perspective, as shown earlier in this chapter, defines the issue quite differently. It also makes quite a different proposal in relation to drugs. The emphasis is on the inequalities of power between social groups and on the need to have a struggle which will change society and reduce the disparities of power. From this perspective a 'power relations theory of alcoholism'[41] has been elaborated. It states that drinking is regulated by power groups in the same way as are all other institutions: that is, the rules are made to suit the main power-groups who in Australia are white, middle-class, middle-aged men. The groups who are vulnerable to punishment as alcoholics are the same groups who are weak in all other aspects of social power—young people, women, and minority groups such as Aboriginals. These subordinate groups need to change the whole social system if they wish to escape being labelled as addicts and being punished accordingly.

The radical pluralist model explains the fact that men drink more alcohol and women take more pills by saying that Australian society is organised more to meeting men's needs than women's. All people need support groups, and men have organised many of theirs around drinking groups in hotels. Women were excluded from hotel bars by law until quite recently, and to a large extent still are by custom. Drinking groups do promote excessive alcohol consumption, but provide social support in exchange. Women, especially, at certain periods of their lives, are excluded from supportive networks in our society. Women at home with small children, middle-aged women whose children and perhaps husband have left, and widowed women in old age often seek support by going to doctors. They are given tranquillisers intead of being helped by referral to support groups which they could join in order to change society and make it more suited to women. Women are pushed back into their low-power positions by having their minds stunned by drugs, which prevents them from obtaining knowledge and money and allows the male-dominated ruling class to ignore their needs. Young people often choose a different remedy for their powerlessness, that of the illegal drug network or the excessive alcohol intake which results in their punishment rather than a more appropriate meeting of their needs.

Radical pluralists perceive an intricate power-play. Governments are described as making elaborate efforts to appear to campaign against cigarette and alcohol promotion, while simultaneously making very certain that their campaign cannot succeed.[42] They license the drugs that bring government revenue, making sure that they choose drugs of addiction on which many people have come to depend, socially and psychologically as well as physically. They do not take away the industrialists' right to promote their drugs, nor counter their expensive advertising with equally effective counter-propaganda. The government and the industrialists are power groups who can, without conscious effort, protect and further each other's interests.[43]

Interactionist theory expresses pluralist views at an individual level. People are seen as having the ability to assess what is good for them and will make choices accordingly. They can see the tobacco advertisements but they can also see the refutations; in society today, with its increasing numbers of action groups and counter-propaganda, no-one is forced continually to submit to the dominance of certain individuals or groups. People can and do act according to their own preferences rather than merely according to societal influences.

In conclusion, drug use is always a reflection of a society and its particular history and values. In Australian society today, a high value is generally placed on the opportunity to seek pleasure by sensory gratification. Drugs are one way of satisfying this wish. The current controversy is about the cost and what to do about it.

8   The changing delivery of health care: old faiths renewed

Community vs institutional health services

The first three chapters of this section have been concerned with the changing patterns of disease and illness in Australia. With the emergence of a range of age-related and lifestyle-related chronic conditions has come a growing awareness that the existing health services are not adequately meeting Australia's health care needs in the late twentieth century.

Institutional services were organised to cope with yesterday's problems, which consisted of acute medical crises and the control of infectious diseases. Today's problems of chronic illness and the longer-term problems of mental disorder and mental handicap were not considered an important part of modern health care delivery. One basic defect is that modern institutional services do not address complaints by handicapped people who have been pushed out of the general life of the community because of their illness. For twenty years or more, people with physical and mental disabilities have complained that they are unable to participate in community life. If physically handicapped, they are blocked by inaccessible entrances and multiple stairs. If mentally handicapped, they are unwelcome in the general community.

But two motives are now driving governments to change the existing patterns of service delivery: first, the need to respond to such complaints, and second, the hope of saving money. Large modern hospitals are extremely expensive to operate, so that there are strong incentives for governments to develop policies which will reduce admissions and the length of time which patients spend in such hospitals. Hence there have emerged twin goals to the restructuring of health care delivery: meeting the wishes of chronically disabled people to be reintegrated into the community, and reducing the cost of caring for them.

It has therefore become important to develop alternative arrangements for managing the health problems of the elderly and disabled, with an emphasis on community-based services, delivered either in small institutions or in people's homes.[1] Examples of smaller institutional settings are hospices, hostels and chronic or nursing-home-type facilities, which are 'low-tech' and thus less expensive. Resources altogether outside the health care system are being mustered to deal with the problems of chronic conditions and handicaps. Already the vast majority of handicapped and frail elderly people live in the community, using resources such as welfare agencies, workplaces, families, volunteers and a variety of domiciliary care agencies. A major response to the AIDS epidemic has been to develop alternatives to inpatient medical management. Thus the network of outpatient medical services and community-based social and health care supports has expanded. As the number of people affected by AIDS increases, the burden on professional and voluntary community organisations will be immense.

Government policies for reintegrating people into the community have been defined in a number of recent reports.[2] Like many government reports, they use the language of moderate pluralism, with words such as 'integration', and 'providing a range and choice'. These policies are now affecting government actions; by gradually closing beds in long-stay hospitals as well as in acute-care hospitals, governments have restricted admissions and reduced lengths of stay. Wilsmere psychiatric hospital in Victoria, for example, discharged its last patient in January 1988. Many of the people who would once have spent their lives in large institutions are being placed in groups in small homes in the general community which is gradually becoming used to seeing them there. This does not mean that all large institutions are now unnecessary: merely that only the most seriously affected people require that kind of care.

While moderate pluralists emphasise that progress and adaptations have taken place in health care delivery, radical pluralists typically perceive barriers to effective change. In the case of community-based services they point out that in order to achieve the goal of saving money but still provide a good service, additional community supports such as domiciliary nurses must be put into the system *before* patients are discharged in large numbers, not afterwards. Governments and bureaucracies are not particularly good at that kind of anticipated service provision and usually appoint such staff only after a number of complaints are made. Radical pluralists consider that this is because government bureaucracies are resistant to changes that would challenge the dominance of the medical elite and its allied interests. People with such a perspective say that when funding is provided for new forms of community-based care, one consequence often is that some money and decision-making power are taken away from doctors and given to other health professionals and administrators. Thus radical pluralists argue that there is generally a period during which the new program swings into action, when people are 'reintegrated into their community', only to find that there are no services available for them although they are unable to manage by themselves. This happened, for example, in NSW in the 1960s with the discharge of patients from mental hospitals, in 1985 when many acute-care hospitals were closed and again in 1987 after the Richmond Report was implemented. Some mental patients were not trained to manage money or use public transport, they had no effective occupation to replace the sheltered workshop or occupational therapy of the hospital, and they did not take their medication regularly. Other people, discharged after an acute episode of a physical problem, were frequently still very ill after surgery or were old, frail and living alone. Often they could not manage at home but no beds were available to provide basic nursing care in an institution. Those who were suffering from a terminal illness needed hospice care; if they were old and frail but not ill or dying, a community hospital, nursing home or hostel would have been the desired location. As budgets everywhere become restricted, however, there are bed shortages in all these institutions. This is another consequence of the tightening of health budgets: people are confronted with having to leave hospital earlier than had been the custom, but often find there is no appropriate care available outside the hospital.

It had been the custom in the past to expect that people would find carers at home, from their families and friends. But this is no longer commonly available. In the past, women outside the paid workforce used to do most of the domestic caring for the younger as well as older family members and these women are now less available. Domiciliary services such as home nursing, household help and delivered meals, which used to be adequate while patients stayed longer and recuperated more fully in hospital, cannot meet the increased demand; governments have increased these services but not sufficiently to meet the growing need due to changed discharge policies. In addition, there is a shortage of nursing staff who find the low wages, poor career structure and unsuitable hours too restrictive and increasingly opt out of nursing altogether, taking up the more attractive work opportunities now available. The consequence is general public dissatisfaction with the health services. There is a real likelihood that the program of deinstitutionalisation may fail because the logistics of its consequences in the community have not been properly addressed.

To summarise this discussion in terms of sociological perspectives, the program of integration was developed by policy-makers with a consensus view. They argued that integration is invariably the rational and sensible approach which will get people out of large institutions into small ones, or into their homes, as quickly as possible. They assumed that families should, and will, rally round and help their frailer members, and that the money governments save by early discharge will be used for other, more needed services. The medical profession and hospitals could then be left to do the highly specialised medical work they are best at doing. From that view, it is pointed out that the government has increased the funding for both institutional and domestic services, though people's expectations for both have grown even more.

This consensus view was subsequently adapted and refined into a moderate pluralist one, whereby it was acknowledged that not all people require the same degree of integration into the community. Moderate pluralists argue that many people do not wish for, or cannot cope with, complete integration. So while some will go to school or work in the general community and live with their families, others will need the professional help and supervision available in hostels, while those with more severe disability and handicap will need care in institutions.

The moderate pluralist perspective is probably the one most commonly expressed at present. First, many institutionalised patients really need or want to be in hospital or nursing homes. It is simplistic to think of significantly reducing institutional services.[3] Extending and improving domiciliary services and hostel accommodation avoids the institutionalisation of some people, but merely delays it in other cases. Community care aims to complement institutional care, not to replace it. Further, care for the aged and infirm can no longer be met by government-supported institutional and community services alone; there is a need to confront and deal with the problems of sharing the responsibility between governments, families, employers, and the local community.[4]

In contrast to those views, proponents of the radical pluralist and conflict views emphasise that the patients have not participated in these decisions because they are relatively powerless to influence events.[5] In the conflict view, deinstitutionalisation is desirable because it would return decision-making to the aged and chronically ill and lessen the profiteering of the medical establishment. People with this perspective believe that in practice, the program is set up to fail because adequate resources are not made available for community services. The community health service is constantly understaffed; this is because members of the dominant class, surgeons and managers of large hospitals, are not trying to make the program a success, and politicians are afraid to antagonise them by forcing them to reduce their expenditure so that money can be made available for alternative types of care.

Alternative medicine: holism

Two systems of health care, scientific and folk, have existed side by side for many years, and in the past they served different populations: the 'medical men' were paid consultants of the upper class, while the 'wise women' cared for the poor, with or without pay. In the twentieth century, scientific knowledge has been able to improve the outcomes when patients saw medical practitioners. As this became known, there was a general movement of patients towards scientifically trained practitioners who still retained their personal relationship with patients. As technology has grown in recent years, however, the practitioners of scientific medicine have become more remote from their patients, their co-workers and the community at large, becoming more involved with their technical roles than with their healing or caring ones.

Increasing numbers of people have been dissatisfied with this change of role and complaints about impersonal and uncaring doctors have increased. This has caused the pendulum to swing, sending some people back to health practitioners who claim to have a holistic approach, which takes into account the whole person, the psyche as well as the soma. But governments have strongly favoured the scientific practitioners, and it is now only the better-off who can consult 'alternative' healers; the health insurance reimbursement structure is such that only registered medical practitioner fees are paid by the national health insurance system. The fees charged by alternative practitioners mostly have to be met in full by the patient, though a small proportion are partially reimbursed by some private health funds.

Alternative medicine is an umbrella term which applies to many different types of health practice which have existed outside the conventional medical system and which have not been given legitimacy by the Australian legislatures.[6] But even the alternative practitioners now have some of the characteristics of the conventional medical system. Just as doctors have increasingly developed new specialties, so have alternative practitioners. Instead of merely 'wise women' and 'midwives', there are now naturopaths, acupuncturists, osteopaths and chiropractors; homeopathic medicine is well institutionalised in British hospitals and used by the Royal Family, hypnotherapy is an offshoot of psychology, and there are even fringe practitioners, such as iridologists and yogi, on the fringes of alternative medicine. At present chiropractors, more than the others, have legal recognition in the form of registration boards, recognised training programs and professional organisations; they also have rights to practise in some hospitals. Chiropractors and osteopaths have postgraduate courses which are recognised by the Higher Education Board. Chiropractic also is recognised for workers' compensation and motor accident insurance purposes,[7] and it has been demonstrated that over the last 10 years chiropractic provides a steadily increasing number of services to Australians.[8]

From all perspectives, it is accepted that alternative medicine is popular because it addresses some of the limitations of conventional medicine. The assumption of the biomedical model is that peoples' physical problems can be treated. Doctors are repeatedly criticised for treating people's physical being separately from their minds, while alternative medicine considers the total person's concerns. Technological and drug interventions that are central to conventional medical treatments are generally avoided by alternative practitioners (though chiropractors pride themselves on taking their own X-rays). Doctors' lack of interpersonal skills is contrasted with the humane and caring attitudes of alternative practitioners.[9] From the consensus perspective, it is considered that scientific medicine has proved its value over the unscientific ideas of alternative practice. Alternative practitioners have not been willing to have their activities subjected to scientific evaluation and there is no evidence that alternative practices are particularly beneficial. From that perspective, it is regarded as dangerous to patients if they seek out alternative practitioners because this may delay help given by a scientifically trained doctor for a curable illness.

From a conflict perspective, alternative medicine has become an issue in the Australian health care system because it is openly challenging the dominance of the medical profession. Almost one million new patients attend chiropractors each year,[10] and since patients have to pay all, or most of the fees, it is clear that they value the services that chiropractors offer. Conventional medical practice is criticised for being fragmented, impersonal and iatrogenic (that is, illnesses are actually caused by supposedly health-promoting activities) and the medical establishment is seen as parochial, conservative and monopolistic.[11] Moreover, science and rationality are not accepted as the sole or even most important bases for health care; emotional, intuitive and subjective experience are more valued. On account of this conflict of basic values, therefore, alternative health care should not aspire to be part of the medical establishment, even if that were possible. As it happens, that is not possible; in the conflict view, the political and economic distances between alternative medicine and conventional medicine make antagonism between them inevitable.

From a pluralist view, it is noted that much of modern medicine has become fragmented; the patients' needs for a personal concerned doctor are too often neglected, and medicine could benefit from incorporating some of the holistic and naturalistic skills into its own practices.[12] Moderate pluralism differs from the consensus view because it does not have a tenet that one basic type of practice can fulfil all needs. It also does not hold that alternative practices need to be approved by the medical profession. For radical pluralists, the objective is not to have a single authority in health care matters; on the contrary, it is desirable to have several independent professional bodies, each with the legal status and financial resources to compete fairly in the health care market. The difference between moderate and radical pluralist perspectives on alternative medicine relates to power.

In the consensus view, legitimate authority to decide health care policy is—and should be—with the medical profession; that profession should continue to play a dominant part in deciding which other health practitioners will be recognised, what sort of work other practitioners can and cannot legally undertake, how they can acquire their clients, what fees can be charged and so forth.[13] Moderate pluralists say that there should be many different forms and providers of health care available for clients; in a free society, people should have the right to consult anyone they wish and to use their own money as they wish. Moderate pluralists also believe that any group should have the right to form associations, recruit new members, establish training programs and attract clients. Thus midwives, osteopaths, optometrists, physiotherapists and psychologists should all be equally able to promote themselves. However, these pluralists would be concerned if some of these groups attempted to do things for which they are not qualified and thus become a danger to the public. Thus they raise the question of who decides who is qualified to do what.

The government's acceptance of a moderate pluralist view is shown by the fact that a number of health professions have increased their legal rights in the last ten years. The growing militancy of chiropractic organisations shows how groups of practitioners can become interest groups, lobbying the government for resources and legislation more favourable to them. However, the right to be registered, to form associations and to become educated is not now the major issue. The real difference between the medical and alternative practitioners occurs at the financial level: when patients go to see a registered doctor, the bulk (or the whole) of the doctor's fees are reimbursed from government funds, so that medical care is free or almost free to the patient. If an alternative practitioner is consulted, there is no government reimbursement at all, and only very partial and reduced reimbursement by some of the private health insurers. There is therefore no way in which alternative practitioners can equal medical practitioners as providers of care and it is this aspect which is stressed from the conflict and pluralist perspectives; there is not a real choice available for even well-off patients because doctors have managed to monopolise government reimbursement.

The self-help movement

Self-help means limiting one's dependency on professionals—especially doctors—for the diagnosis, treatment or ongoing care of a health problem. It is undertaken by individuals in a casual manner when, for example, they decide to follow a diet or measure their own blood pressure; alternatively it takes place when several individuals with a common problem band together and work out a program of care and support, as is done by women who have had a breast removed. The self-help movement emphasises the need for people to be self-reliant, both in relation to particular illnesses and in maintaining their health in general.[14]

The self-help movement has partly grown out of the conservative view that people should take responsibility for their own welfare and that governments should intervene as little as possible. It is also a direct product of the emphasis on healthy personal lifestyle as a means of thwarting the negative effects of industrialisation, urbanisation and other environmental causes of ill-health.[15] Another influence has been the emergence of groups advocating the rights of consumers, in particular consumers of health care. The need to contain the costs of high-tech medical care is yet another reason why self-care—like alternative medicine—is advocated. Both self-care and alternative therapies can be seen as part of the move to deinstitutionalise health services. Bringing care of illness and promotion of health back into the community makes it less bureaucratic, less impersonal and less dominated by the medical profession. The self-care philosophy is akin to that of alternative healers; both call for less dependence on conventional medicine through the development of therapies and organisations that patients themselves can control. Both decry the 'expropriation' of health care by the professions.[16]

Sometimes self-care is undertaken by people who want to escape the unpleasantness of medical treatment or to avoid iatrogenic illnesses. Sometimes the self-care is initiated because people feel that the health services do not take into account the individuals' particular needs and priorities, particularly their desire for information and support which they believe is better provided by other people experiencing similar problems. Most self-care has grown around chronic, disabling and stig-matised conditions for which conventional professionals have no cures and no means of alleviating the pain and discomfort of the patients and their families. As a result there has been a rapid rise in the formation of groups of patients and families who have experienced alcoholism, drug addiction, mastectomy, multiple sclerosis and mental illness. There is also a wide range of groups which aim at weight control, exercising, lobbying against tobacco and alcohol advertising, and various other forms of health promotion. Such groups are formed on the following general principles:[17]

1 Membership consists of those who share a common condition, situation, heritage, symptom or experience.
2 They work on the principle of peer solidarity with no pay-off for professionalism or expertise.
3 They rotate the roles of adviser and advised, director and directed in order to avoid the development of an expert elite.
4 They are self-governing, soliciting donations and subscriptions from the public as well as getting funds from governments.
5 They are cooperative rather than competitive in their structure.
6 They minimise referrals to other agencies or professionals.
7 They offer a supportive phone or fellowship network between meetings.

These characteristics show that the self-help movement is in some ways similar to other social movements such as the feminist and Aboriginal rights movements. All aim to create an emotional, supportive and consciousness-raising fellowship which avoids rules and regulations, hierarchies, competition and judgement which are characteristic of the white male-dominated order of Australian society. Those movements arise out of pluralist or conflict views of the world, although it is important to remember that not all proponents hold such views with equal force. In fact, some proponents of self-care feel that this is complementary to mainstream medical care and should be an integral part of it; similarly, some alternative practitioners have considerable respect for the medical and scientific establishment and would like to be accepted by it.

The consensus explanation of the self-care movement is that it represents only a vocal minority who are not satisfied with the conventional health care system. The moderate pluralist view of self-care follows the same lines as the pluralist view of all health care: a mixed system should be allowed to develop rather than either a medically dominated one or a free-for-all without any government controls. In the interests of controlling costs and maximising benefits and social justice, there should be freedom of competition and choice among conventional and alternative providers, between institutional and community care, and between high-tech and low-tech interventions. The power of each will fluctuate at different times in accordance with changing conditions of need, demand, efficacy and the availability of resources. The radical pluralist perspective, however, focuses on the powerlessness of alternative practitioners and self-help groups, who lack legal recognition and are given only minimal government resources. Dependence on government funding is particularly marked in Australia because there are hardly any private foundations from which funds could be sought. Self-help groups lack influential contacts because they exclude the professionals who hold most power. In Australia, self-help groups are mainly funded from various government sources; they therefore collapse if they cannot get government support of one form or another. One of the consequent problems is that they are somewhat wary of speaking out against the government.

Nutrition policy

'Unbalanced nutrition ranks with smoking and high alcohol consumption as one of the three major risk factors for premature death in Australia'.[18] Diet contributes to our major diseases: cancer, diabetes, cardiovascular diseases, and many others such as gall bladder disease, cirrhosis of the liver, anemia and dental caries.[19] Having said that, it should be pointed out that there is, however, still a degree of controversy about the extact nature of the links between diet and health.[20] Modern diseases are caused by many factors, and risk factors such as diet interact with other possible predisposing factors like smoking, age, sex and genetic endowment. However, there is a broad degree of agreement among all authorities that people should be encouraged to modify their eating habits in order to increase their chances of leading a longer, healthier life. In particular, the main malnutrition problem in Australia is that of excess weight, which is clearly associated with excessive consumption of fat and sugar. Considerable publicity about these dietary inadequacies has brought about an increasing awareness in the past decade of the importance of diet to health. Data on food consumption of Australians over the last decade indicate that changes have occurred and are, in general, in the right direction.[21] However, much diet modification is still needed. There has, for example, been no change in the consumption of fats by Australians.[22]

There are alternative explanations of this pattern of consumption. In the consensus view, the excessive intake of sugar and fat merely proves how affluent our society has become, and that people are free to choose the foods they prefer. This view emphasises that choices are easily available and everyone can decide their own eating patterns. The conflict perspective, by contrast, emphasises the links between malnutrition, ill-health and social class. For example, poor people are said to be exploited by the advertising and fast-food industries.

Alternatively, the nutrition issue can be examined by looking at the more immediate social frameworks in which eating takes place and the attitudes of those who deal in the preparation and presentation of food. These cultural aspects of nutrition are of more concern to people with an interactionist perspective.

When we eat, we react to an internal drive—hunger contractions in our intestines. We all have to eat sometimes. But dietary patterns are learned in detail in all societies, and are a central element in their cultures. Whether a healthy adult feels hungry two, three or four times a day, and when, is culturally patterned and is influenced by social interactions. It is worth spelling this out in more detail in order to see just how complex a behaviour pattern is involved in an aspect of daily life which is so taken for granted.

All societies classify foods in terms of:

1 *Edible and non-edible:* for example, breast milk is not edible for adults in our society, nor is human flesh, horse or dog flesh, though all are biologically possible sources of protein.
2 *The way it is prepared:* Orthodox Jews cook meat and milk in different vessels, and in most societies a whole industry develops around different kinds and shapes and functions of cooking pots and eating utensils. Some foods are customarily eaten soft or hard, cut up into different shapes and thicknesses, cooked for long or short periods of time or eaten raw.
3 *By group or class:* fit for animals but not for people; fit for people of one social class but not another, fit for children but not adults.
4 *By place in time:* some foods are eaten at festivals but not every day,

some foods are for mourning but not for feasting; some food is suitable for the first meal of the day but not for the evening meal, some are edible only in summer or only in winter.

5 *Place of eating:* different foods are eaten at a picnic, in a restaurant, and on the street.

6 *Food taboos:* some foods cannot be eaten during Lent; some cannot be eaten except at Christmas; some cannot be eaten by people who are trying to promote health and some foods are never eaten in certain societies.

7 *Eating manners:* food can be eaten with fingers or utensils; chewed with closed or open mouth; burping may be acceptable or unacceptable.

There are further complications in the cultural variations regarding food. The standard 'good breakfast' in Australian and Britain used to a starchy cereal, some more starch by way of bread, and some protein in eggs or meat. This breakfast might have contained fruit juice, milk, tea or coffee, but not alcohol. This contrasts with the newly developing Australian habit of Continental breakfasts, consisting of bread rolls, butter, jam and coffee or tea—a very low protein meal indeed. Continental breakfasters tend to have a large midday dinner, since their breakfast leaves them hungry by the time the middle of the day comes. By contrast, the typical sandwich lunch is a light, comparatively low-protein meal, leaving its eaters hungry and anxious for a large evening meal. Taste, smell, texture, colour, consistency and temperature are other variables. Thus a food can be nutritionally acceptable but the meal not be appetising because of the way it is prepared.

Migration patterns always have important cultural effects on eating patterns. Successive waves of migrants have made significant changes in Australian eating habits. The early British settlers brought plain roast and boiled meat, porridge, and fish and chips. The Chinese gold seekers made the Chinese restaurants ubiquitous. The central European refugees in the late 1930s and early 1940s brought black bread, rich German cakes and coffee, Hungarian goulash, Viennese apple strudel and German sauerkraut. After the Second World War, successive waves of Italians, Hungarians, Lebanese, Spanish and Turkish migrants have brought us pizzas, pastries and paellas—not to speak of the American invasion of hamburgers and fried chicken. These food changes have brought about the development of a whole new range of businesses such as chicken farms, restaurants and the publication of cookbooks.

There are, in addition, many moral values attached to foods in all societies. Cooking symbolises love and care, and rejection of food becomes a rejection of the cook's love. Men in Australia are not usually the main cook in the home, but they usually cook outdoors at barbecues. Waste of food is seen as a sin by older people who lived through times of food shortages. Fatness or thinness is valued depending on the culture at the time. In parts of Asia, a fat man used to be seen as a high status person because he could afford to eat so much. Some ethnic groups insist on what nutritionists call 'overfeeding' their babies and children, since they regard a fat child as a healthy child with a loving mother. In other subcultures such as in the Australian upper-middle class, thinness is seen as desirable by educated people who are trying to ward off obesity and heart attacks.

In all societies, eating patterns change as outside influences enter the society. Nutritionists point out that the major changes that have occurred in the Australian diet are identical to the changes occurring to diets in other affluent countries. As wealth and purchasing power increase, cereals and root vegetables are dropped in favour of proteins and saturated animal fats, and there is an increased consumption of refined sugar in all its forms. The implication is that the majority of people prefer the taste of such foods, despite the growing evidence that this kind of diet results in damage to health, in particular as a contributing factor in heart disease, cerebrovascular diseases and certain cancers. Hence the promotion of nutritional changes is high on the agenda of the planners of health promotion programs.

Health promotion

Attempts at health education were the precursors of today's health promotion programs. When it was realised that much sickness and disability is associated with people's lifestyles, preventive strategies were sought by doctors, nurses and health educators. This was an extension of the focus of conventional medical practice which is based on treatment of the individual. The assumption behind health education programs was that when people are told what behaviours are damaging to their health, they will change their behaviour. Health education was initially carried out on a one-to-one basis; like conventional medicine, health education focused on the individual. However, the results of these efforts were not encouraging; although people were fully aware that activities such as smoking were damging to their health, they continued to do the things that gave them pleasure. Hence educators decided to change their strategy, and to counter the advertisements of the tobacco, liquor and food industries by equally attractive advertisements promoting healthy lifestyle activities.

In recent years, there has been an increasing volume of complaints about the level of disease in our society. It is ironic that, as more and more treatments and cures are developed, the amount of illness in the community continues to increase. As the length of life increases, there is of course more time to be ill, as well as time to be healthy. It is an old saying that an ounce of prevention is better than a pound of cure. Hence, in addition to the pursuit of cures for the illnesses which we now have more time to endure, professionals are trying to develop effective preventive strategies. It is hoped that some of today's chronic illnesses and disabilities can be prevented, or at least delayed, so that they will occur for a shorter proportion of people's lives.

It should be noted that the call for 'prevention' makes sense only if it is accepted that it does not refer to all conditions and diseases, since some conditions are much more amenable to prevention than are others. In theory at least, some conditions such as accidental injuries and deaths are almost totally avoidable, but this would require considerable environmental modification. AIDS can be controlled but only with the complete cessation of certain sexual and drug-taking practices. And it makes little sense to say that heart disease and cancer can be largely prevented, since death must eventually come as a result of some cause. Even the Seventh Day Adventists, whose lives approach the ideal that lifestyle reformers recommend, die from causes similar to those of the rest of the population, though some years later. It has been reported, in studies comparing Seventh Day Adventists with two general population samples, that the Seventh Day Adventists initially showed 'less impairment of blood pressures, of plasma cholesterol and plasma urate concentrations, and of lung ventilatory capacity...(but) with increasing age, the level of breathlessness, reported heart disease, hypertension, and hypertensive and diuretic therapy...approached that of the comparative groups'.[23] Hence 'preventive efforts can be expected to do only two things: to delay premature deaths among that half of the population which does succumb before the quoted ages and to improve the quality of life of the whole population by improving its health'.[24]

These are clearly worthwhile aims, but they are neither riskless nor costless.[25] Often the risk of a preventive measure cannot be fully understood until after it has been applied to large numbers of people for a considerable time. Furthermore, promoters of particular preventive measures tend not to measure all the costs which offset the savings they calculate; most analyses have looked only to the savings in medical expenses and have not considered some of the other costs incurred, such as people's time in exercising, or the added costs of food purchase and preparation according to new nutritional guidelines. Such research as exists tends to show that sometimes prevention, and sometimes cure, buys more health for the same money.[26] Certainly with AIDS the value of education and prevention has been obvious.[27] In any case, preventive programs usually have to include both preventive and curative efforts, so the most important decision to be made is really what mix of prevention and therapy is best. Only very rarely does a preventive strategy eliminate the condition completely. Unwanted pregnancies will still occur even if everyone uses contraceptives, heart attacks and strokes will still occur even if people exercise and do not smoke. Curative care is still needed for those who suffer the disease despite reasonable efforts to avoid it, as well as for those who have accidents or suffer other diseases for which no known preventive or delaying strategy exists.

The evidence shows that prevention is not a path to lower medical expenditures, even when it does lead to better health.[28] Policy makers with a consensus view often emphasise only cost reduction, and thus imply that a preventive strategy should be used only if it saves money. From a pluralist perspective this makes no sense, since better health is surely a worthy goal in its own right, and should not merely be sought when it comes free. But recent evidence shows that good health does not come free and that prevention does cost money. Hence 'choosing investments in prevention is thus an economic choice like any other. Prevention offers good things at some additional cost...(and so we have to ask)...are the gains in health a reasonable return for the risks and costs'.[29] In some cases the answer is yes: the gain of many disability-free years for a young person prevented from having a car crash, a child saved from drowning, or a thousand measles cases prevented, is obviously worthwhile. But such strategies do require a considerable social investment, and not only from the health sector. For it is not only alcohol that makes roads unsafe: it is also bald tyres, excessive speed, poorly designed and maintained roads, and poor lighting. Children will drown less frequently if all pools are surrounded by fences, and will get poisoned less often if tablets are dispensed in child-proof packs, but these actions also cost money.

Efforts at prevention have been conceptualised as programs of health education, health promotion, or as preventive strategies. The consensus position argues that individuals are, and wish to be, responsible for their own health, and therefore if they have unhealthy habits, they may choose to continue indulging them. Health educators have only the responsibility to give out information which people may choose to use or to ignore. Food and smoking habits, for example, are regarded as areas of individual choice. The consensus view has been expressed by the health policies of several governments, for example the Australia wide 'Help Yourself to Health Campaign' in 1979 which used stickers, T-shirts and balloons to tell people to 'feel responsible for their own health', and the New South Wales Healthy Lifestyle Program which used similar techniques.

The conflict view regards this as a total abrogation of responsibility, arguing that unhealthy lifestyle behaviours are imposed upon people as a result of external pressures.[30] For example, multinational companies use powerful advertising campaigns to sell cigarettes, alcohol and processed foods. But the social and economic analysis of health and illness is not in harmony with a free-enterprise economic system, so people with a conflict view are not optimistic about the likelihood that health promotion will bring about real change.

Proponents of the conflict perspective have criticised the individualism underlying the healthy lifestyle and health promotion movement.[31] They say it ignores the economic and social forces beyond individuals which affect and limit the actions individuals can choose. Real freedom of choice—in health as in other areas of life—is illusory. Rather, one's place in society has far greater effect on what health actions are available and which of them are utilised. If one believes that people can be educated to change their ways, one is implying that poor health and inadequate preventive behaviours are the result of lack of motivation or lack of knowledge, while in fact people's health status and health behaviours are largely determined by their job conditions, and the money they have left over after their rent, food, clothing and transport are paid for. This is all determined by the capitalist structure of society.

It is now known that in Australia, as in other Western societies, premature mortality, chronic preventable disabilities due to work accidents or road crashes and poor preventive health practices are associated with low income, low education and social minority group status.[32] In the conflict view, therefore, preventive health policy should take into account class differences and the economic factors and social structures that reinforce them. Pluralists do not agree; they consider that major social change will not solve community problems and suggest, instead, a combination of approaches. They note that social groups differ in their orientation to health, nutrition, fitness and smoking, and suggest that local conditions should influence program selection. People can be encouraged to join small groups and participate in planning their own local preventive programs. Such activities would be based in the communities in which people live and work, so that health problems can be analysed in the social environment in which they occur. The slogan 'think socially and act locally', can be called a pluralist approach to health promotion.[33]

In the pluralist view, both the changes in health care that are possible and those that are desirable are much more complex than those seen from either the consensus or conflict perspective. Services for sick individuals will continue to be the main focus of health care because people want them and because there are strong incentives for doctors to provide individual treatments. In the moderate pluralist view the allied interest groups in the health sector—doctors, drug manufacturers, private hospitals—do indeed have positive economic, social, health functions. Moderate pluralists would argue that the combination of these interests is not dysfunctional, because community-based, preventive and alternative health care systems can coexist with conventional, curative medicine. They would also argue that in our democratic society interest groups can form around issues if they wish to have service developed; indeed, frequently such groups lobby successfully for these changes. An example they give is the way the gay community and medical groups have worked together to achieve society-wide AIDS preventive education around the practice of safe sex and needle exchange. Another example is in the area of occupational health and safety, where the employers, unions and governments are cooperating to bring about far-reaching changes (see ch 11).

In contrast to the moderate pluralists, radical pluralists argue that there is constant conflict and waste of resources in the tussle between the powerful interests who ultimately can block change. These pluralists would say that health promotion in general is underdeveloped because its proponents do not have political and organisational strength to win support for their cause. Bringing back the disabled and chronically ill into the community, treating people who are ill as if their minds were connected to their bodies, and attempting to avoid accidents and defer or avoid illness are all worthy objectives which, in the pluralist view, often fail. These failures may be partly due to differences in values between professionals and the people whose interests the professionals want to serve. Prevention is an invisible good and is not something politicians can claim as a personal achievement. For this reason, community workers find it difficult to change the practices of politicians who give most health money to hospitals while the community program limps along; the most prestigious health practitioners are still the technologists, not the holistic practitioners, and the strategies of preventive health practice and health promotion lack an adequate funding base while curative medicine receives almost all the attention. Radical pluralists believe, therefore, that society cannot properly implement old faiths, such as prevention being better than cure and home care being preferable to hospital care.

Part III

Technology

9 The diverse effects of medical technology

The development of new technologies

In all developed societies since the 1960s, there has been a considerable increase in the proportion of the national wealth that is spent in the health sector. A number of reasons can be cited, but all are connected to the invention and increasing use of complex medical technologies.[1] At the same time, public health measures which have significantly reduced infectious diseases have resulted in longer life expectancy, while the levels of chronic diseases in later life have increased. As a result of a longer and more comfortable life and an affluent economic system, people have begun to expect higher standards of health care; and because the levels of education in the community have risen, more people can understand the relevance of the available technologies which are daily described in the media.

A technology is essentially a tool outside the human body, which is used to perform a desired task. Medical technologies include drugs, anaesthesia, surgical procedures and instruments, devices implanted into the body, machinery to do tests and the scientific knowledge which enables all these tools to be put to use.

It is important to note that technologies are rarely developed by chance or by lucky accident; preceding their development are concepts, theories and ideas, and accompanying their diffusion are explanations of their purpose and capacity. When the actual device such as, for example, a ventilator, has been perfected, it cannot merely be bought and used; it requires support systems, space, technicians, spare parts, and skilled staff to operate it and understand its outputs. Specialists to decide when and how the technology can be used are a basic necessity; they check whether it performs according to the manufacturer's claims, whether it is cost-effective, and what damage it may cause to the patient or the health worker as a 'side-effect.'

Not all new technologies consist of large, expensive machines which require capital, support systems and expertise. Low technologies, such as a relatively cheap drug or a simple procedure, may be simple to use and staff may require only brief training in their application. Vaccines for immunisation, simple contraceptive procedures, and stress management programs are also examples of this type of technology. But the fact that some technologies are simple and cheap does not mean that they have little social impact. Just because they are simple and cheap, they may be very widely used and in that way affect a large number of people.

One example of a cheap technology which has had extensive societal consequences is the birth control pill, which is now one of the most widely used drugs. It has been accused of causing cancer and heart disease, and of being imposed on women without adequate testing. Yet millions of women have accepted its risks because the pill has offered almost complete control of fertility. The pill's widespread use has changed women's position in the family, in the economy, and in society. Women have been able to rely on their ability to continue in the workforce and earn their own incomes, and have therefore increased their power relative to men both in the family and the community. Since sexual intercourse now mostly leads to reproduction only by choice, sexual customs have changed and sex can be a purely recreational activity. But since sexual morality has underpinned some of the most cherished values such as love and family relationships, the existence of the pill has had an enormous moral impact on the whole of society, not only on its users. Even our housing structures have changed, since young people now frequently move away from the parental home in order to lead independent sex and social lives without taking on the responsibilities of family life.

Even inexpensive, 'low' medical technologies, then, have the potential to create widespread social change. However, the greatest modern controversies tend to centre round the so-called 'high technologies': organ transplants, nuclear magnetic resonance (NMR) scanning machines and intensive care facilities are examples, and they create the greatest impact on the media and hence on the public mind. They are also, of course, the most expensive and the money spent on them has increasingly become a major part of the government's expenditure on health.

The cost of medical technologies

Certain characteristics are common to most modern medical technologies. They are generally expensive, and some technologies are extremely expensive, and it is their cost which has caused health policy to enter the political debate, where it is inevitably going to remain since it is only governments which can pay the full cost of technological health care. Very few people will reach their death, whenever that occurs, without experiencing a disease or deterioration which will result in their being prescribed considerable amounts of technologies. Tests, drugs, surgery and resuscitative machinery will accompany their last months, weeks and days. These are so expensive that it is no longer possible for people on average incomes to save enough money to pay for health services for serious illnesses. Apart from the risk of sudden accident or serious illness, which applies to everyone, even healthy people can no longer expect to go through middle and old age and merely to pay for an occasional medical consultation.

Commonly, the outcome of a visit to the general practitioner will be a series of tests, one or more prescriptions for drugs, and perhaps a referral to a specialist. The full cost of these services is likely to be as much as an average wage-earner's weekly income. If further tests or treatment are then ordered, or a stay in hospital with possibly some surgery performed, the cost of a single such episode will add up to several thousand dollars. Without government funds and some kind of health insurance, bankruptcy would be a common occurrence. Rarely today is only one doctor involved in an episode of serious illness, and in the case of an accident there are always several specialists involved as well as many hospital services. These activities are due to the complexities of modern technological medicine. No doctor can single-handedly manage a modern hospital service which includes provision of drugs, surgery, diagnostic tests, X-rays, nursing and various ancillary services. Nor do the costs start only when the patient first attends the doctor or hospital. In order to provide a modern health service, drugs must be developed and tested for effectiveness, safety and purity; they are then marketed and sold. Screening tests must be developed and checked for accuracy; then the biological material has to be run through complicated machines and the results interpreted by specialists who receive long periods of training. Hospitals have to be built, stocked with machines, and staffed with skilled people. A number of different specialty groups have to be trained to understand and operate all this technology and to organise the necesssary personnel.

It is therefore no longer possible to return to a situation where the relationship between one patient and one doctor is at the core of a health system. In every industrialised country, there is increasing government involvement in health care. In a conservative medical newsletter, a doctor pointed out to his readers who had been demanding that governments should leave medicine to the doctors, that 'anyone who seriously believes that health care can be simply a private contractual matter between patient and doctor—on a par with what of a plumber or architect and his client—is suffering from a good dose of fairy-tale-itis'.[2] In every industrialised country, which means every country where technologies of many kinds are being developed, the continuing increase in health costs has made health a major political issue with economists becoming the main consultants to governments.

The medical specialist in a technological age is no longer an individual entrepreneur who can deliver health care according to personal inclination. Complex services require complex organisations, support systems and training processes and cannot be left to individual specialists' preferences. High technology specialists are now members of large teams, managing expensive resources, and are forced to be accountable for their use of money because it is paid mostly by the government. Because individual patients cannot afford to pay for all the care they might use, the whole community has to pay through the tax or insurance system. But people are always reluctant to pay taxes and insurance premiums, so there is always a shortage of public money and no government can afford to provide all the health personnel, technology and facilities that could be used. The availability of both expensive technology and skilled staff is therefore limited and some kind of rationing has to be introduced. No country can afford unlimited access to services like neonatal intensive care, cardiac surgery or organ transplants, so decisions have to be made, whether openly or secretly, about the way in which these services should be rationed.

In the days when the doctor's main task was to diagnose, prescribe and possibly to do simple surgery, the cost of medical technology was not an important problem. Health costs were limited because fees were charged only for the work that doctors were able to do with their own hands and minds. Technologies have changed this situation, because technologies are essentially extenders of the doctor's own mind and body. Machines help in diagnosis, prognosis, decision-making and treatment, and the machines do not run by themselves but require specialist doctors to interpret their findings, nursing staff to monitor information obtained from machines and apply doctors' instructions, engineers to improve the techniques, technicians to correct malfunctions, and buildings to house all these machines and people. Hence, since the 1960s, an increasing amount of the attention by the media and the public has been focused on the cost of the new technologies used in the health sector. Attention is often focused on the initial capital cost of the equipment. At one extreme, a nuclear magnetic resonance scanner, for example, costs one to two million dollars. However, a great deal of money is also spent on less expensive technologies such as renal dialysis machines or intensive care cots for tiny newborns, because those are bought in larger numbers.

But the capital cost of technologies is small compared with the cost of operating these machines. In the past, hospitals used to be grateful when voluntary associations raised money to donate a machine: now such gifts are referred to as 'a cuckoo in the nest', because from the first year the new machine usually needs far more in consumables, maintenance and staff than it originally cost. In about three to five years, the machine is likely to become obsolete and because people have come to expect its use, it becomes hard to resist replacing it with what, by then, is usually a more complex machine. 'The prize for being one of the first hospitals to purchase a newly developed machine is to become the first with an outdated model'.[3]

Not only is high technology expensive in itself, but it tends to generate expenditure on other items that may individually be comparatively cheap, but whose accumulated use adds up to very large sums. This is because each patient is given more tests and treatments; a test, as well as giving information, frequently also raises questions, which are answered by further tests, surgery or drug trials.

High technology is usually first installed in specialist hospitals and used on patients who are selected as being the most likely to benefit from its capacities. Initially, therefore, the costs are relatively restricted. But once the first results seem encouraging, they are made public by enthusiastic manufacturers. Well before any full evaluation is made, large numbers of doctors and patients are tempted to try the new technology. These doctors are not so skilled, and the patients are not so carefully selected as were the first group; they tend to be less in need of the new technology, and less likely to benefit from it.[4] The total costs rise as the number of patients treated increases and the severity of conditions regarded as suitable for treatment is reduced. Rarely is a proper trial carried out, but the procedure becomes standard practice until, after a considerable period, its damaging side-effects or ineffective results become very obvious. In a technologically biased society, the assumption is generally made that a new technology will be an improvement, and the onus of proof is more strictly put on those who doubt its usefulness than on those who claim its benefits.

The costs of modern health care now have the potential to distort the governmental budget mechanism, and the whole question of health care delivery is being regularly reviewed. It has become clear that health care, like all social goods, has to be rationed, but the basis of that rationing is still being debated.

The effects of technology on health care delivery

Medical technology has now become so pervasive in Western societies that, whether ill or well, everyone's life is affected. It surrounds us all, from birth to death, including the prevention of conception and the assisting of couples who find difficulty in conceiving. It screens people in pregnancy, birth, mid-life, old age and throughout the dying process; it is available in health and attempts to treat us in illness. Immunisation, drugs, surgery, tests and life support machines are a part of everyday life. Because healthy everyday life has been so affected by medical technology, the whole of society has been affected by the health sector.

It is also for this reason that medical technology has totally changed the way health care is delivered in Australia.

Doctor–patient relationships
It is widely assumed that the doctor–patient relationship is the core of medical treatment. When medical technology was in its infancy, people who perceived themselves as ill would put themselves in the hands of a doctor, who knew them and their families and who would be in charge of the treatment during the whole course of the disease. This does of course still happen, most commonly in rural areas where specialist services are sparse. It is much less common in Australia's urban areas, where 85% of the population lives, and where technologies and specialists are more available. It is also uncommon, even in rural areas, when serious illness occurs and patients are transferred to the specialist hospitals in urban areas. When a technology is developed, a considerable amount of expertise is required to know when and how it shoud—or should not—be used; expertise is also needed to interpret the results it shows, to assess the seriousness of any side-effects, to determine whether to continue or discontinue using that technology or to try another one. Often a number of specialists are needed to make all these determinations for one condition, and when patients have several health problems simultaneously, specialists with different training are called in to treat each condition.

In most such situations no single doctor is in charge of the patient's treatment, and in many situations no doctor coordinates what is happening. An elderly patient living at home may, for example, be tested and treated for angina, hypertension, diabetes, glaucoma and urinary problems, each by a different specialist in different consulting rooms. In the meantime the general practitioner dispenses sleeping tablets and occasional referrals, but does not know the full treatment the patient is having because one specialist has referred the patient to another specialist, rather than returning the patient to the general practitioner. In cancer treatment, to give another example, surgeons, radiotherapists, chemotherapists and oncologists may all be treating the patient, and when the patient is admitted to hospital various duty registrars and resident medical officers will be in charge at times of crisis, so again there is no single doctor who has an on-going relationship with the patient. The more complex the technology, the greater is the number of specialists who become involved, so that in hospital the patient often does not know whom to consult about a particular problem, and there is little possibility of developing and maintaining a traditional doctor–patient relationship.

Thus the role of the hospital doctor has now fundamentally changed, particularly in the case of those doctors who specialise in high technology medicine. Instead of making independent decisions about treatment, 'according to personal inclination, inspiration, intuition, or prejudice'[5] doctors have to work together with a team of specially trained staff; resources such as operating theatres, respirators, and neonatal intensive care are not always available when and where a particular doctor wants them. Even if money were unlimited, there would not be enough skilled staff, and particular resources such as organs suitable for transplantation are just not available for all who could use them.

The consequences of these newly developed medical abilities are not always straightforward. The situation will be better understood with an example: the need for kidneys from cadavers to be transplanted to people whose own kidneys have failed. The shortage has been such that pressure groups, such as Kidney Foundations, have succeeded in persuading governments to place an endorsement on every driver's licence which each driver may sign stating that in the event of the driver's death by accident, the kidneys or any other organ may immediately be used for transplantation. For each individual who receives an organ the donation is a benefit, but overall, these gifts will pose a serious imbalance in our health services. This is because the staff, the money and the expertise must be taken away from other needed areas of health services, leaving many equally valid needs unmet. Clearly, while each medical intervention may seem to be extremely useful, the overall effect of doctors' and patients' demands may become a serious problem.

A further aspect of new inventions is that high-technology medicine has resulted in the development of many more medical specialities and sub-specialities, as well as specialties in nursing and in the other health professions. A consequence is the development of inter-specialty rivalries, with certain doctors demanding that technologies be provided for their particular specialty which may not necessarily be in the best interests of the total patient population. One example is that of computerised tomography scanning for head injuries in accident and emergency departments, where demands are often made by clinicians that everyone with a mild head injury should be scanned. This would increase the accuracy of diagnosis but most scans would be found to be normal; the costs would be very high, and the consequence would be shortages of money and skilled staff for other sections of the health service.

Priorities for use of all such high technologies, which are inevitably in short supply, have to be determined between various specialist groups. Indeed, there is evidence that some demands for increased availability of particular resources come more as a result of rivalry between, for example, neurosurgeons and neurologists, or between heart and liver transplant surgeons, than from patient need. These rivalries increase at times of economic pressure and resource restrictions, since

for many doctors conspicuous private consumption (e.g. a Rolls Royce) has been replaced as a status symbol by conspicuous public consumption. To be seen to be developing and expanding HT (high technology) procedures signals success in the competition for scarce resources—as between

specialties, between hospitals, and between individuals...high technology
(is) one of the major divisive influences in medicine today.[6]

The impact of technology on nurses' roles

Traditionally, nurses more than doctors have spent time at the patient's
bedside. Nurses, as the carers constantly present, observed the patient,
learned what were the indicators of problems and decided when the
doctor had to be called. Traditionally, also, patients have asked nurses
for information and advice when the doctor has seemed too busy or
when the medical explanation has been too esoteric for the patient's
understanding. In modern hospitals, technology has affected nursing as
much as medicine and traditional nursing roles have had to change.
Nurses are the people who have constantly to use technology and for
them, its development has resulted in continuous retraining and in their
having to work in an organisation that has become much more complex.
A number of nursing specialties have evolved and as in every other field
in modern society, the more specialised technical tasks have higher
status and receive higher pay, while basic nursing care is relegated to the
lowest level in the organisational structure.

If one considers hospitals from a radical pluralist or conflict perspective, nurses do not rank very highly in the power structure. They are not
always involved in decisions to purchase or install various technological
devices; they have frequently received inadequate training to deal with
the complex technologies with which they are confronted and which
they are expected to understand. Nursing has generally been regarded
in terms of the 'manual labour' content of the hospital's tasks, and
nurses' training has been inadequate to deal with the modern health
environment.[7] A certain ambivalence surrounds their role, and nurses
themselves, doctors and patients are not clear about what is now expected. The move of nursing education into Colleges of Advanced
Education was welcomed by nursing organisations but aroused considerable protests from doctors, who complained that nurses would be
turned into technicians; they asked who would do the basic nursing
tasks such as turning and bathing patients. Yet at the same time, there
are complaints by doctors and nurses that the nurses are not always
sufficiently trained to cope with the technology that they have to use.
Sometimes nurses see themselves as torn between these two opposing
demands, which creates an ambiguous situation of considerable stress.
Unless adequately trained, nurses find it a stressful and fearful experience to work in high technology environments, while the same environments present an exciting challenge for the technologically highly
trained nurse.

For all clinicians, whether doctors, nurses or other health workers,
the availability of technologies changes the way in which they perceive
patients, and how they make their clinical observations. Instead of
relying on clinical judgement, doctors now rely on tests and nurses look
at the various monitors instead of at the patient. They lose, or never

acquire, many of the observational skills which older doctors and nurses used to have. The trend now is to train professionals in technological skills, with the consequence that they cannot function without their machinery. After such training, they tend to prefer newer machines which give even more detail and accuracy, even when, as often happens, more knowledge and more detail do not improve the outlook for the patient. For doctors, 'it fulfils a psychological need. . . Instead of relying on clinical judgment, now they rely on a battery of tests, many of which they don't see, don't know how to interpret, or indeed are not relevant'.[8] The nurses today. . . 'use the equipment all the time and can't function without it. . . long before any of the monitors. . . were brought in, you could tell by looking at the patient the difference and changes in condition. Nowadays, the kids don't see that at all, they just look at the machines'.[9]

Technology and the hospital
Medical technologies have changed the whole nature of the hospital system. It has already been pointed out that as technologies diversify, so specialists must be trained to use, develop, research and repair various machines. These specialists come not only from occupations such as medicine and nursing, but from biomedical engineering, from the basic sciences, and from various technical training courses. As more and more is done for each patient, doctors and nurses become fully occupied clinically and new types of specialist professionals such as physiotherapists, occupational therapists, speech therapists, social workers, psychologists and dieticians carve out their own niches. Even the housekeeping tasks have become more complex: catering, purchasing, cleaning, waste disposal all require departments of their own.

With so many departments and so much technology taking up space, the hospital's buildings have grown larger. Computers have to be used to track the whereabouts of patients as they move from X-ray to surgery to radiotherapy before reaching their own beds. Staff and patients cannot become acquainted in the short time available. The frequently undervalued administrators have to tie all these activities together; unless rosters are drawn up and supplies of food, linen, machinery and drugs bought, unless staff are recruited, salaries are paid and machines repaired, patient care would very rapidly become unsatisfactory. The health industry in general and hospitals in particular have, as a result of modern technology, become big business. This has had an important effect on community employment levels, on the education industry, on manufacturing and building, and on government budgets.

Social impacts of medical technology

When technologies were first introduced into the health sector, the tendency was to assume that they would all benefit the patient and that the money they cost was well spent. Reports of a few patients treated successfully were generalised. It was assumed that what was good for a few patients was good for the population as a whole, and it was not for some time that the side-effects, risks and lack of success of a technology became clear. However, it became evident by the 1980s that all too often, the damage inflicted by a technology outweighed for many patients the benefits that had been expected, because no adequate evaluations were done before the technology became widely accepted. The prestigious medical literature is full of examples.[10]

In all developed countries since the 1970s, there has been some attempt to assess technologies, in particular the very expensive technologies, before they are widely introduced. These attempts have, however, not been very rigorous or effective. When working with technologies, or when seeing a technology being used on an individual, it is difficult to widen one's perspective to consider the effect of the technology beyond the patient and the hospital. In order to understand the ramifications of medical technology on society, it is necessary to consider its impact on individual patients, their families, health professionals and beyond these, to the effects of medical technologies on the economic and legal systems, and on social values and ideals. The discussion below concentrates on the 'high' technologies such as intensive care units, complex surgery and investigative technologies, as these have had the most dramatic impact on the health system.

Implications for the patient
When confronted by a sick patient, the doctor's task consists of four steps: diagnosis, prognosis, decision and management.[11] At each of these steps, technology is today used as a basic tool. Diagnosis which used to be reached by taking a history and examining the patient is today aided by technological investigations. The ability of computers to store and collate information about large numbers of patients produces one of the most effective ways of using high technology: systematic data, collected about many patients and analysed, is far more accurate and informative than any single clinician's experience can be. A more accurate prognosis can be reached by using these tools. Modern drugs assist in the treatment of a great many diseases, enabling people with conditions such as diabetes or hypertension to lead normal lives. Modern surgery enables many diseases to be cured or reduced in severity. Decision-making and management in medicine, must, however, always be made under conditions of uncertainty. Technology often helps to reduce this uncertainty and may be extremely beneficial to the patient, but on the other side of the equation, technology is often used to excess to reduce this uncertainty. This happens, for example, when extra tests are made to confirm an already established diagnosis. Doctors, trained to do 'everything possible', sometimes find it difficult to resist the temptation to try a particular treatment or to use a new technology, even when the likely benefit to the patient is very limited. Such situa-

tions are most common in the intensive care wards, where attempts at rescue may result in the patient surviving but in a very damaged condition.

The real difficulty for patients today is that there is so much treatment available, and that for many chronic diseases there are no 'best' treatments. The technologies aim to reduce the impact of the condition, but generally cannot cure the disease. Hence choices have to be made, trading off the pros and cons of various treatments against one another. Clearly such decisions, whether made by doctors or patients, cannot always work out successfully.

These tensions tend to be exacerbated by admission to hospital because modern hospitals are very complex, impersonal institutions where there are inevitable breakdowns in communication and efficiency. In small non-technological institutions like nursing homes, or in long-stay wards like spinal units, patients can develop relationships with each other and the staff, but in the high-technology institutions where each day's stay is very expensive, there is no time for human relationships to be developed, and the experience of having a serious illness with its inevitable anxiety is not alleviated by the presence of impersonal technology and overworked staff.

Implications for the patient's family and social network
If the technology used for the patient is successful in reassuring, curing, improving quality of life or extending life at a reasonable level, then clearly the patient's family and friends are extremely grateful. On the other hand, it must be remembered that many patients who now reach hospital have progressive disease, the ultimate outcome of which cannot be significantly changed. Hence on many occasions families suffer as much as, or more than the patient.

Technology may be lifesaving, and people with a consensus or moderate pluralist perspective tend to regard it as such. Someone who has had a coronary bypass will be able to lead a full life after a period of disabling angina, and the whole family will benefit. From other perspectives, however, people tend to look critically at technology. A person who has a bypass might suffer a disabling stroke during or after the operation. Similarly, the family of someone who has been brain damaged by a head injury and kept alive, will be grateful at first but may later express regret on account of the negative side effects. Thus if the family has to care for a member who was kept alive by technology, but left seriously handicapped physically or mentally, the initial gratitude may gradually be followed by other emotions. A very premature baby, kept alive by intensive neonatal care, may have a number of handicaps which may require great changes in lifestyle for the whole family. Some families regard this as a challenge, but others have major problems in coping with such a situation, and regret the technology which was responsible for their ordeal. A person disabled by spinal injuries needs special accommodation and regular help with daily living; an accident victim rescued after serious head injuries may be intellectually impaired, have outbursts of temper and not be able to work again. Someone receiving haemodialysis needs adequate space for the kidney machine, plus a family member ready to intervene and prevent the patient from bleeding to death in case the machine malfunctions. In such cases, the original gratitude may later mingle with resentment.

Implications for health professionals
The person who today enters a training course for one of the health professions is being educated for a very different role than used to be the case. In order to manage, understand and interpret the findings of the complex new technologies, specialists with extended training are needed, and merely wishing 'to help people' is no more than a good beginning. Complex machines force complex specialties to develop, which requires a long and arduous education. The medical super-specialists at the top, such as cardiothoracic or neurosurgeons, each require their own retinue of assistants who carry out segments of the task, and many of these tasks are stressful and exhausting. Histori-cally, bureaucrats have been unpopular, but no high-technology hospital can function without managers to organise the many categories of people and equipment. The more complex the technologies and the knowledge, the more organisers are needed to coordinate the staff, machinery and patients. Financial as well as management expertise is needed since each hospital spends many millions of taxpayers' dollars per year.

Inevitably, in such a large organisation with responsibilities which involve life and death, tension at times is high and morale fluctuates. When this is combined with actions by governments aimed at reducing costs, the workload increases, stress levels rise, and inevitably problems occur. The pace of the work is to some extent set by the machines, which limits the kind of social interaction that used to be common between staff and patients, or among the staff themselves. Shift work is an essential part of health work and always has the potential to create difficulties of availability of appropriately qualified staff who are scarcer as their qualification become more esoteric.

Implications for the economic and legal systems
It will be obvious from earlier sections of this chapter that new medical technologies are expensive in themselves, and have caused health budgets to use an increasing proportion of taxpayers' money. But the economic implications go well beyond the inflationary trend of health budgets.

People who would earlier have died relatively quickly from their diseases are now kept alive, but not healthy, for years. Instead of requiring short periods of care, they may require intermittent care for some years and constant care for a relatively long time before death. As more people are screened for hidden health problems, more inter-vention results; this may lessen people's earlier disability or delay death, but it costs additional money to provide services for the problems discovered. Other difficult situations occur when handicapped children are kept alive for many years instead of dying as they used to do in infancy or early childhood. They not only continue to use health services, but require special schooling, sheltered workshops, pensions and possibly nursing home care for many years. More carers are needed to look after these people during their periods of illness. All these ex-tended lives increase the size of the non-working population dependent on the workers, and taxes will have to be increased to pay for pensions, superannuation and life insurance, as well as extended periods of health care. The Paradox of Time states that 'Time converts one decade's achievements into the next decade's dilemmas'.[12]

The legal system, too, has been affected by medical technology and there are further consequences still to come. Already death has been redefined from the cessation of the heart to brain death, so that people can be declared dead while their hearts are still beating in order to keep their organs in good condition for transplantation. Attitudes to death are beginning to change as a result of medical technology. The new technology of terminal care has had the incongruous effect of making many people afraid of being kept alive for longer than they believe is appropriate, and several Australian States have followed the example set by almost every American State and have passed laws giving patients the right to refuse medical treatment in order to be allowed to die. As more people with debilitating illnesses and of greater ages survive in society, the permissibility of euthanasia becomes a public issue and is likely to lead to further changes in the law. The legality of artificial insemination, embryo-freezing and -thawing, and surgery for mentally handicapped children have all been referred to lawyers for decision and that debate is far from over.

Effect of technology on social values and ideals
The effect of the contraceptive pill on societal values as they relate to sexual relationships has been described above. But from the consensus point of view many other medical technologies have profound effects on social values, ideals, beliefs, habits and rules. Our society is now undergoing a fundamental reassessment of the value of life and death.

When life was likely to end at any time as a result of an uncontrollable infection, prayer and hope were the tools by which people sought to procure health. Human life was certainly not regarded as sacred, which was a word restricted to the deity and the clergy. Now, death is general-ly regarded as premature if it occurs before the age of 60, because life expectancy has increased, and a great deal can be done at all ages and in all health conditions to stave off death at least for some time. Two major effects have occurred as a consequence.

First, our capacity to extend life seems almost godlike, so that human capacities are considered somewhat sacred. Second, the distance between what is considered sacred and what is considered profane has shrunk: this enables people to regard earthly human life as having qualities approaching that of the immortals. Emile Durkheim, the French sociologist, said that the essence of religion was not found in beliefs about the supernatural, but in the making of a distinction between the sacred and the profane. The sacred used be to set apart, treated with awe and respect. It was regarded as being polluted by contact with things ordinary and everyday, which were the profane.[13] It is therefore a major change to have some community groups refer to each human life, including embryonic and foetal life, as being sacred. Once a life is said to be sacred, all sorts of consequences follow: every means must be used to conserve it, even if it is insensate, incapacitated, or undeveloped; in our society, this usually means using technologies for that purpose.

From the radical pluralist perspective, it is frequently said that our society has become 'medicalised', that is, dependent on medical professionals and medical technologies for many daily needs. Governments demand medical certificates before giving people pensions, medical prescriptions are required before drugs can be obtained, employers require certificates of illness before wages are paid, doctors have to certify continuing incapacity for workers' compensation to be paid. Technologies have extended doctors' powers to a previously unimagined extent, and these capacities are then generalised so that it is often assumed that doctors' knowledge, of human nature, and of ethical behaviour, is as expert as their command of technology. It is only recently that this assumption has been widely questioned and the debate about the way medical technologies have affected social life as well as that of individuals has been extended to include experts in the law, in ethics, in sociology and in psychology.

Alternative perspectives on medical technology

It is clear that medical technologies have made fundamental changes in societal values as well as in individuals' health. However, the assessment of those changes is itself a value judgement, dependent on one's perspective.

Examined from the consensus view, technology in general and medical technologies in particular have positive functions. For an individual patient, technology is assumed to extend life and make disabilities more bearable. Hips can be replaced and club feet straightened. Doctors, clinics and hospitals can provide better care for more people. Diagnosis is more accurate, and many diseases can be controlled. The consensus perspective emphasises the benefits of technology and regards the risks and costs as a price which is worth paying.

In this view, developing new technology is called progress and progress is seen as inevitable and good. Medical scientists have an important role to play in developing and testing new technologies. Private businesses as well as governments are needed to fund the research into and the manufacture of new technologies. Technologists and medical professionals are assumed to be motivated by their concern for people and the welfare of society. They are said to deserve the rewards they get in money and status because their work has responsibility and importance. The consensus perspective applauds the techno-business model in which technology is considered an 'irresistible and unchangeable force which determines and shapes social change'.[14]

Moderate pluralists accept that there are advantages and disadvantages to technologies in health care. Many illnesses have been cured, many lives extended, and a great deal of increased comfort obtained by modern surgery, drugs, implants and other inventions. Without modern technology, kidney failure would spell inevitable death, many couples would have no child, many tiny children would not have survived. Many people would be severely disabled or blind, many with disabilities, hypertension and heart disease who are leading normal lives supported by drugs would be dead or disabled. People with many mental illnesses would be permanently in hospital if there were no psychoactive drugs, and women would not be able to control their fertility effectively without contraceptive technologies. Moderate pluralists would not accept that powerful and wealthy people obtain most of the benefits of technology. They would point out that all industralised countries have a public health system available to the disadvantaged, and in Australia (even before the introduction of Medicare) no one has ever been turned away from a hospital emergency department for inability to pay. Further, moderate pluralism sees power as being divided among different groups who have a stake in technological developments. For example, within a hospital, the heart transplant unit will be competing for resources with the neonatal intensive care unit; in the community the Cancer Society is one interest group competing for resources with others such as the Spastic Centre and the Heart Foundation.

The radical pluralist and conflict perspectives, in contrast to the consensus and moderate pluralist perspectives, take a critical view of technology. Both these perspectives focus on the powerful groups who fund the research into and development of medical technologies, as well as those who prescribe it. They emphasise that scientists and academics—the developers of technology—get jobs, money and prestige from developing their products; manufacturers and retailers make huge profits out of the sale of their products. Doctors are seen as having the power to demand and get increasingly high rewards for prescribing these technologies for their patients who, because they are less informed and less vocal, cannot question or resist; journalists and media organisations are seen as benefiting financially from exaggerated claims; politicians and members of hospital boards gain popularity for making technologies available. Thus it is the powerful and wealthier people who primarily benefit from the growth in medical technology.

The conflict perspective sees the economic motivation of the capitalist upper class, to which doctors and drug companies belong, as being the thrust behind technological development and exploitation of the poor. Thus they stress that patients are coerced into believing all technological interventions are beneficial, whereas in fact much technology is of no value, or may even be detrimental to patients' health.

Radical pluralists point out that there are greater financial and social rewards for high technology than for low technology; therefore more interest groups are formed to promote high technology than there are interest groups promoting low technology. This explains why *in-vitro* fertilisation has attracted much more funding than has research into health promotion. Radical pluralists stress that choices are made about which technologies to develop and how to distribute the benefits, and a key factor in the resulting decisions is the political pressure exerted by various interest groups. Associated with this continuous power struggle are interactions among individual doctors, patients and politicians, which also affect the total decision-making scene. It can be seen from this that interactionism and pluralism are closely related although they differ in their units of analysis: interactionism focuses on individuals while pluralism focuses on collectivities.

It should be obvious from the above analysis that the introduction and use of medical technology cannot be regarded merely as an obvious way of improving patient care. Depending on one's sociological perspective, technology is seen as saviour, villain, or as a complex array of advantages and disadvantages.

10 The ethics of rationing health care

The need for decisions

Medical technologies have had social impacts on a scale far wider than the direct delivery of health services, and one consequence is the considerable literature debating their effectiveness, ethics and costs.

The social, sexual and moral experiences of Western nations have been radically modified by the technologies of medicine, and it is commonly stated that Western societies have become medicalised. Medical terms are used to describe situations far removed from the health sector. Society is referred to as 'sick'; the economy is 'healthy' or 'unhealthy', and health care itself is a major preoccupation of all political parties. Governments have become closely involved in the protection of human life, with courts having to adjudicate between doctors, relatives and social workers to decide whether a baby or a dying adult should be treated by all available modern technology or be allowed to die. As each expensive new technology is introduced, governments are now insisting on an assessment being made of its cost, its potential achievements and its value. Decisions have to be made as to whether certain technologies, which may benefit a small number of people, can be afforded by a society which has many people who have needs and demands which are not being met.

Such debates have never before been needed. When it was impossible to replace a baby's diseased liver, people were not faced with debates such as whether it is moral to make a public appeal for a liver from another dead infant for the transplantation, or whether the child's reaction to the necessary drugs will so badly affect its future that the treatment should be abandoned because it is more damaging than helpful. Doctors who once had no choice but to accept a patient's death are now forced to make such decisions every day. Ethical discussions have become so pervasive that right-to-die groups are arrayed against right-to-life groups; social workers and lawyers debate with doctors and parents whether or not to operate on mentally handicapped children who would otherwise die. Ethics committees are set up by governments to decide whether research should be permitted on embryos which have been artificially created in a laboratory; law reform commissions debate whether people should be allowed to sell their organs. Governments find themselves trying to rein in the costs of health services while simultaneously being pressured to provide *ex gratia* payments of hundreds of thousands of dollars to provide risky overseas treatment for a dying patient.

Because more possibilities for diagnosis and treatment now exist, doctors' roles have expanded. As definers of medical need and medical possibilities, doctors can accept or reject a patient's expression of need. For example, a couple's inability to have a child of their own may be regarded as trivial or important, a medical problem or a social problem. Infertility may be regarded as a challenge for doctors who may demand research funding for the problem, or it may be seen as a problem for the couple to accept. Doctors can lay stress on, or trivialise patients' complaints. They can respond to a complaint of headaches by ordering many tests, by ordering tranquillisers or by taking a careful history; they can respond to a complaint of angina by doing coronary bypass surgery or by conservative medical treatment. They may emphasise the risks, or the likely benefits of the treatment they recommend. When many alternative courses of action are available, the range of choices is broad.

Evaluating the impact of medical technologies

Because the consequences of medical technology are vast, a major industry of medical technology assessment has sprung up. The meaning of technology is interpreted differently by the various active participants.[1] To the doctor, the focus is on the safety and effectiveness of drugs, tests, surgery, medical devices and technical procedures, since the doctor's purpose is patient care, safety and quality of life. The doctor's technology assessment strategy therefore aims to answer the question 'Does the technology achieve the intended outcome'? This seems, but is not, a straightforward question. The 'intended outcome' must be carefully defined, that is, the evaluation must define what is meant by the 'improved' state of the patient's health, how this is measured and over what time horizon. 'Improvement' may be interpreted as reducing tumour size for a few weeks or months, and 'effectiveness' may mean the ability to diagnose but not treat or cure a disease. More complex assessment criteria, such as relief of pain, ability to lead a normal life and retention of full intellectual ability are more rarely included, while effects on relationships with others are almost never measured. Thus the definition of a 'successful' treatment may be the salvaging of a handicapped child, although that may result in family disruption, or the 'successful doctor' may rescue a severely injured adult from death only to condemn that person to a life with severe paralysis or considerable pain.

The economic questions are somewhat different from the medical ones. While the medical ethic looks to achieving the greatest good, however defined, for the individual patient, the economic ethic is concerned with what is best for society within clearly defined limits of available resources. The relevant economic questions are: can the benefits justify the costs incurred, and what are we giving up by using this particular technology? The economist is concerned with evaluating the technology from the point of view of the total health care system, as contrasted with the point of view of the scientists who invented the technology in order to increase human knowlege, the commercial interests which make profits out of it, the practitioners who use it to increase their status and intellectual satisfaction, and the patients who hope to benefit from it. 'A favourable effect on patients is a necessary but unfortunately not a *sufficient* condition for the optimum level of utilization of a new technology within a health care system to be positive.'[2] Patients and doctors might believe that some treatments would be justified at any cost; economists would not agree because they would always be aware that other treatments would have to be foregone to pay for the one whose price was so high.

From the consensus perspective then, it is assumed that technology is beneficial for the individual, the family and society as a whole. It improves people's comfort and extends life. Diagnosis is much more accurate and made at an earlier stage of disease. Technologies which continue to be used have survived because they are functional for individuals and for society; they have succeeded in improving patient welfare, while ineffective technologies soon fail the tests of research and cease to be used by doctors. Technology supports the value of each individual human being by assisting doctors in their efforts to help each patient, regardless of cost. Thus the essential function of medical technology is to help in the support of the most basic value common to all members of society: the belief in the importance of each individual and in the sacredness of each human life, no matter how young or old, well or ill. Doctors, nurses and technologists are all working together to improve and extend human life.

People who hold a conflict perspective emphasise quite different aspects. First, there is the point that resources are scarce and that people are fighting over these scarce resources. Technology is one such scarce resource, and people who take the conflict view consider that the more powerful, higher status and wealthier people in the community receive an excessive proportion of the desired, scarce resources. Hence the poor, or low-status groups such as recent immigrants, would be likely to receive fewer technological interventions than the better-off, though they might need them as much.[3]

The second aspect of the conflict argument is that a great deal of technology is not beneficial in any case. There is now a large volume of evidence describing the damage done by technologies such as drugs, surgery and tests.[4] The research base on which technologies are introduced is commonly inadequate because the manufacturers are so determined to make profits as soon as possible.

The life-cycle of new medical technologies has been described by several writers and though they differ in details, all have the same essential features.[5] After an enthusiastic beginning based on only a few selected cases, the technology is quickly adopted and widely used, being tried on all sorts of patient populations. The media describe it as a new breakthrough and a large number of people demand it. It is then found not to be as widely relevant as was at first thought and its disadvantages gradually become more apparent. Stories of the damage caused by the technology begin to circulate and better quality research begins to be done. Gradually its qualities and limitations become defined and the technology is either used in a more restricted way, is replaced by a new technology, or is abandoned altogether.

The conflict theorist emphasises that this whole process is damaging in a number of ways. First of all, it is damaging to the patients on whom it is inappropriately used but who do not understand its risks because the full facts have not been presented to them. Secondly, providers have a large financial stake in introducing the technology quickly and, as a result, are tempted to neglect proper assessment.

Third, stories of iatrogenic disease—or disease caused by medical treatment—are common and give strength to the conflict view that the promoters of the technology use their power and take advantage of the gullibility of doctors and patients in order to benefit themselves. In doing so, they allow patients to sustain damage as a 'side-effect'. Some eminent physicians now talk of the 'medical-industrial complex'[6] and entrepreneurs take advantage of the extremely profitable health sector, whose money-making capacities are based on a safe income from governments. The conflict perspective holds that in a fee-for-service government-funded system, the costs of technology are largely ignored because no one has any incentive to consider them: patients do not have to pay, while doctors are certain to be paid. As a result, manufacturers know that any device which is even marginally better than the existing technology can be readily marketed, because doctors and patients look primarily for medical efficacy and hope that the technology can be advertised as causing improvement before the contrary evidence is available. Benefits accrue to the manufacturers and doctors, and the losses are met by the taxpayers. 'Consequently, even a technology that could only infrequently be cost-justified can still be expected to proliferate'.[7]

In Australia, consensus-oriented entrepreneurs have moved into profitable ventures such as the nuclear magnetic resonance scanner.[8]

The pioneer importer said: 'I think the Government should applaud private enterprise for being prepared to take the risk of introducing this expensive new technology'.[9] However, not everyone agrees: a conflict-oriented researcher said 'It concerns me that a machine in private practice is there for profit. There are pressures to pay for the machine, which means there needs to be a rapid turnover of patients. Pressures in public hospitals are indirect, there is not the stress on the radiologist. Better medicine is performed that way.'[10]

A similar analysis has been made of the artificial heart program in the United States. The conservative media publicity deals with the suffering patient, heroic in the fight against death, who is presented as an underdog battling against great odds. The conflict view is quite different: 'the story. . . is not just one of compressors and blood clots, respirators and ventricles. It is the story of the nation's (perhaps the world's) most efficient and most profitable chain of private sector hospitals, and how it managed to hijack one of the most sensitive areas of medical research to the city which houses its corporate headquarters'.[11] The hospital chain gains an enormous amount of free publicity and many routine patients, so the shareholders reap the profit.

The fourth argument from the conflict perspective is that technology, because of its enormous expense, distorts the whole health care system. The use of technology is a running sore in a continuing debate, because technology encourages emphasis on cure as compared with prevention. Because so much money is spent on high-technology acute care, other parts of the health system such as preventive services, occupational health services and services for the chronically ill are all under-resourced; they have low status, inadequate numbers of staff, and receive inadequate attention from policy-makers. Here again, conflict theorists point out that it is the poor, elderly, Aboriginals and low-level workers who suffer disproportionately from these problems, and who receive the least attention.

From 'resource allocation' to 'rationing'

In times of peace and prosperity, the word 'rationing' is not one which is commonly used to describe how people obtain goods they need or want. Yet increasingly, the word 'rationing' is being used to describe how health resources should be divided, instead of 'resource allocation' which is a less stringent description. The word 'ration' is defined as 'to put on, or restrict to, rations'[12] and is described as being similar in meaning to 'stint, skimp, hold back, be parsimonious'.[13] It is usually used in wartime and other times of crisis and implies that people cannot buy as much as they would like because some of the goods are needed for the war effort and are reserved for the troops. In such times, rationing means that a fair and reasonable share of what is needed is distributed by a superior authority to everyone in the community.

'Allocate', on the other hand, has no overtones of scarcity or equity, being defined as 'to set apart for a particular purpose'.[14] To allocate is similar in meaning to 'divide, carve up, share out, distribute'.[15] Policy-makers used to talk in the 1960s of allocating scarce medical resources, which implied that there was a general sufficiency. Now, the discussions increasingly refer to the need for rationing, which connotes an emergency in which everyone has to accept that some preferences or needs will not be able to be satisfied.

These problems have arisen essentially because of the availability of new technologies, which, by extending medical capacities, allow doctors always to make just one more effort, to develop yet another technique. Hence all discussions about the rationing, allocation or distribution of health resources are underpinned by the belief that because something more can always be done, the *demand* for health resources has no natural limit. But the *money* available for health care does have a limit which is set by the willingness of the taxpayer to meet the bills.

The Tragedy of the Commons
In an attempt to explain this situation, society has been compared to a group of herdsmen whose cattle share a common pasture. While the number of animals is small in relation to the size of the pasture, each herdsman can add to his cattle without damaging the pasture. But as the herd grows, the pasture cannot supply all their needs. Each herdsman believes that if he adds just one more animal it would make no real difference. But if all herdsmen act in this way, the common pasture will be ruined. What is possible for one, is impossible for all. This is known as 'The Tragedy of the Commons'.[16] According to this analogy, the total resources available for health care are the commons and all doctors, patients, hospitals and pressure groups make their own demands. Consequently the common pasture is devastated and everybody must now submit to the rationing that has become essential.[17] Medical ethics have always been based on enjoining doctors to do everything possible for their own patients, without regard to the rest of society. 'In caring for an individual patient, the doctor must act solely as that patient's advocate, against the apparent interests of society as a whole, if necessary.'[18]

It is this ethic which is now challenged because the medical commons has become overgrazed. More and more expensive techniques and devices have been developed, many of which have limited effectiveness in relation to their cost. While they make diagnosis slightly more accurate, marginally prolong life, or relieve symptoms of an illness, the expected benefits are very small relative to the costs. Hence the medical profession is coming under increasing pressure from governments. Their practice style can no longer be based on the precept 'Do no harm'. Instead, doctors will have to shift to a style based on the precept 'Employ a treatment only when you are sure that it will make a noticeable improvement'.[19] It is now recognised in every Western society that it is not possible to give every available treatment to everyone who could use it; the two existing heart transplant units in Australia can only exchange a few hearts a year. Similar limitations apply to liver, kidney and corneal transplants. By focusing only on the patients in front of them, doctors are led to believe that the patients who have managed to gain access to their surgeries are more in need of attention than the ones who, for whatever reason, have not managed to gain entry; sometimes doctors are so busy transplanting twelve new hearts, for example, that they forget the hundreds of people outside who need simple open-heart surgery. The latter cannot gain entry because there is neither money nor nursing staff available.

As medical costs rise and more interventions can be made, it becomes more obvious that ethics which direct doctors to give maximum treatment to their own patients at whatever cost are being challenged. At the State and Federal levels, finance ministers reduce total budgets; health ministers then instruct their departments to reduce costs; hospital boards are then told that their allocation is reduced but that they are not to cut services. So staff who resign are not replaced, beds are closed, operating theatre time is reduced, equipment is not replaced, waiting lists grow longer.

> But no one seems prepared to make the long-term decisions such as whether the next million health dollars should be spent performing more coronary grafts and increasing neonatal intensive care beds, or providing more community care for the aged and mentally ill, proper support for cancer patients to die in their homes, and a decent preventive health program. The usual result is a sad and generalised neglect, with everyone complaining of chronic fiscal starvation. Inevitably, however, the worst affected will be the poorer areas and patients, and the less glamorous and less influential employees of the system.[20]

These complaints are now being echoed by many doctors, as the reality of the restrictions hits home.

> In 1985, (in Australia) medical research funds are apparently at a standstill, yet suddenly $500 000 are apparently found (to send a baby to the United States for a liver transplant). There is an urgent need to start talking about health care priorities in this country and to try to build a health care programme that is going to take us into the 21st Century—not just to the next election.[21]

One response to the problem of cost allocation is the development of Diagnosis Related Groups, known in the health system as DRGs. Evolved in the United States, and now to be introduced throughout Australia, their purpose is to prevent the 'overtreatment' of patients in hospitals. In this scheme, patients are grouped according to their diagnosis and the severity of their condition, and the average cost and length of stay in hospital of each group is calculated. Hospitals are paid according to these estimates; that is, they are expected to keep the patient only for as long as the average length of stay for that particular condition. If the patient is discharged earlier, the hospital can make money; if the patient is kept for longer, the hospital has to pay the extra costs without reimbursement. Governments, and health funds, see the scheme as a protection for the taxpayer or fund contributor. However, many hospital administrators and doctors emphasise the potential problems. For example, hospitals might discharge patients too soon, or might take insufficient account of social reasons which sometimes make later discharges necessary. Economists, politicans, doctors and patients give different answers to the following questions. Should patients be sent out of hosptial at the earliest possible moment to save money, rather than be kept in longer for their best health benefit? Should people be kept longer in hospital, or even be admitted to hospital in the first place, for social rather than medical reasons? Should people be transferred from a more specialised hospital to a less specialised one when they improve, to save the more specialised—and expensive—bed, although this transfer will probably add to the discomfort of the patient and sometimes the patient's visitors? People with different perspectives, and different professional backgrounds, will, once more, endorse different views.

It is clear to many people in the health care field that there needs to be an extended public and political debate about the goals of the health care system. This reflects a moving away from consensus assumptions which hold that the health system was functioning well before there was major government interference with the private sector. The growing adherence to conflict or radical pluralist perspectives is reflected in the fact that many questions are now being asked about the goals of the health care system and the best way to determine them. For example, should the health system be aiming at prolonging life, improving its quality, increasing the productivity of the population, making life more enjoyable or some other goal? How are these goals to be placed in order of priority? Should funds be allocated at all for more technological development and research, and is existing technology just to be extended to those who need it? Similarly, the conflict perspective is reflected in such statements as: 'The ethical issue in health care today is cost. All the philosophical and theological reflection in the world will not produce change. Economic reality will. The catalyst for change will come from the economics of high-technology medicine'.[22] Nor is there much time available in which to make decisions. Health care used to be viewed as a social problem; now it is seen by politicians as mainly an economic problem. 'Social problems can be left to fester: budget-deficit problems require more immediate solutions'.[23]

The debate about the ethics of resource allocation may come to a crisis level when the costs of AIDS begin to limit other public expenditures. Various estimates have been made which differ from each other because they make different assumptions[24]. There is, however, one certainty: the costs will be enormous. These will either have to be paid through the general taxation system by increasing taxes, or by reducing some other health or social expenditures. Depending on their perspectives, people will have different opinions as to the total amount of public money that should be allocated to AIDS and the method of its distribution. From the consensus point of view the public contribution should be limited to prevention among the high risk groups and care of the most needy among those infected; expenditures should be decided by the medical experts. Moderate pluralists would argue that that all affected groups, ranging from drug users and recipients of blood transfusions to medical researchers, can lobby for the support they require and all groups will eventually get funding appropriate to their needs. Radical pluralists will also consider the lobbying process but assume that less powerful groups, such as recipients of transfusions, prisoners and drug addicted prostitutes, will miss out while the more powerful, such as the alliance of gay groups and the medical research and clinical groups, will achieve their goals.

Justice and ethics in the rationing of health resources

If one believes that the products of the health services must be freely available to all, then one accepts that decisions must be made about the method of their distribution. Rather than medical considerations, theories of social justice, ethics and morality are at the heart of the answer to the questions: Who gets what? Upon what principles do we divide up the health pie? The principles and beliefs one holds about social justice, and the decisions one makes, will depend (as always) upon the sociological perspective one adopts. The fundamental difference between the consensus and conflict perspectives about social justice is whether one believes that wealth belongs to individuals or to all of society. In other words, do individuals have special claims over particular property they own or buy, or does society as a whole have a right to decide how the total wealth is to be distributed?

A classic tale illustrates the difference between these two views. Imagine a forest in which there is a native tribe and one deer, which is caught by a young man. The question is 'Who shall have the deer?' The young, fleet member of the tribe says 'The deer belongs to the one who has caught it' meaning 'those who cannot or will not exert themselves, deserve to lose the deer'. But an older, weaker member replies, 'No. The deer belongs to all of us to be shared equally. Catching deer is not the only task we have to fulfil. Some have to tend the land, bear the children and worship the gods. Some are by nature weak and ill. That is no reason for them to starve. If you are the one who catches the deer, that is no reason for the rest of us to go without food'.[25] The individualism of the young tribesman is an ideal often associated with the consensus perspective; it asserts that wealth is created by individual effort and therefore belongs to the individual who created it. This extends to the belief that all people must be able to have free choice in the disposal of their own property, whether it be large or small, and those who have little property have no right to take any away from those who have a great deal. For example, from the consensus view, taxation is an infringement of basic rights. The older tribesman probably holds a conflict perspective; he believes that economic production is social in character, since everyone enters the world owning nothing and no one can survive without the help of others. Hence, the only way in which a society can work is to distribute all its goods equally among its members. For similar reasons, all people should have an equal share in decision-making, or else decisions will favour the strongest and disadvantage the weak.

The moderate pluralist view is exemplified by Rawls' 'difference principle',[26] which asserts that the aim of a society should be to distribute social goods in such a way that it improves the standard of living of the worst-off. It is possible that by giving some people an advantage, they will work harder and create more social wealth; then everyone will be better off. In this situation, an unequal distribution is better than an equal one because the overall welfare is increased. As an example: if the government believed that by giving doctors high incomes they would work harder, the conclusion would be that the health system would be improved because the worst-off patients would be better-off. In such circumstances, an unequal distribution of resources is the policy that should be adopted. Thus moderate pluralism is not merely a compromise position between consensus and conflict, but a distinctive view based on a belief in liberty and the best possible benefits for all.[27] It is also a view that takes into account the interdependence of social structures and social issues, by emphasising that there is never one simple, unchanging explanation or solution.

Systems of resource allocation

Western societies have developed three basic types of resource allocation systems in health care which have been implicitly based on the three perspectives of how society works: a free market, a mixed and an egalitarian system.

The free market system is based on the belief that 'the natural lottery is morally neutral',[28] that is, we may be born clever, healthy and rich, or stupid, ill and poor, but this is no one's fault and there is nothing unfair about this. It may be sad but it is not unfair, so no one has the responsibility to do anything to help the unfortunate. This is clearly based on the consensus perspective and is rather Darwinian in its assumptions: the fittest will survive, the unfit will not, but this is in the interests of society as a whole.

A health system based on the free market model would allow suppliers to sell their goods at the highest price they can obtain, with consumers choosing the best quality goods at the lowest price they can find. It is assumed that consumers and suppliers are equally knowledgeable and that consumers are all equally able to get to a source of supply, even if their condition is likely to be a low-profit one for the provider. Further, it assumes that consumers know what they need, can bargain with the supplier and can change suppliers if they are dissatisfied with the quality or price of their original purchase.

It should be noted that no modern health system works on the pure market model. But sections of some modern systems are based on a market model; for example, when a surrogate mother sells her services, as is now frequently done in the United States, or when someone sells one kidney to someone who needs it, as is done when poor Indians sell kidneys to wealthy Americans. No such free market transactions have been permitted in Australia, although the private, fee-for-service system of paying for doctor visits has obvious free market elements. But since modern technology has priced health services well beyond the individual consumer's purchasing power, no technological health service can operate its services entirely on this model, no matter how often some medical practitioners advocate it. Another reason that no developed country has a price market medical system is that the disadvantages of the price market model are too great. To be consistent, a market system would allow a careless or unfortunate person to die for want of medical care; that is not acceptable today in Western societies like Australia. People who, out of choice, have not made provision for illness would become freeloaders in a price market system if they were treated for compassionate reasons. But since the market model specifically avoids compassion, some other mechanisms must be introduced to enable everyone to have a basic minimum of care in time of need. Thus even the rigid marketeers have moved from the consensus price model to the pluralist, two-tier model.

Mixed, two-tiered systems are based on the moderate pluralist model and the Australian system is such a one. It is assumed that different health care arrangements can, and indeed should, co-exist in a society. It is assumed also that if the distribution is made fairly, people do not object to differences in access and treatment. Two-tiered systems are set up to ensure that everyone is entitled as of right to a reasonable minimum level of care but, if people wish to do so, they can buy more care from those who are willing to sell it. This, in modern technological systems, usually has to be purchased on the basis of private health insurance, which offers more luxuries than the basic public health insurance which is available to all.

However, the insurance process does not work as effectively in the health sector as it does, for example, with fire or motor vehicle accident insurance. Insurance is an effective mechanism for assisting people who meet a disaster of which there was a low probability, but which produces a large physical or financial loss, such as a fire or burglary. Only a few houses will burn and be burgled and the maximal loss is fixed by the value of the property lost. The companies therefore calculate the total risk and compensate those who lose in the lottery. But there is a great difference between fire insurance and health insurance. No one is very likely to have a house fire, but everyone is almost certain to incur large health costs before death. Hence health insurance is 'not a pooling of small risks but an enormous distortion of incentives'.[29] This means that there is no reason why anyone should try to be economical in their use of health care. If one has paid for it, why not use it, especially as it is expected to do good and even possibly extend one's life. A simple analogy is the experience of going out to dinner with a group. If the bill is to be divided equally among the group, large eaters and drinkers are advantaged and small eaters and drinkers are penalised, so the incentive is for everyone to consume more than they would have done, had they been paying only for themselves. In the same way, each of us knows that if we all use much more health care, insurance rates will eventually rise; but we also know that our individual use will not be noticeable. Hence we continue to use as much as we believe will benefit ourselves, regardless of cost, since the insurer is paying. The provider who is paid by the insurer and is certain of receiving that fee also has no incentive to economise; rather, the opposite is the case. The provider will receive the grateful thanks of the patient, the respect of peers and adequate remuneration if no account is taken of cost when treating insured patients. It is a classic case of the tragedy of the commons, and is a problem which governments have not yet solved.

Egalitarian systems are based on a radical pluralist model, which assumes that though people are not all equal, equality ought to be the ideal for which a society strives. In a free market system, 'equal' means that no impediment is put in the way of those who wish to sell and buy health care; in a two-tiered system, 'equal' means the provision of a decent minimum to all. In an egalitarian system, however, 'equal' means that no one has more than anyone else except by medically defined need; nor is anyone allowed to obtain more by purchasing it. The benefit is that all are aware that they are served equally well or badly. Egalitarians believe that health care is part of the social glue that holds societies together, that it is one method of redistributing wealth in the society so that the powerful will lose some of their advantage while the poor will benefit from getting extra resources. An egalitarian health system aims to have all members of the society feeling and acting as a large communal network, rather than working against one another in a competitive, aggressive environment.

There are, of course, disadvantages in egalitarian systems. There is little incentive for the providers to work hard since they cannot offer the consumers any extra benefits; consumers get their entitlement and nothing more. If the providers are on a salary, they can gain no extra fees nor develop a large private clientele which will pay them more. There is also no incentive to become highly productive, since extra productivity will only benefit the consumer but not the provider; in fact, the provider might actually benefit from reducing productivity, since the pay would be the same for doing less work.

Difficult choices

It is clear that choices have to be made in any modern health system: choices between services, to decide which ones are to be provided and how lavishly; between patients, some of whom will receive better and quicker service while others fall behind; and between providers, some of whom will receive high pay and lavish resources while others work in poor conditions for low pay. These choices imply that someone has to do the choosing and make some very difficult decisions. Those people are the politicians and administrators, whose choices will inevitably limit the autonomy of doctors. The issue is no longer *whether* such autonomy should be limited: 'It is how to define a framework for rationing that conserves resources without sacrificing the provision of good care or the morale and commitment of the physician'.[30] The problem is that while technology is continually being developed, there is no equitable way of rationing care, since new technologies must *inevitably* be scarce. When new treatments are being introduced all the time, new interest groups will emerge to take advantage of them, and when combined with technological innovation this will result in fragmentation and poor coordination of delivery of services.

In the immediate future, there is likely to be an increasing number of complaints about the Australian health care system as funds are reduced, and this will happen even more as new technological inventions are developed. Australia will have a distinct two-tier service in which the people restricted to basic services will receive crisis care when needed, but will have to wait, sometimes for considerable periods, for elective care, while those who are willing to pay extra will be able to have convenient and comfortable services when required. Prices for health insurance must rise unless technological innovation is strictly controlled. Politicians will be under pressure to provide more services while reducing costs, an impossibility while technological services have the highest status. Rationing will have to become stricter, and it is likely that the health sector will remain in a state of turmoil for some considerable time.

11 Occupational health

A newly recognised public health issue

If any social group is to survive, its members must do certain work. From the smallest family to the largest social aggregates, the performance of work is an integral and essential part of group life. The nature of the work that is performed, and the method by which the particular performers are selected, differs of course between groups and at different times in history.

Industrialised Western societies have moved away from having most work done within the home and its surrounds, to a position where work is defined as something that is done for monetary reward away from home, at specified hours, by certain people.

At all times and in all societies, certain hazards are a consequence of work. Fishermen risk drowning, explorers risk getting lost, miners risk a collapse of the tunnel and timber workers risk cutting off their fingers. Historically, these risks have most often been regarded as something to be accepted as part of the job, about which little could be done apart from prayer to the gods and exhortations to be careful.

Public attitudes to the health of workers have only recently emerged from a long period of indifference. Children used to be sent into the mines and up chimneys from the age of five, pregnant women did likewise through economic necessity; the hours of work at heavy labouring jobs for both sexes and for children were so long that many collapsed and died at work.

In Australia, conditions of workers during the nineteeth century were not as bad as in Britain and Europe. This was partly because the population was far more mobile and labour was in undersupply, so that people could move away from an employer if conditions were too unpleasant. Industry was less developed than in Europe, and more people were self-employed and able to determine their own working hours and conditions.

In general, it was left to individual employers to ensure the health of their workers, although safety and workers' compensation legislation has been in existence in Australia since the 1890s. However, that legislation covered only part of the workforce and was poorly enforced. Protection from occupational diseases and death was virtually non-existent because there was no data on how much illness was work-related. Workers, whether self-employed or working for wages, were left to see to their own health and safety at work.

Occupational health did not become a political issue in Australia until after World War II, when new legislation was developed to provide for a more proactive attitude to problems arising from work-related accidents and diseases, and 'to provide for a completely new view of the importance of workers, their needs and capabilities in the occupational field'.[1] This concern with workers' well-being was fostered by the International Labour Organisation (ILO),[2] which was established in 1919 as an agency of the League of Nations, but, like the League itself, was more or less inactive until it was brought into a formal relationship with the United Nations at the end of 1946. In recent years, the ILO has become a forum for the consideration of occupational health and safety policy and legislation throughout the world.

By the early 1970s, occupational health and safety had become a matter of serious concern in most developed capitalist countries.[3] This was triggered by the increasing mechanisation of work as well as by economic recession, with a consequent increase in unemployment rates. Instead of demanding higher wages, or accepting 'danger money', unions began to demand changes in the conditions of work, and in particular the establishment of new rules for the health and safety of the workforce. The Australian workforce is very highly unionised and when in the 1970s, Labor governments were elected in most States and in the Commonwealth, pressure was successfully applied to State and Federal governments to pass legislation which would change the rules about the way the health and safety of the workforce was to be protected. At that time, employers were beginning to be dismayed by the cost of workers' compensation premiums: by 1980 it was estimated that workers' compensation premiums cost employers almost $11 billion per annum.[4]

Until recently, most workers' compensation payments were made to workers as a result of accidents, but during the 1970s there was an increasing number of successful claims for diseases people had developed through their work. Diseases resulted, for example, from exposure to dangerous chemicals and to excessive noise; some workers suffered severe stress reactions, and painful repetition strain resulted from excessively fast and repetitive muscle movements. These conditions resulted in such expensive compensation payouts that workers' compensation premiums had to rise. In this book, following official usage, the term 'employment injuries' refers to all accidents in the workplace and on the journey to or from work, as well as to occupational diseases.

The human costs of accidents and diseases also began to receive more publicity. By the late 1970s, it was clear that social attitudes were changing. There was a general concern with human rights. It was no longer acceptable to allow people to be killed and injured at work without taking some preventive action; a generally increased consciousness of health and safety permeated the workplace. South Australia had passed legislation to this effect in 1972; Tasmania, Victoria and NSW followed with Acts which were identical in their major features and in most of the detail[5]. During the debates prior to the passing of the NSW Occupational Health and Safety Act in 1983, for example, the social and economic costs of occupational disease and accidents were starkly exposed. It was claimed that accidents and diseases in the workplace surpass all other sorts of tragedies. For every Australian injured on the road, six were injured at work. In NSW alone, there are about 250 deaths per annum through accidents or disease at work; in 1985–86 there were 114,443 employment injury cases resulting in an absence from work of at least three days.[6] The costs, direct and indirect, of fatalities and injuries in Australia each year, are estimated at more than $12 billion.[7] It is important to note, however, that in the 1980s there has been a *decrease* in occupational fatalities and accidents, while the incidence of diseases, reflected in the volume of compensation claims, has *increased*.[8]

Occupational *health* presents a somewhat different set of problems as compared to occupational *safety*. While the task of occupational health services is to prevent diseases, the task of occupational safety is to prevent accidents. Employers sometimes prefer to deal with prevention of accidents since accidents are very visible: they occur suddenly, the cause can often be relatively easily identified and fixed, and employers can see immediate value for money spent on prevention. Occupational disease, on the other hand, often takes many years to develop, the cause is difficult to find and often almost impossible to change, so that employers can see no immediate value for the money they spend on preventive strategies.

Progress or reform in occupational health?

One can interpret the history of occupational health and safety in Australia in different ways, depending on one's perspective. The consensus view is that technological advances have allowed changes to be made in the organisation of work so that efficiency and productivity have improved; this benefits employers and workers in both the public and private sectors. In the consensus view, the rewards of technological progress far outweigh the tensions and difficulties experienced in industries, offices and factories as they modify their workforces and modes of working. While people with a consensus view talk of progress, a key concern of those with a radical pluralist or conflict perspective is that not all change is progress, and that steps to alleviate the damage done are taken much too slowly. The conflict perspective is concerned not with progress but with restructuring work; present arrangements are seen as destructive, unstable or unsatisfactory, and this is essentially because of the unequal distribution of money and power. Not only is there constant conflict between the capitalist owners and employers who have power to decide on conditions in the workplace and those over whom they dominate, but that situation will remain so until there is a more equitable distribution of that power. This can only come about by reforming the basic institutions of society; the conflict perspective is thus concerned with radical and rapid social reform rather than with gradual progress.

From the consensus perspective, the commissions of inquiry and the legislation with respect to occupational health and safety that have taken place in Australia represent progress, especially when compared with conditions in England and Australia a century ago. From the radical pluralist and conflict perspectives, the inquiries and legislation are always too little, too late. A moderate pluralist view is that major improvements have been made and the workers have wrested considerable power from employers, though more needs to be done to reduce occupational accident and disease.

Interactionist perpectives do not concern themselves with the wider societal picture; rather, interactionists are concerned with what caused a particular accident. They ask, for example, whether a worker is accident-prone, or whether he or she is malingering or pretending to be ill as a personal response to the job, co-workers or some other problem.

Critics with a moderate pluralist perspective give five major reasons for the slow pace of improvements in occupational health: lack of knowledge, lack of data, lack of interest, until very recently a lack of legislation, and a lack of the resources needed to enforce the legislation when it is finally in place.

Lack of knowledge
For many years very little was known about occupational disease. No one considered that working conditions might cause long-term illness. The earliest work was done on pneumoconiosis in coal miners, but for years, even positive results were ignored because employers refused to believe that they were responsible for deaths which occurred twenty years after exposure. Company doctors conspired with employers in this cover-up. Although coal had been mined in Britain for 700 years, it was not until 1934 that British doctors began to accept the fact that coalmine dust produces a slowly progressive fatal disease. This deliberate turning

away by the medical profession has been called 'the greatest disgrace in the history of British Medicine' by one of the doctors who tried to protest on behalf of the miners.[9]

Most doctors know little of occupational medicine and there is still no course in occupational health in general medical training. In medical schools, the now well-known occupational hazards, such as coal dust and asbestos, are discussed, but only in the context of the diseases they produce. There is no course which teaches about occupations that are likely to endanger workers; toxicology is hardly taught and students do not visit workplaces, examine work practices or assess chemicals. Most doctors know little of occupational disease. They are taught to treat sick people, not to think epidemiologically. They have little incentive to hunt for environmental causes of illness unless these can be discovered radiologically or pathologically. Doctors' advice to a patient with occupationally caused disease is more likely to be 'change your job' than 'get the employer to change the causative factor'. This attitude stems from a lack of knowledge both of working conditions and of occupational hazards. It also stems from doctors' greater concern with the individual patients who consult them than with whole groups of individuals such as the workers in a factory or office block. The medical profession has traditionally been very individualistic in orientation, emphasising doctors' responsibility to their individual patients in the one-to-one doctor–patient relationship.

Lack of data
Knowledge of occupational disease is growing rapidly but has been and still is severely handicapped by a lack of adequate data. In Australia as in many other Western countries, new work procedures and to a lesser extent, new chemicals are usually considered safe until proven otherwise. This is in sharp contrast to new therapeutic drugs which have to pass stringent testing before being considered safe. Drugs can be tested on animals before human exposure occurs, and so can chemicals to some extent, but work practices and procedures cannot. For these, it is only possible to gauge the effects of particular procedures and machines after they have been in operation for some time and after considerable damage may have occurred.

Until 1987 there have been no reliable Australia-wide or State statistics on work accidents and diseases. The best data available have been workers' compensation statistics, collected in each State separately[10] These document in considerable detail the different types of accidents and diseases occurring in different occupations and in types of employment; they also show the variations in compensation claims made by men and women, and relate these to country of birth and age. The National Occupational Health and Safety Council is now moving towards ensuring the comparability of data across States, through the establishment of a national set of compensation-based statistics. This data set was first published in 1987.[11]

Epidemiological studies are increasingly being used to describe occupational health problems and to assess their outcomes. Epidemiologists often follow up clinical observations with systematic study and examinations of large numbers of workers. In this way, they try to see whether the suspected causes in the work environment (physical, chemical, social and psychological) really are contributing to the injury suffered by the workers.[12] The first occupational epidemiology report was published in Australia in 1955, and such studies are increasingly being supported by governments, industries and trade unions so that health hazards can be recognised and action taken before they have damaging effects.[13] Epidemiological investigations have been carried out in Australia in a variety of occupations and have included study of the effects of asbestos and uranium mining, the effects of job stress on bus drivers, ambulance drivers, nurses, police and firefighters, the effects of machine noise on workers' hearing, the respiratory problems of waterside workers and so forth.

Lack of interest
Until recently, as already discussed, employers were not interested in occupational injury; this lack of interest stemmed from a lack of knowledge of the extent of accidents, diseases and death in the workplace. However, there was also a considerable lack of interest by employees and their organisations, the trade unions. The reasons for this lie not only in lack of knowledge but in the low priority that used to be placed on health. The common pattern for dealing with occupational injury used to be that each individual accepted cash compensation rather than that workers as a group forced the creation of a safer workplace. An individualised, adversarial relationship formed the basis of Workers' Compensation Law. But changes are now occurring. Apart from the already-mentioned Occupational Health and Safety Acts in various States, the most significant recent initiative was the establishment in 1984 of the National Occupational Health and Safety Commission (NOHSC). Its task is to develop a tripartite approach, with the Federal Government, unions and employers working together to develop a national strategy. Research, training and education are some of the planned activities of NOHSC. One of its first tasks was the development of a system for collecting reliable national statistics on occupational accidents and diseases. In the past, governments have only been concerned with the dollar cost of these problems, which is why workers' compensation data were collected but governments did not allocate funds for the full investigation of the causes and consequences of occupational injury.

The social profile of occupational damage

Workers' compensation statistics and death rates do not show the full cost to individuals of work-related injury. Every day in NSW, someone is killed at work, frequently leaving a family without a breadwinner and children to be brought up by a single parent. Many of these deaths are of young, healthy people; most of the serious accidents happen to men since fewer women are employed in occupations where accidents result in death or serious injury. In the 10 years from 1975 to 1985, 82% of all employment injury in NSW were workplace accidents, while 10% were occupational diseases. The rest were non-workplace work accidents.[14]

An enormous number and variety of diseases are related to work. Some major problems are damage to the nervous system and development of cancers as a result of exposure to pesticides and other chemicals, hearing loss as the result of continuous exposure to loud noise, and exposure to excessive heat and cold which may result in unconsciousness or even death. Long-term exposure to radiation can result in leukaemia and other cancers, and can damage sperm, ova and the foetus, as well as other body tissues. Back injury is another common problem, and chronic back pain can result from trauma, from overloads in lifting, from falls and from prolonged poor posture. The present epidemic of repetition strain injury is an example of a disability that was underreported for a long time and whose causes therefore continued unchecked. Its symptoms are aching, weakness and tenderness of muscles; it occurs most commonly in keyboard operators and is sometimes so disabling that the person cannot lift a cup of tea, use a knife, write, or drive a car without extreme pain.[15] Other problems related to keyboard and visual display unit work are eyestrain and blurred vision, headache, poor sleep and backache.

The two most frequent diseases which result in workers being incapacitated for longer than three days, and thus putting in claims for workers' compensation, are noise-induced deafness and diseases of the musculoskeletal system (including tenosynovitis, bursitis and synovitis). In 1984–85, three-quarters of all disease cases were in men and 69% of the disease experienced by men was due to deafness. Among women, tenosynovitis, bursities and synovitis, along with other diseases of the musculoskeletal system and connective tissue, all now known collectively as occupational overuse syndrome (OOS), increased considerably in the 1980s and by 1985–86 comprised 77% of disease cases.[16] Another modern industrial epidemic is back injury. In fact, the most common type of injury resulting from workplace accidents in NSW is due to over-exertion and physical stress. This includes strains and sprains, and is mostly due to lifting and carrying[17]. Backache, like OOS, is often hard to diagnose, lacks objective, measurable medical signs and incapacitates people for a long time. It affects men much more than women, on account of the different kinds of work done by men and women: women are protected by law from lifting excessive weights while there is no maximum load legislated for men. Women, however, work far more commonly in jobs which require small, delicate movements repeated many thousands of times a day. Reports of repetition strain began among process workers, mainly migrant women, who developed painful lesions of the wrists, hands, arms, elbow, shoulders and neck as a result of rapid repetitive movements. An early study of all patients presenting to a health centre with relevant symptoms showed that 88% were women and 90% were migrants.[18] Seventy-four percent were process workers in factories, doing jobs such as continually cutting sheets of plastic with both arms raised above the head, packing coathangers (8000 per day) and squeezing them into a cardboard sleeve. Usually the required movements were rapid, repetitive and required some strength. Little attention was paid to this as a problem until it spread in epidemic proportions to Australian-born women working as data-process operators in offices, affecting almost half the women working in some offices such as Telecom and Australia Post.[19]

Stress as an occupational health issue

Stress has in recent years been blamed for much physical and psychological illness and disease. The problem of discussing stress begins with the fact that there is no agreed-upon definition of that condition. Recent definitions range from the Macquarie Dictionary's statement that stress is 'a disturbing physiological or psychological influence which produces a state of severe tension in the individual' to the suggestion that 'stress now is a diffuse concept that can be readily invoked to explain random events...In some ways it can be compared to ghosts who influence fortunes in traditional societies.'[20] There is, however, wide agreement that people under stress experience an unpleasant state of tension, which varies in severity from time to time depending on its cause and the condition of the person under stress. It is caused by a mismatch of the demands of the environment and the individual's capacity to deal with the resulting tension.[21]

The first modern writer on stress was Hans Selye, who in the 1940s developed the idea that various forces could act on the body to produce a stress response and this could, under various circumstances such as genetic predisposition, nutritional deficiency and infection, cause disease.[22] Although stress is by no means confined to the workplace, it is easier to study stress systematically in the workplace than in diffuse domestic or urban settings. Hence most of the recent stress research has focused upon work-related stress.

Occupational stress studies reflect the different assumptions held by various researchers. People with a consensus perspective believe that the existing divisions of responsibility and authority between management and labour are necessary and functional; that work satisfaction and effective stress management will increase if management introduces improvements, and also if workers have reasonable expectations of their job and its rewards. A consensus perspective is generally held by management and therefore by the researchers working for management. 'Studies initiated by management are generally concerned with ergonomic studies and the identification of stressors in specific work environments'.[23] In focusing on the workers' attitudes, management has initiated job attitude and satisfaction studies. From the conflict perspective, however, it is assumed that the political and social aspects of the work environment are the major and overriding causes of workers' stress and that these must be restructured if workers' health is to be protected.

In general, the research shows that people in different occupations have very different stress levels: the greatest stress is not experienced by executives, as is often believed, but is instead experienced by low-level, unskilled workers and by workers in occupations where shiftwork is essential, as in the health service, the police force and in transport.[24] Particular aspects of work tend to be perceived as stressful by workers. The most important stressor is a feeling that one lacks control over one's work, that one is unable to influence decisions and has a feeling of uncertainty about one's future. Having to do repetitive work, especially under close supervision, undertaking tasks which cannot be successfully achieved and having to do too much work in the time available are also significant stressors.[25]

Occupational stress has now become an issue that concerns employers, because in a number of cases, workers have received compensation in industrial courts.[26] Simultaneously, researchers have begun to define more accurately the physiological and pathological consequences of stress by examining, for example, the level of hormones excreted in the urine of workers under various conditions.[27] Their findings show that workers have significantly raised hormonal levels at particular times and in particular conditions. Hence it becomes far more difficult for employers to argue either that workers who are unable to cope with their work are unusually weak or that work stress does not cause physical damage. In the pluralist view, stress is multicausal, the result of many factors interacting in a complex way. It is necessary to identify physical as well as organisational factors in the immediate work environment as well as in the wider society; in addition to individual attributes, economic, social and political factors must be examined. There will need to be changes both in the job and the way it is organised.

Perspectives on occupational health and safety

In discussing occupational health and safety, as with any other issue, one's world view or perspective determines what one looks for and finds. We have already mentioned the traditional ethic of members of the medical profession who feel responsible for the individual patient rather than for society in general. Likewise, when medical practitioners are employed by management, they tend to look at each illness presented to them as an individual event unless they are presented with a large number of similar cases in a short time. In any case, many workers do not wish to see the company doctor about personal problems. Hence workers often go to doctors outside the workplace, who see few cases from any one industry and therefore judge each case as an isolated example of individual problems. Company doctors on the other hand do not all see the sick workers from their firm. Therefore they cannot examine the health profile of a whole group of workers and the impact of the work environment on that. The company doctors' approach is generally based on a consensus perspective, with the assumption that workers should adapt to the workplace because managers have made it as safe as possible, given the available finances and knowledge. People with a conflict perspective have called the consensus approach 'victim-blaming', because it regards workers' own habits and risk taking as the main cause of occupational accidents and illnesses.[28]

The conflict perspective asserts that occupational injury and disease are largely caused by the conditions under which workers must work—the physical, chemical, social and psychological environment—and these are seen as originating in the organisation, which in turn is controlled by management. Thus occupational stress, for example, can be seen either as the result of employees' personalities and coping styles (functionalist view) or as a product of an unsafe work environment and organisation of work (conflict view).

In the consensus perspective, it is assumed that managements provide working conditions and health services for workers that are as good as possible, because that serves the interests of management as well as workers; healthy and safe workers will be productive and efficient. While employers have a responsibility to provide a safe working environment for their employees, the latter have a responsibility to work hard and follow the safe work procedures set out by management. If safety measures or medical services fall short of what is most desirable, it is only because the management lacks the knowledge or, more commonly, the resources to provide it at this time. Accidents and disease are therefore seen as being largely due to workers' negligence or vulnerability. From the consensus perspective, the large compensation claims by workers represent abuse of the employer–employee rights and responsibilities, and prolonged absenteeism is often thought to be malingering.

A very different picture is seen from the conflict perspective. Here it is pointed out that the well-being of the employees is not a priority for management; in fact, the interests of employer and employee are perpetually in conflict because one represents the capitalists/owners while the other belongs to the oppressed class. Employers aim always to reduce costs and increase productivity. In this way, employers in the private sector can make greater profits and employers in the public sector can efficiently provide necessary services. Inherent in the conflict perspective is the assumption that employers will always be tempted to understaff, to increase working hours without increasing pay, and to provide poor conditions for workers. Management is always likely to use untested procedures and substances because evaluation takes a long time, and this delay causes loss of profits.

In the conflict perspective, employees need to fight for the power to make changes in the conditions of their work; this, of course, is the ideology of the trade union movement. One way of ensuring that workers' interests are taken into account is to have the workers—or their union—employ their own doctors as is often done in Scandinavian countries. In these cases, workers are more likely to see the same doctor with all their health problems, so that the doctor sees a population of workers who are all exposed to the same environment, and will notice when a series of similar conditions is brought for attention. It is only in this way that multiple cases become obvious and the medical worker becomes alerted to a factor in the work environment which might be the cause. In addition, when the doctor is employed by the union, workers' interests are the prime goal and the doctor is not tempted to conceal problems which are potentially expensive for the employer. Employers in many industries have succeeded in concealing from the public the damage done to their workers as the asbestos producers did for many years.[29] People holding a conflict perspective believe it is impossible for doctors to act in the best interests of both management and the workers, which is what the consensus view proposes.

Disparate views on repetition strain (OOS) demonstrate very clearly the two perspectives. OOS is one condition which causes considerable absence from work, and from which women suffer more frequently than do men. Yet OOS is frequently not considered to be a genuine medical condition. In the consensus view, doctors have the expert knowledge to make diagnoses and it is in the interests of patients to comply with doctors' judgements and advice. Since doctors can find no physical signs of a disease, they believe that repetition strain is not a real medical problem. They therefore believe it to be psychosomatic, which means it is a result of the workers' personality or inability to cope. It may be a conscious attempt to exploit the compensation system and the employer, or it may be malingering.[30]

The alternative views from a conflict perspective is that OOS is indeed a disabling condition, a new type of musculo-skeletal disorder which does not fit well-established disease categories. It is due to a lack of fit between workers and their instruments of work, and this arises out of the way the work is organised. Employers have adopted technological advances such as word processors, have separated out the keyboard jobs from clerical jobs in the name of efficiency, and have ignored the possible ill-effects for the workers. From the conflict perspective, employers were able to ignore the injuries caused to workers because the employers had the power to dismiss workers, particularly women in keyboard and assembly-line jobs who were ill-informed about their rights as employees and were not adequately represented on workers' committees. The conflict perspective emphasises the powerlessness of workers to change the conditions of their work that contribute to injury and disease. The mere fact of powerlessness can itself cause serious stress.[31]

It is well known that migrants are disproportionately located at the bottom end of the workforce, filling the jobs Australians reject; this was, after all, one of the main reasons they were allowed to enter Australia. For example, non-English-speaking women are much more concentrated into production process-worker and labourer positions than Australian-born women. Such jobs have been characterised as having 'low pay, low promotion prospects, hazardous working conditions and shift work'.[32] One major report described working conditions in some factories with a large male migrant workforce as consisting of 'arduous labour, deafening noise, everpresent fumes, extremes of temperature, and various hazardous machines'.[33] Seventy-five per cent of workers expected to develop permanent disability if they continued to work in these conditions, and 58% of workers had lost work time as a result of accidents, most often back, shoulder, leg or arm injuries. Eighty-seven per cent of workers were of non-English-speaking origin, almost all from rural backgrounds with only a primary school education, and most could not speak English. From a consensus perspective, the injuries could be explained by the workers' lack of familiarity with the Australian work scene, their inability to speak English and lack of education, all of which affect their competence. The conflict perspective argues that employers consistently exploit all low-level workers, and particularly migrants, and make no serious effort to improve unpleasant and dangerous working conditions since such workers are powerless to make demands.

Pluralists believe that as long as we concentrate on finding *a* cause or *a* cure, no real change will occur, and 'cause–effect thinking is literally the curse and blinkers of the safety world'.[34] In the pluralist view, the aim should be to try to explain and understand occupational injury as an important phenomenon, rather than blaming either the workers or the managers. The problem should be studied as a 'damaging occurrence'; a series of events which have in the past culminated in damage to persons, property or production and may do so again if no changes are made in the system. The pluralist perspective examines the interrelations among the workers, the technologies, the work environment and the wider political and social environment. Pluralism assumes that some modifications are needed in all these and will vary from one occupation to another. The various Occupational Health and Safety Acts are based on this perspective: they mandate a tripartite agreement between unions, employers and government. The moderate pluralist assumption is that each group has a point of view which it will defend. Power and resources are divided among the three groups, who must all make efforts to change the work, the workplace and the workers in order to reduce the cost and scale of the damage. No one person or group can be regarded as the perpetrator or the victim; all need to share the responsibility for bringing about change. 'Complexity' and 'shared responsibility' are words which reflect a moderate pluralist view of occupational health and safety.

Occupational health in the age of technology

This chapter on occupational health has been included in Part III because the impact of technology in the 1980s has made occupational health a major political issue. However, this chapter has only touched on the issue of occupational health, since a full discussion of the impact of technology on the organisation of work would be out of place in a book on health and society. It should be emphasised that the impact of technology on workers' health will increase rather than decrease and the field of occupational health is likely to become an increasingly important one for health workers. There will therefore be a need to develop new ways of dealing with the problems that this will raise.

One of the problems of assessing occupational damage is that most statistics combine the most serious injuries with the trivial, so that it becomes difficult to believe the enormous total of 'injuries'. Serious injuries tend therefore to be belittled. A more effective method is to classify damage to people into several categories, so that the serious problems can be urgently addressed. A coherent one is a three-stage classification:[35]

Class 1 Permanently alters the future of the individual (fatality, quadriplegia, paraplegia, amputation, disabled back, disfigurement, serious psychological disturbances).
Class 2 Temporarily alters the future of the individual (short-term lost time, accident from which the individual fully recovers).
Class 3 Inconveniences the individual (minor cuts, bruises, sprains etc., which hurt and discomfort a person but do not stop him or her from carrying out normal activities).

It is obvious that the major problems are those in Class 1, which accounts for 85% of money costs and human suffering. Recognising this, some governments have made the establishment of comprehensive, workplace rehabilitation programs a major part of their occupational health and safety policy. In NSW for example, all employers, large and small, are now required by law to have arrangements in place whereby injured workers are assisted in taking up their old or alternative jobs as soon as possible. Provisions are to be made for retraining if necessary; medical and support services are also to be available.[36]

Part IV

Accountability

12 Public participation in health care

The meaning of accountability

In all Western societies, populations have increased and become more urbanised, with governments being involved with the people's lives much more than in smaller communites. Governments in large cities have to make complex arrangements to enable citizens to live in comfort, to move about from one part of the city to another, and to maintain a safe, sanitary environment. It is governments that provide, for example, the transport, communication, education, sanitation and welfare services which everyone uses daily. We cannot live without these services, but at the same time we may find them quite intrusive; if, for example, a rubbish tip is placed near a residential area, the residents are likely to object. On the other hand, residents may demand services that do not as yet exist in their area, such as a children's playground or a health centre. In doing all these jobs, however, government departments tend to work to their own priorities, which may be different from those of the general public; hence in recent years there have been increased demands by people that governments be more responsive to them in the detailed arrangements that are made. This is why the word 'accountability' has become a watchword used by groups of citizens when they demand that they should be consulted on a continuing basis by government departments and politicians, to ensure that services are provided as needed and in a way that fits the priorities of the people whose needs they are meant to serve.

Accountability addresses the issue of how people, who give authority and property in trust to someone else, can ensure that their rights are responsibly exercised and in a way that follows the interests of the owner of those rights. The usual way is by appointing an agent who has the necessary time and the expertise to do the work, and who is trusted by all parties. The question then arises, how is accountability actually to be exercised and by whom? When people are accountable for something, it means they owe a duty to those to whom they are accountable. They are responsible for what they hold in trust for someone else and they have to justify the way they have discharged their duty. The very word implies that someone owns a tangible or intangible property which can be counted or valued. Agencies which have been nominated to ensure government responsiveness to citizen needs are complaints departments, consumer affairs departments, ombudsmen, citizen lawyers, and patient representatives. The number of such representative groups is growing rapidly since government activities are increasing: pensioners' groups, Right to Life, conservation groups and women's groups are a few examples. Some are attached to government departments; others are formed as volunteer groups.

Alternative perspectives on public participation and its effects

'Participation' and 'accountability' are terms used from pluralist and conflict perspectives; the consensus perspective has no need for them.[1] From the consensus perspective, demands by consumer groups to have a say in decision making are merely attempts by radical fringe groups to overturn the views of the silent majority. Writers on participation frequently distinguish between public *action* and public *involvement*.[2] Public *action* is often regarded as the more democratic: it is action initiated by members of the public and controlled by them for purposes they determine. It includes public interest groups, local action groups, self-help groups of all kinds and voluntary service groups. Public *involvement* is seen as being initiated and controlled by governments to gain support for decisions already made, or to develop discussion and consultation on issues yet to be decided. It includes activities like Royal Commissions, public hearings, consultation with advisory committees, discussion documents and attitudinal surveys.

From the consensus view, it is believed that the public's elected representatives and public servants who obey their instructions are both willing and able to develop the best possible services, and that they know better what is good for people than do ordinary members of the public. This view holds that health services are mostly satisfactory and require only fine tuning, and that in any case, ordinary people do not have the technical and administrative skills necessary to make a contribution. Furthermore, if members of the public are dissatisfied with public health services they can, in Australia's mixed private and public system of health care, always choose to get the services elsewhere.

The consensus view assumes that the same fundamental values are shared by everyone in Australian society; that most people are reasonable and are willing to put the public good above their own, especially in the important area of health; that the best health care should be available but cannot be given to all citizens equally; that professionals and elected representatives have obtained their decision-making positions on their merits and can therefore be trusted to act in the best interests of the majority of the population; that social, economic and technological changes in our society are gradual enough not to create major problems; and that any disagreements and problems that do arise can be resolved by reasonable people reaching consensus. It follows that the elected representatives are accountable to all or most of their electorate. If they do not do their job satisfactorily they will not be re-elected; public participation is therefore not necessary. A good example of a statement from this perspective is a column in a newsletter for the medical profession, 'The Medical Letter'[3]. The columnist describes how the Consumers' Health Forum was lobbying to have a consumer representative placed on the Australian Pharmaceutical Manufacturers' Association's (APMA) committee which monitors and investigates breaches of the APMA's advertising code of conduct, and comments: 'Consumerism can be taken to ridiculous lengths and this could be a prime example ... perhaps the Consumers' Health Forum would better occupy its staff in the formulation of practical and productive suggestions.'

There are several points that must be remembered when considering what public participation can, and what it cannot, achieve.[4] First, most people living in a democratic society do say they value public involvement and are therefore tacitly acknowledging a pluralist view of society. Most people believe that participation will enable governments to select out, or develop, those proposals which are acceptable to most groups, rather than to only a few. There are different ideas on how this participation should be organised: by electing agents, by nominating representatives, or, as suggested from a more conflict-oriented perspective, by citizen groups controlling government services by electing representatives to administer government programs instead of allowing bureaucrats to make decisions for them.

Second, it is very clear that the overwhelming majority of people are uninterested in participation. The small proportion of active 'joiners' is not representative of the population as a whole; they are higher in income, education and occupation, and their leaders are more frequently male. 'The flaw in the pluralist heaven is that the heavenly chorus sings with a strong upper-class accent'.[5] In almost every case a small group initiates a movement, but usually fails to gain a more 'representative' involvement. The reason is that it is not possible to find a large number of ordinary people who have both the considerable time and the interest needed to monitor government decisions.

Moderate pluralists believe that everyone has a right to form a group and lobby for what they wish to achieve, and that recent legislation has enshrined that into the societal framework. They also emphasis that consumerism in health has won many victories during the 1980s. The Consumers' Health Forum referred to by the columnist cited above was set up with an office and paid staff in Canberra in 1986 to advise the Federal Minister for Health on policy matters. Moderate pluralists believe that both the public and the administrators comprise many disparate groups. Administrators are like some people but unlike others in the community. Moreover, representatives often have less than adequate technical knowledge and some of their electors know far more. Inevitably, public servants and politicians must decide among competing and opposing interests, and when they act in what they believe to be 'the best interests' of the public, a large or small proportion will not agree with the decisions made and indeed, will believe that such decisions are in their worst interests. The government's role is to be the guardian of the public, to protect the weakest groups and to restrain the strongest.[6] Radical pluralists agree that consumers have won new rights but consider that the weaker groups, who may not know how to lobby effectively, will always have less influence than the more articulate and powerful, while from a conflict perspective, the consumer legislation does not give equal rights to the rich and poor consumers; the poor will still not be able to have their voices heard. Values are not shared by the whole community, and in particular, the values of disadvantaged groups are never taken into account. There is rapid social change, with which many people cannot cope. All decisions advantage the more powerful groups in the community. Hence it is impossible to elect representatives who can understand all or even most of their electorate, and therefore there can be no accountability to the electorate. Instead, politicians and administrators are people in power, who are concerned with their own interests and those of their own social class, neglecting the less powerful people. The only way in which the less powerful can protect themselves is to participate actively and continuously; otherwise they will find their interests ignored. At present, moderate pluralism seems to be the dominant perspective held by government legislators. These legislators seem to believe that the role of consumer groups is a preventive one as much as an curative one: to ensure that certain decisions to which there would be objections, are not made; to see that certain programs are not abandoned; or to force governments to institute programs responding to new needs which have not existed before. Thus pensioner groups monitor legislation which has relevance particularly to the aged, and diabetic groups ensure that diabetic children's camps are not abandoned as a cost-cutting exercise.

'Exit' and 'voice' in the health system

The pluralist case for consumer participation is based on the observation that in a mixed public-private system, when the functioning of an organisation such as a hospital deteriorates, its consumers and its employees have two basic choices: *exit* and *voice*.[7] When exit is the option exercised in hospital care, patients choose another hospital and staff resign. As a result revenue drops, beds are empty and the remaining staff are overloaded. Management notices that staff are leaving the service and revenue is shrinking, and tries to remedy the situation before going out of business. When voice is exercised, consumers and staff complain to management or to some higher authority but continue to use and work within the health care organisation.

When consumers in a market for easily substitutable consumer goods are dissatisfied, exit is the obvious and easy option. For example, if one brand of soap no longer gives a good lather, it is easy to change to another. It is more cumbersome to change from one grocer to another and it requires considerable resolution to change one's dressmaker or hairdresser, but it can be done. However, there are some organisations from which it is very hard or even impossible to exit. These include one's nation, state, religion or family. In such organisations, voice tends to be used more commonly than exit; only as a last resort do we exit from an organisation we care about.

There are costs for consumers in both exit and voice. Exit involves the costs of obtaining information about other products, of learning to find one's way round a new organisation and of feeling disloyal. Voice involves the costs of time, money and emotion spent in trying to change an organisation, and is generally more personally taxing than exit. This is both because our personal time is a precious resource and because people who complain are not usually popular. Consumers, therefore, can only afford to use voice for causes that are of particular importance to them. Phone calls, letters of complaint, and returning faulty goods take time and energy which most people cannot regularly afford. From the consensus point of view, everyone has the right of both exit and voice from almost every societal institution. On the other hand, from the radical pluralist perspective, both the options of exit and voice are readily available only to educated, articulate and energetic people who are accustomed to protesting if services do not reach standards they feel are acceptable. At the other extreme are people who are handicapped, ill or old, and sick people with no energetic relatives who have to accept the standard of service that is available. Still from this radical pluralist perspective, it is not surprising that public demands for complaints mechanisms arose first in the field of consumer durables such as cars, television sets and swimming pools. It is easier to tell when one's car is faulty than when the planning of health services has been inadequate or one's own medical treatment has been ineffective. Complaints are particularly difficult to make if the health services are fragmented into an uncoordinated private sector plus public services provided by Federal and State governments, as in Australia. Most people's access to health services begins with an approach to a general practitioner or hospital emergency centre. The idea does not occur to most people that they could or should have participated, years before, in the planning and development of at least those services which are provided by governments. It is only when they or their families are struck by chronic sickness or disabling accident that they become aware of the difficulties that are faced by many people in dealing with our health services. When people are in the crisis of an illness they are not capable of demanding participation, and when the crisis is over they want to forget the experience as quickly as possible. When they are disabled or chronically ill, they usually lack the energy needed to demand changes in service delivery. Only the families of the chronically ill, disabled and handicapped and those who are elected as their agents are likely to have enough motivation to be interested in long-term participation in health service planning and organisation.

Further, because a large proportion of health service delivery in Australia is done by the private sector, formidable obstacles are placed in the way of any member of the public who does want to participate. The difficulty of interfering with a powerful government bureaucracy on the one hand, and the powerful medical and other provider pressure groups on the other, would deter all but the most assertive, informed and persistent consumer. No matter how health services are organised, voice rather than exit has to be used as the major resource to prevent deterioration of such services. Having entered the system it is not easy to exit from one's health provider, whether public or private. In the middle of a highly mechanised childbirth, a woman can say she will have her next child elsewhere, but for that delivery she has to stay where she is. It is not easy to change one's hospital or doctor in mid-treatment nor to develop one's own health education or relaxation program. If a government's policy states that the market should regulate all services and that doctors and hospitals should compete for patients, consumers have to use voice to ensure that they obtain both the medical and ancillary services they feel they need, at a reasonable cost.

Hospitals which provide poor food, long waiting times, uncomfortable waiting rooms and no privacy can sometimes get away with this if their reputation for medical services is good. In theory, consumers could shop around before entering hospital, but this is not generally done. It is the doctor, not the patient, who usually chooses the hospital, since the patient has insufficient technical knowledge to evaluate the medical facilities available or because beds may not be vacant elsewhere. In any case the chosen doctor is accredited only at certain hospitals. If the treatment or accommodation is unsatisfactory, consumers can write letters or complain to the hospital board or the ombudsman after discharge, but this is no comfort to the person at the time of the illness.

For all these reasons, health consumer organisations with broadly based interests have been active in Australia since the 1970s. The Medical Consumers' Association of NSW and the Health Consumers' Association of the ACT were both set up in 1976, and are both still functioning. In the meantime, the Commonwealth Department of Health published a paper 'Health Care and the Consumer' in 1985[8] which listed the various avenues available to consumers for the investigation of their complaints, and in 1986 set up the Consumers' Health Forum referred to above. In 1986 the NSW Government announced that Area Health Boards would be appointed; their members are responsible for delivering all the public health services to their area, so that hospital and community services can be integrated. Regionalisation of health services permits the participation of interested people in planning and organising health services in a coordinated way. If a board is responsible for all health services in a given area of region, the members have to develop ways of assessing needs and demands; the board has to decide on methods of judging what can and should be done, and what cannot. However, it is still difficult to ensure that Board members are effective in representing their community, and there has been no satisfactory answer to this problem.

Radical pluralists would therefore argue that both voice and exit are thus difficult to use in regard to health services. Exit is often impossible, and people are not capable of using the voice mechanism effectively unless they are trained to do so. Participation through voice is a skill which needs to be developed and fostered, while exit requires only one simple decision and action. The theory of exit and voice explains why any public enterprise can deteriorate *more* when it has competition, contradicting the traditional economic model which states that competition keeps competitors on their toes. When government transport, housing, education and health services deteriorate, the most aroused and vocal clients—to whom quality matters most and who are able and willing to use voice most effectively—are the first to leave the service. The people who remain will be the weakest and poorest and will have to accept whatever standard of service is offered to them because their only alternative is to have no service at all.

Public involvement in private and institutional health care in Australia

The Australian health care system has been described as a closed system with respect to the public's capacity to know what is going on in all sectors of the system.[9] This is clearly written from the radical pluralist or conflict perspective; from the consensus perspective, this question would not even have been asked and from the moderate pluralist perspective it would have been assumed that groups could lobby to find out information if they wished. The whole issue of the need for consumer input into the established system was originally raised by people with a radical pluralist perspective, who argue that the clinical decisions of doctors in private practice are not open to either the scrutiny of professional peers or of patients. While doctors are legally accountable, there are in fact, few malpractice actions; complainants cannot afford the costs and the delays, and doctors are reluctant to testify against one another. Furthermore, each patient going to a doctor's surgery is isolated from other patients. All the information patients receive comes from the doctor. Patients do, however, have the right to seek additional opinions, both from other general practitioners and from more than one specialist. The only primary health care which is open to somewhat more scrutiny is that provided in the general practice departments which have been established in some hospitals.

The institutional sector includes public and private hospitals, psychiatric and mental handicap hospitals, Veterans Affairs hospitals, and private for-profit and not-for-profit nursing homes. The main channel for consumer participation in hospitals and institutions in Australia is through the Area Health Boards. Board members are not elected as they are in New Zealand, but are appointed by each State government in Australia; while women and ethnic minorities are now usually represented on boards, appointments made on the basis of political alliances are still the most common pattern. Since board members do not have to receive any training, their abilities in defending and furthering the consumers' interests are not developed. Moreover, all boards meet in private and their deliberations are kept confidential. Journalists cannot publicise decisions and the public has very little idea of what goes on, what problems exist and what is planned in 'their' area. Similarly, the board often has little information about the level of satisfaction and complaints of the public it purportedly represents.

Sometimes there are other channels for public input in hospitals. In NSW the Complaints Unit in the Department of Health investigates all manner of complaints by members of the public regarding the quality and delivery of health care.[10] One of the aims of this complaints system, which is being extended to other States, is to 'review the complaints in the broader sense of what they say about policy and administrative practices of the Department'.[11] As mentioned above, patient representatives work in some hospitals, while other hospitals circulate statements on the rights and responsibilities of patients.

Public and non-profit nursing homes and psychiatric, geriatric and mental handicap hospitals are run by administrators. In some states, a small group of people appointed by the Health Minister or by the Medical Superintendent of the institution is appointed to visit the institution periodically. No public reporting of such visits occurs; the only public information available is through the annual reports of the State Health authorities which usually deal with their activities and achievements during the year.

The private institutional sector is even less penetrable to outsiders, though acute private hospitals come under the informal scrutiny of patients and their visitors. However, no peer review and no scrutiny of the quality of medical care is required. Private nursing homes are even less scrutinised. Since many long-stay patients have visitors infrequently or not at all, there is not even much scrutiny of the accommodation and meals. To address this deficiency, in 1980, the Australian Consumers' Association began to make inspections of nursing homes and the Australian Council of Health Care Standards arranges a program of accreditation for long-stay institutions.

Public participation in community health services

Community health centres, mental health centres, baby health centres, assessment centres for handicaps, women's refuges, alcohol and drug rehabilitation centres and geriatric centres were set up after the Federal Labor Government in 1973 provided each State with the finance to set up a community health program. The community health program named primary care as the appropriate point of entry to a comprehensive health system. Citizen participation was originally not a major aim of the program, except for 'consultation', but by 1976 more emphasis was placed on 'participation of the community in decision-making processes affecting health care in the community so that individuals are brought into a close relationship with providers of care'.[12]

The administration of community health centres varies from State to State. Some are outreach posts of hospitals run by the hospital's administrators who are responsible to the Board of Management of the hospital. A number are independent entities, set up by specific interest groups such as women's health groups, unions and voluntary organisations; they deal with such specific problems as mental breakdown, occupational health, multiple sclerosis or alcohol and drug addiction. These are run by the community groups or boards which sponsored them and are the only ones with true community participation. Finally there are community health centres run by the health departments or commissions in each State. Depending on the philosophy of each department, these health centres will either be run directly by public servants, be responsible to the central or regional office, or be relatively autonomous and run by a board of directors appointed by the government. In a very few cases, the board members are elected by the residents of the community the centre serves.

In December 1980 a Community Health Association was formed, consisting essentially of staff members working in community health services. This Association has strongly recommended the development of participatory structures for consumer consultation, recognising that the lack of a public outcry when community health services are threatened is a result of the present lack of consumer involvement in the planning, management and delivery of community health services.[13]

As a result of pressure from some of the conservative medical associations such as the General Practitioners' Society and the Australian Medical Association, most State governments have not employed salaried doctors in health centres so as not to give 'unfair competition' to private practitioners. However, the Doctors' Reform Society has lobbied strongly for salaried general practitioner services in community health centres. General practitioners in private practice do not generally refer patients to health centre staff such as social workers, psychologists and community nurses. Nor do people generally refer themselves to community health centres when they know that there is no doctor available for consultations. This is another consequence of the lack of community involvement in the running of community health services; in New South Wales there is no citizen pressure to act as a counterweight to the pressure used by the medical associations. The contrast between the two States of New South Wales and Victoria demonstrates this point well. In New South Wales, where almost all the centres were opened and are run by the NSW Health Department, no salaried medical practitioners are employed by the health centres. On the other hand, in Victoria the majority of the centres were established by local community groups and do employ general practitioners.

One of the objectives of the Community Health Program of 1973 was the involvement of local people in decision-making which concerned their local health services. A small trial project in consumer participation was set up in one municipality in NSW.[14] Its goals were to educate the public in how to participate, to help the public to understand cost issues, and to make public officials more responsive. The consumer group tried to achieve joint management of the local health centre but that was not acceptable to the staff of the centre. Another aim of the consumers was to establish self-help groups in the community, but this never gained much momentum and funds were cut off after a short time. It was not until 1976, with the formation of the Medical Consumers' Association of NSW, that funds were again made available for another consumer participation trial, known as the Western Health Involvement Project.[15] Problems abounded in relation to financial cut-backs, secrecy in the Health Department bureaucracy, staff changeover, and lack of access of consumers to the decision-making bodies, so that the consumers were never involved in the policy-making process of the Health Department. Despite a number of successful activities, such as the establishment of support groups and information dissemination, the consumer group ceased its activities fifteen months after it began. As mentioned, area health legislation now mandates this. In Queensland, community involvement in setting up the community health centres mandated by the Community Health Program was limited to consultations with community representatives prior to the establishment of each centre. Ongoing participation in the administration of the centres was explicitly forbidden by the government.[16] However, community participation was legislated earlier in other States. In 1980 the Victorian Health Commission made a serious commitment to consumer participation, with a major recommendation being that District Health Councils should be set up, consisting of representatives of committees and managements, local councils, other health service providers and, 'if thought desirable', additional representation of the community at large.[17]

From the late 1930s until the mid 1980s, therefore, the health planning process carried out by the various State and Federal health departments had virtually no consumer input. With the consensus perspective dominant, accountability was believed to be satisfied by the parliamentary election process. However, community perspectives changed during the 1970s and by the 1980s a moderate pluralist rather than a consensus perspective was dominant. With this new approach, the Federal Government as well as governments in most States, responded to the argument that accountability could not be adequately satisfied by the parliamentary election process.

Regulation of the professions

Almost all recognised health professions in Australia are registered by the States, with accountability thus being formalised. Registration boards' tasks are to ensure that the educational courses for professionals are satisfactory, that the registered members are competent to practise, that there is an ethical standard for the profession and that incompetent or unethical members become deregistered. All registration boards consist of a majority of the members of the relevant profession, but there are usually additional members appointed by governments for particular purposes. Consumer representatives are now appointed to some registration boards, and there are usually lawyers on the boards to ensure that the legal responsibilites of the profession are kept in mind.

In the past, the professions were generally able to regulate their own affairs with little scrutiny by outsiders because it was assumed that they were more concerned with their patients' welfare than with their own advantage. This was in accordance with the traditional, consensus view of the conflict-free relationships between health professionals and their patients.[18] This assumption has been challenged by unfavourable evidence. When doctors went on strike against Medicare many people considered that this showed doctors were more concerned with their income than with their patients' welfare. Recently there has also been a great deal of publicity about excessive pathology testing and excessive surgical intervention which increases doctors' income. There are also occasional reports of fraudulent practices by doctors. To all but extremely consensus-orientated people, it is now clear that doctors' and patients' interests are not identical. Hence

it can no longer be assumed that the community will accept, without question, the degree of self-regulation afforded in the past. Higher standards of education and knowledge in the community inevitably lead to greater demand for community participation in activities previously reserved to the elite and informed few...after all, the practice of the professions is a public business.[19]

Each year, more public money is spent on professional services, so more demands are made for accountability, for a community voice in the way those funds are spent. Government policy in several countries has moved in this direction.

The four perspectives' views on accountability demonstrate this linking characteristic of pluralism. To the conservative, consensus outlook, accountability is an element of any business relationship. The doctor-patient relationship is seen as such a relationship, where the patient buys the doctor's expertise and caring concern. From this perspective, the doctor–patient relationship is the central element in the health care of Australians; doctors are directly accountable to their patients, and governments and bureaucracies have no part to play. In the conflict view, the issue of accountability exists at a very different level. It is really the 'haves' who should be responsible to the 'have-nots'; the ruling class, which includes the medical profession and allied enterprises, has to be made truly accountable to the workers. Governments should strip these capitalists of their economic power which would stop them structuring the health system on their own terms.

To moderate pluralists, professionals should be accountable to their clients, just as governments should be accountable to the public. Just as there are many different power relations in society, so there are many different expressions of accountability: doctor to patients, medical profession to the public, and government to the public. Government is the guardian of the public—it is there to protect the weak and restrain the power of the strong[20] In fact, it is accountability that keeps power in check, and it is the balancing of power that keeps society orderly and stable. To radical pluralists, accountability is the essence of the continuous confrontations between the medical elite and consumers, and between governments and consumers. Accountability reduces the power that providers (of services or funds) have over recipients. This is why acountability is resisted by doctors and politicians, and why progress towards true community participation is so slow.

The moderate pluralist perspective on consumer participation has recently become the most common. On the assumption that professional bodies are basically set up to protect the income and power of their members, it is felt that public participation is crucial in order to ensure a balance of power, to guard against the misuse of professional power and to ensure that the bodies charged with regulating the professions will be accountable to the public. Regulatory professional bodies are charged with two functions: to protect the professional interest and the public interest. But there is a real danger that this will result in a conflict of interests, and that the professional body may promote the professional interest at the expense of that of the public. Moderate pluralists argue that a strong lay participation would make professional regulation a more 'open system' by providing a direct link between the profession and the community. This in turn would go some way towards ensuring that the regulating body is responsive to societal needs. Additional arguments are that lay participation would help to promote mutual cooperation and overcome community apathy, and that justice must not only be done, it must *appear* to be done. The moderate pluralist view emphasises that the mere appointment of a public representative to a regulatory body is not sufficient to ensure that the public interest is safe-guarded. The important question is *who* is appointed: will appointees be knowledgeable, assertive people or 'lame ducks'; how many non-professional members are appointed as compared to the number of professionals; how much administrative support are they given in their search for information? It is not hard for professionals to conceal all sorts of effects from lay members: a judicious manipulation of agendas, and a monopolisation of secretarial assistance can ensure that no information will be revealed which shows the profession in an unfavourable light.

Towards success in public participation

There are as many definitions of participation as there are writers on the subject, but essentially it is seen as a bargaining activity between decision-makers and other people who were previously excluded from that process. Because it is a process, the bargains which eventually result cannot be predicted or controlled.[21] Hence, participation essentially is untidy, unpredictable and expensive, characteristics which are disliked by both bureaucracies and politicians. Nevertheless, participation in a democracy is as essential as it is difficult. The issue from a moderate pluralist perspective is how to develop participatory strategies that have the fewest disadvantages, not to close such openings as have been made. Several basic requirements for the success of a community participation program will be discussed below.[22]

Community development
There needs to be some general community development to set up a climate in which people feel able to participate. It is essential to establish official structures which make participation part of the *necessary process* through which public servants must go in order to do their work. Without written rules and regulations, and instructions for carrying them through, officials will not risk their careers by giving out information to outsiders or by allowing outsiders into their decision-making network.

Before setting up participatory projects, it is essential to set up these organisational structures or the projects will inevitably fail. People who are just beginning to participate will not persist in a climate of indifference, delay and obstruction. Bureaucrats must be given staff resources and official sanction to deal with consumer groups. Money allocation for such projects is essential, but it is only a beginning. If politicians are genuinely committed to encouraging the community to develop a voice, they must lay down participatory structures by legislation and regulation and ensure that department heads then monitor the contacts with the consumer groups. It is essential for consumers to have access to information and to programs which educate consumer groups in what kind of information to request and how to use the information obtained. Sufficient time must be given to the projects so that officials and community participators can get to know one another and develop some trust in each other. Allocating sufficient time will also enable participators to become educated in their area of interest and as a result, to become useful to officials in helping to generate ideas. Until this happens, officials will regard the participatory groups as time-wasting and ineffective, and will not pay much attention to the participators' ideas. Time must be given to lay people to enable them to learn how to participate effectively.

Devolution of power

At this point it is useful to examine briefly the theory of regionalisation and devolution of decision-making. Palmer[23] describes the three models of regionalisation which have been considered and applied in different countries to overcome such problems as maldistribution of resources, lack of integration, proliferation and inefficient utilisation of health services, and a lack of community involvement. The three models are:

1 A *hierarchical* system of institutions and services within defined geographical areas. This means that patients move from local treatment centres to community, district and teaching hospitals depending on their degree of illness. In this model, no power is devolved to the local areas and the aim is a centralised control of the system to create a maximum degree of efficiency and economy of patient management. This is the system used in Britain by the National Health Service.

2 Central administration *delegates* responsibility for administration and planning to a system of subordinate administrations located within a defined set of geographical areas. This is the system used by the Health Department of New South Wales for its Area Health Boards. Each board is given a budget, and must make its own allocations to all services within its jurisdiction.

3 The central health authority *devolves powers* of policy and decision-making to a system of authorities located in a defined set of geographical areas. The local authorities are empowered to include local community members in their decision-making processes. This is the proposal put forward by the Victorian Health Commission in 1980 where it was stated that

... The Commission regards the opportunity for local residents to participate in decision-making as an integral part of its concept of regionalisation. *The major concern of this paper is to examine ways in which producers, consumers and organisation of health services can exercise an effective say, at regional and local levels, on what they get and how resources are used.*[24] (Emphasis added)

It seems fairly clear that without a genuine devolution of power and full commitment to regionalisation, community participation is almost inevitably doomed to failure. Perhaps the first important thing the promoter of a participatory project must do, therefore, is to establish as far as is possible what are the goals of participation in this particular project. Yet this is extremely difficult given that, as pointed out above, the whole participatory process and its results can neither be predicted nor controlled by any of the groups involved in the process.

Achieving legitimacy

In democratic systems, the easiest way to achieve legitimacy is by means of an election. Members who have been elected can claim to have the right to speak for the community that elected them; they can claim to be accountable to the community because they have to submit themselves on their record for re-election. Elected members can also claim that they are representative of their electors. There are many flaws in these arguments, but they are broadly accepted in the community. Anything other than the electoral process, then, always has to be justified before it is accepted. The next best procedure is probably that of appointment from specifically nominated subgroups, such as a representative of the paraplegics, the aged or the mentally ill. These people should then report back to their own organisations. Then it cannot be said to such representatives: 'You may be a disabled woman, but you cannot speak for anyone except yourself'.

Of course, some valid criticisms can be made of such appointments. One criticism is that participants selected in that way do not properly represent those sections of the population which are least well served by the public services—the deviant, the poor, the migrants, the less educated. But none of these critics have suggested any way of solving this problem, nor have solutions been found in Britain and the United States, where participatory projects and structures started some years ago. Further, it must be recognised that a more articulate group has a far better chance of influencing the bureaucracy than a group of inarticulate or poorly educated people who would accurately represent the weak and voiceless consumers of health services. These groups certainly need representation, but it is their own articulate members and friends who are called to represent them. The experience of all participatory plans demonstrates that so far, at least in Australia, the only effective way to develop participation is through the activities of concerned people who use their voice to take up issues on behalf of less active people. In the British Community Health Councils, which are the most fully developed participant institutions in health services, a similar bias exists. But the Councils have been extremely successful in their main function of making managers aware of how users see the health services.[25]

Maintaining interest

For most policy issues, the recipients of any policy develop and retain an active interest only while they can clearly see the benefit of such policies to themselves, their families or their property. Generally, only people who are affected will make efforts to influence policies. For health issues, as for many others, there is no 'natural constituency' and we are all potential consumers who hope that they will never be actual consumers. Hence it is likely that volunteers who participate as 'general interest' consumers will not be typical consumers, but will be people who have had unfortunate experiences with the health system. When they realise that no quick fix is possible, they tend to lose interest.

However, people who are already working for voluntary organisations, or who have to report back to a local authority are far more likely to retain a longer-term interest in such a project than people who merely participate as individuals. Ordinary citizens should not, of course, be excluded; they can always attend meetings and be coopted into working subgroups, but until they have shown a serious and longer-term commitment, they should not merit full appointment to a consumer body established by government. If anyone can join and be a member of the executive of such an organisation, there is no status attached to that work. If people have to attend a number of (sometimes dull) meetings, have to read a considerable amount of difficult material, and have to spend money and time in getting to and from these meetings, there needs to be some more substantial status attached than the vague feeling that one is doing something for the community.

Transferring power

It is considered by people with a moderate as well as a radical pluralist perspective, that if community participation is to have any impact, there must be real power transfer to the participants. Pluralists differ, however, on their assessment of how easily and quickly that can happen in our society. Pateman distinguishes 'full participation' (where citizens have equal power to decide the outcome of decisions) from 'partial participation' (where citizens can only influence decisions) and 'pseudo participation' (where those who have power try to create the illusion that outsiders are participating in the making of decisions).[26] The parameters of the rights and duties of such groups need to be spelt out by the government at the beginning.

Spelling out success

A number of prerequisites must exist before a participatory project can have a real chance of success, and indeed, promoters of such projects should insist on these conditions being met before committing time and effort to them. Fourteen principles of effective consumer participation have been identified on basis of a pluralist understanding of how health systems and political processes work:

1 The structure of the health department must be a properly regionalised one, that is, real power must be devolved to the region.

2 The Health Minister and the central administration must be committed to a belief that their organisation will benefit from the addition of a consumer voice in the decisions made by their department.

3 The consequence of such a commitment is that resources must be made available to the department to enable it to deal with such a consumer council. There will be meetings after normal working hours, long debates, requests for information and some frustrations for both sides. Unless resources are provided for the administrators, long-term participation by representatives of the public will not occur, because frustrations will exceed successes.

4 Some community development has to be done in the local areas where the council is to be set up, to raise the consciousness of the public and make people aware that participation is a possibility. Only in such an atmosphere will it be possible to find enough active participators who will have the stamina to work with governments on a long-term basis.

5 The participant group should be given a title (such as Regional Advisory Council) and, to be manageable, should have a maximum of thirty members.

6 The council should be composed of representatives of established organisations. They must be accountable and known to be accountable to those organisations. If possible, members of the council should be elected as representatives by the members of voluntary organisations. A proportion of places on the council (about one-fifth) should be reserved for nominees of the local or State government and be required to report to the Minister at regular intervals.

7 The organisations which are represented must be selected so that all important pressure and voluntary groups in that community have an opportunity to be represented on the council. Ideally, the health department should contact all trade unions, clubs, societies and self-help groups in the area to ask if they are interested in being represented on the council. If more groups are interested than there are places available, a ballot should be held to select those which will be represented on the council for the first two years; thereafter all places should be declared vacant and a new ballot should be held to give other organisations the opportunity to have their voice heard. The nominees of the local council could be renominated twice for a maximum of six-year term. These representatives and nominees

should be obliged to report back to their organisations at regular intervals.

8 The rights and responsibilities of the council should be set down in writing at the beginning. *Rights* should include the right to visit local hospitals and health centres (by arrangement with staff); the right to meet with representatives of the various unions of health workers; the right to be represented on health department committees which are planning programs in their area; the right to have regular meetings at specified intervals (every three months or so) with senior administrators; the right to be informed if a service is to be wound down; the right to obtain statistical information collected by the department. *Responsibilities* should include the responsibility to keep matters confidential if so requested and if reasons are given for that request; the responsibility to recognise the constraint on resources; the responsibility to accept a cut-back in some services if others are being expanded. There is also the responsibility to attend educational seminars and to become familiar with health issues (see principle 9). A Consumer Annual Report should be required to be a public document, and the health department should have a duty to respond to this.

9 It should be mandatory that council members attend a certain number of in-service training courses each year. Such courses could be run by universities and colleges of advanced education in the region; council members should attend some in-service courses run by the health department. This would give members the ability to use effectively the information they seek. Joint training courses with health department staff would enable the development of informal links between council members and health administrators. Council representatives should always receive invitations to attend and contribute to conferences held at middle management level, in order to give the consumer view to managers.

10 Funding for the council should be made available on a long-term basis, for a minimum of five years and preferably ten years. Funds allocated should be sufficient to allow for (i) at least 2 staff members; (ii) offices in a reasonably prominent location; (iii) some resources for research to be done from a consumer viewpoint to complement research done by governments; (iv) some publicity to be developed and distributed; (v) special projects to be completed at the council's request, such as registers of local doctors and their services.

11 Meetings of the council should generally be held in public, like local government meetings. Media releases should be issued before and after meetings. Few members of the general public will attend but if journalists can be induced to come, the council's activities will be reported and the general level of interest in health matters will increase in the community. In this way potential new council members can be recruited and trained. Confidential matters can be

dealt with in a separate part of the meeting and the press can be excluded from that section.

12 The Council should form sub-committees to carry through special tasks. Particular attention needs to be paid to establishing sub-committees to regularly examine the situation of mentally ill, mentally handicapped, chronically ill and disabled people in that community. Regular visits should be made to institutions dealing with the care of such people, and some of the council's research budget should be used to examine how satisfactorily the problems of these people are dealt with. Openness in that sector is crucial as these groups are the most vulnerable.

13 The council should have the right to include members of the general public in its subcommittees and former members who have been retired could continue to assist the council in that capacity.

14 Evaluation of the council activities and achievements should be built into the project and resources made available to do this. The evaluation team should not come from the health department. Funding should not be dependent on the outcome of evaluation for at least the first five-year term of the council.

13 Professional accountability

Defining the term 'profession'

In every society, certain work has to be done. Food, clothing and shelter have to be provided; children, the weak and the old have to be cared for; the sick have to be treated and the dead have to be buried. Children must be educated, gods worshipped and disputes settled. All these jobs have to be divided among the people, but that division can be done in a number of different ways. In all societies, some tasks are prestigious while others have low status; some work is more highly paid than other work, and some jobs are regarded as difficult, dirty or dangerous while others are easy, clean and safe. In Western societies, one aspect of this division of labour has come to be known as a division between *professional* and *non-professional* occupations.

The major implication of the term 'profession' is that when an occupation calls itself a profession and is accepted as such by law and by the public, it gains a number of advantages. The most significant of these are high status and freedom to control its work. Professions usually also have control over a number of lower status occupations. Hence the term 'profession' is not so much a descriptive term as one which implies value and prestige.[1] People who practise an occupation often try to improve its social status and the push to become a profession is one way of moving the whole group up in the social hierarchy.

In the theories of professionalism, three characteristics are accepted as being essential before an occupation can call itself a profession and thus obtain the considerable increase in prestige that the title gives. First, professionals must have knowledge in a particular area, and this can only be achieved by years of study followed by examinations which test that knowledge and exclude students who do not reach a required standard. Second, the training must be broad and generalised rather than narrow and specialised; in particular there has to be a gap between the knowledge and its application to specific cases, so that a professional has to be able to interpret the knowledge that has been learnt. Thirdly, the professionals must use their judgement in order to do their work.[2] These characteristics distinguish professionals from technologists and enable professionally trained people to expand their knowledge throughout their careers. Through the possession of special knowledge, professions define an area of work as peculiarly their own, and demand the legal right to exclude unqualified people from the practice of the profession. All professions state that they have a service orientation, meaning that their prime aim is to serve their client's interests. To this end they form a professional association which describes their code of ethics, whose aim is usually to regulate the conduct of the relationship between the professional and the client. If the public accepts the profession's claims to specialist knowledge and ethical behaviour, the profession is granted the legal authority and gains the exclusive right to work in this particular field. Its members are licensed to do certain things which others are not permitted to do; they may even claim a mandate to tell society what is appropriate in their field. In this way, for example, doctors are enabled to define health and illness, to prescribe drugs and do surgery, and to define what training is necessary to become a licensed practitioner of their profession.

In the consensus view, the professions perform important social functions. The medical profession, the highest ranking profession in the health field, is regarded as having the vital task of maintaining health and healing illness so that the work of society can go on. In order to motivate some of the most competent people to do this work, the consensus view advocates that they must be given rewards in money, prestige and authority that are commensurate to the difficulty of the task.[3] In this view, it is regarded as important for professional training to take a number of years, partly so that the trainee can acquire the complex and specialised knowledge that is needed, but also so that the student becomes socialised into an acceptance of the attitudes and values that are regarded as appropriate to that profession. In medicine, these attitudes are clearly set down. Doctors receive their qualifications as a result of examination success and not because of their personal characteristics; they are not supposed to develop emotional relationships with patients because such involvement could cause the doctor to lose the objective, calm judgement which is necessary. In their relationships with patients, doctors are supposed to limit their activities to specific patient problems; advice on matters other than health-related problems is not to be given. Doctors are not supposed to have favourites among their patients; rather, they are expected to treat all patients with equal interest and care. Moreover, doctors are to put their patient's welfare before their own interests. From the consensus perspective, it is believed that since doctors are carefully selected by objective criteria and have their attitudes developed over years of training, they can cope responsibly with a considerable degree of freedom and autonomy over the way they practise. It follows, then, that they should be permitted to set the standards of their profession, its activities and fees.

An alternative to the conservative, consensus view of professions as special occupations which have certain rules of behaviour, such as a code of ethics and a service orientation, is a belief that the true aim of the professions is to control and organise other occupations.[4] In this conflict view it is considered that the hierarchy of health workers in a society always parallels the social hierarchies of that society. The division of labour is not according to the difficulty of the task; rather, it is a division by social class. The powerful upper class allocates to itself the most prestigious and remunerative tasks, leaving the dirtier and less interesting work to lower class. In the conflict view, the push for professionalisation is a way to increased income, power and prestige and a profession's autonomy ultimately benefits only the professionals themselves. The public pays a high price for services rendered yet is prevented by the profession from finding out whether they are being well or badly served. Conflict theorists say that physicians, as representatives of the ruling class, aim to maintain control of new medical technologies in order to have power; they also use restrictive practices to maintain their control over the growing field of other health occupations. At present they have control over their own professional associations, they decide which graduates are admitted to the various medical specialties, they control the assessment of the quality of their work, they control the division of labour in health and the very organisations that are supposed to regulate the doctors in the community interest.[5]

From the moderate pluralist orientation, occupations are seen as interest groups which attempt to legitimate themselves by upgrading their training and getting public recognition of their status. From this perspective, the best way to safeguard professional standards would be to encourage constant debate among occupational groups over the truth and reliability of each one's knowledge, since that is the basis for their legitimacy. It is through continual evaluations between occupational and consumer groups, that the power of each occupation is kept in check.

While moderate pluralists believe that the power relations among the professions are constantly changing, the radical pluralist view is that the imbalance of power among the health professions is very slow to change. In the radical pluralist view, professions are longterm interest groups, whose power, or lack of it, derives from their unique history, objectives and economic situation. The medical elite is not equated with, or seen to be representative of, the ruling class. In the past doctors have had the power to dominate health care policy-making, but now that profession is struggling within its own ranks and with other health workers, governments and consumer interest groups, to hold on to its power. At the same time, other occupational groups, such as nurses, allied health professionals and alternative therapists, are struggling to obtain a greater share of the decision-making and income.

Autonomy of the professions

Freedom and the opportunity to make one's own decisions is one of the most valued human rights in Western societies. The more power one has, the more one has freedom to make choices. It is therefore to be expected that people in the more prestigious professions will demand the power to decide the important aspects of their work. Consensus writers use the term 'freedom', while conflict and pluralist writers refer to power. Here we use the word 'autonomy' as a relatively neutral synonym.

Two types of autonomy concern health professionals and doctors in particular.[6] One is that they should be able to make and implement decisions about patient care and have some control over the work that is to be done. The second major area of professional autonomy is being able to decide on the conditions of one's work, including where the work is done, which patients will be treated (and which, if any, can be refused treatment), how much to charge for one's services and which other health workers will be involved.

Doctors, as the most powerful health professionals, have been able to decide on the content of their work, as well as on their working conditions. However, this freedom is currently being reduced by the increasing costs of health care, as well as by technological changes. Technology has forced a number of doctors to cease being private practitioners; increasingly they have to work in hospitals for a salary, which makes them much less free to decide their conditions of work. Because governments have had to step in and meet the major costs of health care and pay for most of doctors' incomes, governments have been able to reduce the great degree of autonomy previously enjoyed by doctors. Doctors' autonomy is also reduced by the national health insurance system, Medicare, because its computers are able to monitor private doctors' practice patterns. One of the major ways in which a profession can maintain its autonomy is by concealing information about its members' earnings and by not allowing itself to be observed at work. In a country with a free press, this is no longer possible for anyone whose income is received largely from public sources, as doctors' incomes are; doctors' autonomy decreases as their openness to the public increases.

Autonomy is not an absolute quality; it is a matter of degree. How much autonomy a group demands and obtains depends upon its prestige, the importance with which its work is regarded and also the risk to consumers from the practitioners' activities. The consensus perspective holds that professional freedom is necessary because doctors are so important and knowledgeable; doctors are a universally recognised profession precisely because the functions they perform are so indispensable that they deserve the reward of autonomy. The conflict view is that the medical profession has maintained its independence because of its economic and political allegiances with the dominant, ruling class in Australian society. To moderate pluralists, the main reason why some occupations have more autonomy than others is that some have been better able to lobby for their autonomy; the medical profession in Australia has always demonstrated its power to influence political and legal decisions.

From a radical pluralist perspective, there are three basic groups of health workers distinguished by their relationship to the dominant medical profession. These groups are: *direct competitors* (chiropractors, naturopaths, osteopaths, hypnotherapists); *independent non-medical specialists* (dentists, optometrists, pharmacists); *subservient groups* (nurses, and technologists of various kinds).[7]

The direct competitors are independent private practitioners who earn their living by charging a fee for each service, but because they are not regarded as 'proper' doctors there is no government subsidy via public health insurance for their work. Their patients must pay the full fees and their incomes are therefore far lower than those of doctors. Effectively, they are excluded from registration as *bona fide* medical practitioners. They may, however, have their own licensing arrangements and there is no legal restriction on their activities provided they do not intrude on the doctor's legal territory. It is only doctors who may do whatever they wish upon a patient's body; the independent competitors cannot, for example, prescribe drugs, do surgery or sign death certificates.

The independent non-medical specialists such as dentists, optometrists and pharmacists may own and operate their own offices and control their own licensing boards, but there are medical practitioners on those licensing boards, while there is no dentist, pharmacist or optometrist on the medical registration board. There is no formal control of their activities by the medical profession, but these professionals are forced by law to limit themselves to a small area of the body or mind, or to a technological expertise auxiliary to medicine. Some of these professionals, such as physiotherapists, psychologists and social workers are subservient when on the doctor's territory but are able to set up independent practices elsewhere. They have autonomy provided they do not expand their activities beyond their designated area.

Subservient groups form numerically the largest part of the workforce in the health field and consist mainly of nurses, with the addition of technologists of various kinds. They cannot set up an independent private practice; they do not control any area of the health service; they must be supervised by doctors and must obey doctors' orders. Doctors choose what activities to delegate and to whom. These subservient groups have limited responsibility for the consequences of their activities, can diagnose and prescribe only under certain circumstances, and can treat only by permission of the doctor. They are clearly low in autonomy and have freedom to define only very limited areas of their work. The nursing profession has now begun to demand greater autonomy over the conditions of its work, and the government decision in the mid 1980s to move nursing education out of hospitals into colleges of advanced education reflects a move in that direction.

The changing roles of doctors

No matter whether people receive health care in institutions or in the community, this care is largely delivered by paid staff generally trained as professionals. The key person in the health delivery system was, and still is, a medical graduate, but the doctor's role is increasingly uncertain as the organisation of the health system is in a state of flux.

It used to be taken for granted that patients had their own doctor, who looked after them throughout the course of an illness and, indeed throughout their lives. The general practitioner was a generalist who held a holistic view of the patient and indeed of the whole family.

With the advent of complex technologies and the development of new medical specialties, this role hardly exists; general practitioners have, for example, been barred from most hospital practice. The complete interdependency of patient and doctor, and the self-sufficiency of their relationship, is a thing of the past. The one-to-one doctor–patient relationship cannot apply to the treatment and management of chronic conditions. It is only in brief episodic illness that the one-to-one relationship between patients and doctors remains, and such episodes are a decreasing proportion of Australia's health problems. In general, people with chronic conditions need to be helped by a number of different professionals. While doctors maintain an all-important role in the diagnosis of chronic conditions, the care, support and long-term management of these conditions is just as effectively done by other professionals. Even in the diagnostic and treatment stages, the doctor no longer works alone; tests are done by radiologists and pathologists while treatments involve nurses, pharmacists, physiotherapists and occupational therapists. There are increasing pressures to provide community care after discharge. As a result, community nurses are becoming more important since much of the regular contact is with them. Inside hospitals, various professionals such as physiotherapists, speech therapists and social workers are carving out niches for themselves with the aim of developing a primary relationship with patients. Outside hospitals, alternative practitioners such as naturopaths are increasingly sought out by patients.

Thus it is argued from a moderate pluralist standpoint that, as patterns of illness and the nature of health care procedures change, the doctor's role is inevitably diminishing while that of other professionals is increasing. Another factor in the changing balance of roles and statuses is the rising level of patients' awareness of the range and limitations of modern medical care. People's greater knowledge of treatment alternatives leads them to question their doctors' decisions. They shop around for doctors who have more knowledge, charge lower fees or do different procedures; they undertake self-diagnosis and self-medication or turn to 'alternative' medicine; they can meet with other people with similar conditions and give each other the advice they feel is not available from the professionals.[8]

The argument that the doctor's role is diminishing relative to other professions goes as follows: each new type of specialist is an expert in an ever more limited area, but the more limited the area, the more easily it can be taught to less highly trained people. Technology, which until now has buoyed up the doctor's role and status will, by the end of the century, enable lower-level staff to replace the doctor.[9] It is argued that we are entering a 'post-physician era' where the six major tasks now performed by doctors—taking a medical history, doing a physical examination, ordering tests, diagnosis, beginning treatment and making a prognosis—will be done by lower-level workers—'more efficiently and reliably than by physicians and often in a manner actually preferred by patients'.[10]

The argument continues: medical treatment already involves only the matching of a supposedly pathological condition with an available medication which itself is a technological product, and that in any case, this medication is no longer dispensed by the doctor but by nurses or by the patients themselves. The only real remaining task performed by the doctor is choosing of the proper kind of technology for the patient, and it is the technology that does the actual curing. In the future, it is suggested, the computer will be better equipped than the doctor to make these decisions, thereby rendering the doctor obsolete. The doctor is therefore being deprofessionalised, having given up the priest-like function that used to be the main purpose of doctoring. Medicine has learned to rely upon science for total justification of its existence because in our society, scientists are more highly valued—and paid—than priests. But science is no longer in need of doctors and will, instead, move on to the creatures that have been created by scientists themselves—the computers.

To many people with a consensus perspective, this is an exaggerated scenario. Even if the computer can perform the function of treating the patient as well or better than the doctor, the tasks of consultation, discussion, reassurance and comforting are still central, and cannot be performed by anyone but the doctor. It may well be that this will become the prerogative of the general practitioner, who will have to interpret for the patient and the family what treatment is being given, its probability of success and what alternatives are available. Choices need to be discussed with a knowledgeable person, not with a computer. Conservatives would argue that this knowledgeable person can only be a doctor; that the authoritativeness and trustworthiness of doctors *vis-à-vis* their patients is what patients need and like best. Moderate pluralists, however, see gradual changes as inevitable, with other professionals such as nurses and social workers jostling for more central roles in patient care.

Radical pluralists do not see the inevitability of change; instead, they see confrontations constantly taking place between the elite medical profession and others, and point to the strategies that are used to block changes to existing roles. For example, the medical profession also uses complex arguments against the practice of osteopathy and independent midwifery in hospitals.

Professionalising nursing

Some of the same factors which are causing doctors to work less autonomously than in the past are leading in the direction of more autonomy for the nursing profession. The increased number of chronically ill and disabled patients is causing a redistribution of hospital beds from acute to chronic, with more work for nurses in long-term care. There are also new roles for nurses in the community, where they are involved in coordinating a wide range of community-based and institutional services. In both these new work settings, the emphasis is on 'total patient care'; this means an expanded role for nurses and often more autonomy than for the acute hospital nurse. There is a move away from intuitive, individualised nursing care towards a science of nursing which emphasises nurses' independent and professional role.[11] There are also more nurses working independently or through agencies, rather than in salaried jobs.[12]

A number of factors have caused an increased demand for highly skilled, registered nurses.[13] There is more advanced medical technology which calls for greater skills from the nurses who must use it. Most patients in acute care hospitals are acutely ill because they are only admitted while they are acutely ill, and are discharged as soon as possible, without a period of convalescence in hospital. Hence the hospital nursing staff cannot rely on having patients manage some of their own nursing care. Not only in the acute hospital, but also in chronic care facilities, nurses have more complex work to do. Long-term care patients are more dependent than in the past because they have been discharged earlier from acute institutions, and because the dying process has been extended in time.

There is an increased number of older people who have multiple disabilities and chronic diseases, and there is a growing emphasis on home care, where the nurse may be the only regular carer to see the

patient. Hence psychological as well as physical support is given by the
visiting nurse, rather than by the doctor.

For all these reasons, the daily work of nurses has become more
difficult; the emotional and physical demands on them have increased,
with both technological and interpersonal skills being necessary for
competent performance. At the same time a severe shortage of nurses in
Australia has developed. By the mid 1980s large numbers of nurses were
leaving the profession and not enough new ones are attracted to it. This
was because of the relatively low salaries, inadequate career structure
and poor working conditions in nursing, as well as the alternative jobs
now available to women which are less stressful, better paid and which
frequently allow more autonomy in decision-making and control over
one's work.

Only now, when the need for highly skilled nurses is high while they
are in short supply, are nurses succeeding in their demands for greater
recognition of their status as professionals. In this quest they have
imitated the steps taken by other professions: the hospital apprentice-
ship training system is being replaced by education in tertiary institutions, and nurses' interests are advanced by well-organised professional associations. At the core of these actions is the search for
autonomy over the conditions of work, and the issues of responsibility
and accountability are stressed.[14]

Unlike the medical profession, nurses have not traditionally mobilised
their full strength as a group to force changes in their own role and in
health policy. However, by the mid 1980s the nurses were using work
stoppages and other militant actions to obtain changes they wanted:
more nursing positions, a clinical career structure, childcare and better
pay.[15] A hallmark of professionals is a belief that what they have to say
is of public importance, and nurses have begun to grasp this nettle.
Another requirement of an aspiring profession is to show the public that
it has unique knowledge which is not only important but is so specialised
that it can only be practised by someone trained in that occupation.
Further, the aspiring profession usually claims that its work is so techni-
cally complex that only its own members, who know all about it, can
monitor its quality. In this way, an aspiring profession justifies its claim
for autonomy. According to these criteria, it is debatable that nursing
can ever achieve full professional status. Some say it makes no claim for
unique knowledge, nor that difficult judgements must be made by
nurses alone for effective patient care. Some would also assert that
people other than nurses can monitor the quality of nursing care.

Whatever the outcome, the reasons for the nurses' search for professional recognition are seen to be different, depending on one's perspective. According to the consensus view, minor moves are part of a naturally evolving change in occupational roles and are aimed at benefiting
both the nurses and the patients. Moderate pluralists see a gradual
process of lobbying and negotiation which will lead to reforms which

are acceptable to all parties, while radical pluralists see the nurses' struggle against the power of the medical establishment as a long and difficult process, and unlikely to be very successful. In the conflict view, the nursing occupation represents the exploited, powerless, lower class of health workers which is united around issues such as gender discrimination and unequal pay.

Health care teams

When the explosion in scientific knowledge began in the early part of the twentieth century, a strong trend to specialisation developed. No one person was any longer expected to be able to learn all that was needed for proper patient care. Medical specialists' training became longer, and their fees and prestige became higher than that of generalists; one example is the fact that specialists receive more reimbursement than general practitioners for the same procedures. Hence medical specialisation is still flourishing, but it is now obvious that medical services are uncoordinated and fragmented, resulting in large gaps in patient care. From this has come the widespread realisation that there needs to be a more effective approach, in which specialists of the same profession as well as differently trained professionals work together to prevent overlaps and gaps in the health care of their patients. According to the 'team' philosophy, only a service which is delivered by generalist doctors, nurses and social workers in coordination in the community or in a community hospital (rather than in the specialist wings of a teaching hospital) can be truly accessible, continuous and effective. The team must have a known and stated goal, such as the provision of assistance to mothers and babies, the care of handicapped children or the care of elderly people in a particular geographic area. If the team is to be effective, its members will need to train together and learn each other's methods of working. Some undergraduate courses, as well as in-service training, need to be undertaken jointly.

The very concept of teamwork is a consensus one, because it assumes that agreement can and should be reached by all health workers in the interests of the patient. There is an implicit assumption that the health care team will be led, democratically but decisively, by a doctor. Differences of opinion and style among the team members will be outweighed by the shared belief that integrated and comprehensive care is best. In the consensus view, teamwork leads to increased understanding of the needs of patients and communities and to more coherent and effective work-role relationships. Members know their respective tasks and the whole team develops high morale.

New team models are now developing, where the team leader is a non-medical coordinator of a program, such as a community palliative care service. Disciplines and occupations such as nursing, physiotherapy and social work are having a greater say, and are shifting some of the decision-making power away from the medical profession. In this case, team relations are based implicitly on a model of moderate pluralism. This perspective stresses the fluidity of teams, which form and disband according to fluctuating patient needs, and incentives available to the professionals. Teams work neither under conditions of complete consensus nor complete domination, but rather in an organisational climate of constant negotiation of roles, responsibilities and rewards. Interactionists would emphasise that these negotiations are very much influenced by the experiences, values and expectations of the participants in any particular team. The radical pluralist view, on the other hand, emphasises that no matter how the rhetoric of teamwork is presented, the team members remain unequal in status, power and income, with doctors usually receiving two or three times as much pay as nurses and social workers. Nurses and social workers never have the opportunity effectively to challenge doctors' decisions or to have an equal influence in planning a program. Further, people with a radical pluralist perspective raise the question as to how much autonomy is compatible with teamwork. Their view is that 'the autonomy of one occupation is necessarily the subordination of all others. Professionalism...legitimates the current division of labour within the health institutions, the main feature of which is the domination by doctors'.[16] This view would hold that equality in decision-making is not possible in the current Australian health system. In the conflict view, a health team would be possible only if all workers were paid the same salary and had equal legal rights and responsibilities.

Women as health workers

The total health work force consists of many occupations; doctors and dentists are at the top of the hierarchy and beneath them are people such as physiotherapists, radiographers, dieticians, nurses, chiropodists, health inspectors and ambulance officers. Of the health workers shown in Table 13.1, 76% are female. Women still far outnumber men as registered, enrolled and dental nurses and as cleaners, ward helpers and kitchen hands. There are relatively few women professionals, or in the trades and among the plant and machine operators. The gender division of labour is extremely marked in the health industry.

In the consensus view, it is not surprising that the lower levels of the health work force are made up predominantly of women; caring for the sick has always been the work of women. The domestic, supportive roles of women in homes are naturally extended to their work outside the home, which is why women choose—and are best suited to—jobs in health, welfare and education, rather than in the aggressive and competitive world of business and industry. Further, women's domestic and caring roles in the health sector are important in facilitating and complementing the doctors' work of healing. Nursing first arose as a complementary function to doctoring, and the society which defined nursing as feminine could readily see doctoring as intrinsically masculine. If the nurse was idealised Woman, the doctor was idealised Man. The very qualities which fitted women for nursing barred them from doctoring and vice versa. Their tenderness and innate spirituality were out of place in the harsh, linear world of science. Men's decisiveness and curiosity made them unfit for long hours of patient nurturing.[17]

Thus the differentiation of health occupations along gender lines can be seen as natural and, believing that this state of affairs is recognised and accepted by everyone in society, the consensus perspective does not give much consideration to job stress and job dissatisfaction. It is the proponents of the conflict perspective who have highlighted the subordination of women in health occupations and agitated for change. They have pointed out that there are hardly any women in positions of real authority in hospitals or health departments. The subordinate occupations such as nursing consist overwhelmingly of women: over 90% of nurses and occupational therapists and 83% of physiotherapists are female while only about 22% of the medical profession and 13% of dentists are female. All the female-dominated professions receive less pay per hour than those that are dominated by men. Hence the incomes of women in the health services are well below those of men; the subordinate, female-dominated occupations such as nursing receive relatively low pay because the arbitration commissions used to give lower awards to female-dominated occupations because women were not considered to need money to keep a family.

Even female doctors earn less than male doctors because they are more often in salaried jobs than in private practice and because the specialties they tend to choose—such as general practice, medical administration, paediatrics and psychiatry—are less well paid than others. Women doctors cannot easily gain access to specialist training posts because the selectors are afraid that they may take maternity or child-care leave.[18] While from a consensus perspective this is acceptable because hospitals need a reliable supply of doctors available twenty-four hours a day, from a conflict perspective this is seen as discrimination against women. Women, in the consensus view, are more suited for those specialties which require less physical strength; for paediatrics rather than orthopaedics, for example. In this view, surgery is highly paid because it carries a greater degree of risk and urgency than the work of other doctors, and so greater incentives and rewards ensure that more male doctors will chose this specialty. From a radical pluralist perspective, however, these are specious excuses made by the male, medical elite to prevent females from gaining access to the more highly paid and valued specialties. From this perspective it is also pointed out that female socialisation has affected the political activities of the women in the health work force; neither the nursing bodies nor any other female-dominated groups who work for salaries rather than as private

Table 13.1 Persons employed in the health industry by occupation and sex, 1986

Occupation	Hospitals and Nursing Homes Male	Female	Other Health Male	Female	Total Persons	Percent of total who are female
MANAGERS AND ADMINISTRATORS: GROUP 1	**3 200**	**4 896**	**1 205**	**832**	**10 133**	**57**
PROFESSIONALS: GROUP 2						
General medical practitioners	5 012	2 152	11 480	3 248	21 892	25
Specialist medical practitioners	2 086	636	4 938	698	8 358	16
Dental practitioners	195	46	4 936	712	5 889	13
Pharmacists	584	828	48	50	1 510	58
Occupational therapists	72	1 566	41	462	2 141	95
Optometrists	5	6	1 079	289	1 379	21
Physiotherapists	254	2 419	650	2 022	5 345	83
Chiropractors and osteopaths	3	–	1 128	193	1 324	15
Speech pathologists	14	489	8	346	857	97
Radiographers	1 036	1 452	421	1 122	4 031	64
Podiatrists	40	114	232	492	878	69
Other Professionals	5 155	9 089	3 064	4 409	21 717	62
Total Group 2	**14 456**	**18 797**	**28 025**	**14 043**	**75 321**	**44**
PARA-PROFESSIONALS: GROUP 3						
Registered nurses	8 888	103 024	602	13 659	126 173	92
Other para-professionals	2 630	3 874	5 916	4 545	16 965	50
Total Group 3	**11 518**	**106 898**	**6 518**	**18 204**	**143 138**	**87**
TRADESPERSONS: GROUP 4						
Food tradespersons	2 436	4 990	47	114	7 587	67
Other tradespersons	7 289	1 177	3 652	760	12 878	15
Total Group 4	**9 725**	**6 167**	**3 699**	**874**	**20 465**	**34**

Table 13.1 Continued

Occupation	Hospitals and Nursing Homes Male	Female	Other Health Male	Female	Total Persons	Percent of total who are female
CLERKS: GROUP 5	**3 547**	**24 261**	**1 326**	**38 938**	**68 072**	
SALESPERSONS AND PERSONAL SERVICE WORKERS: GROUP 6						
Enrolled nurses	1 825	28 358	85	1 327	31 595	94
Dental nurses	5	301	29	7 726	8 061	100
Other salespersons and personal service workers	591	3 904	416	1 665	6 576	85
Total Group 6	**2 421**	**32 563**	**530**	**10 718**	**46 232**	**94**
PLANT AND MACHINE OPERATORS AND DRIVERS: GROUP 7	**2 171**	**467**	**558**	**601**	**3 797**	**28**
LABOURERS AND RELATED WORKERS: GROUP 8						
Cleaners	3 166	15 451	254	2 346	21 217	84
Laundry workers	726	3 516	11	95	4 348	83
Kitchenhands	1 532	11 924	22	254	13 732	87
Ward helpers	8 885	22 793	251	689	32 618	72
Other labourers and related workers	3 987	3 571	561	490	8 609	47
Total Group 8	**18 296**	**57 255**	**1 099**	**3 874**	**80 524**	**76**
INADEQUATELY DESCRIBED/NOT STATED	**968**	**1 964**	**395**	**897**	**4 224**	**68**
TOTAL	**66 302**	**253 268**	**43 355**	**88 981**	**451 906**	**76**

Source: Based on *Australian Institute of Health Workforce Information Bulletin* No. 13. Nurse Workforce 1986, AGPS, October 1988, Table D. Reprinted in C. Grant and H.M. Lapsley in *The Australian Health Care System 1988*, Australian Studies in Health Administration, No. 64, p. 128

practitioners have been quick to strike or to be vocal on health policy matters such as Medicare.

Lack of assertiveness on the part of women would be interpreted by consensus-oriented speakers as evidence that they agreed with the majority of doctors that Medicare benefited neither patients nor practitioners. However, that lack of assertiveness would be interpreted by the conflict theorists as evidence that women and lower-level workers have been so oppressed that they are no longer capable of articulating their views. It would be argued by moderate pluralists that different female-dominated occupations are at different stages in the process of achieving professional status and have gone about it in varying ways. Women doctors, for example, have for some time been quite assertive and vocal about sexism in the medical establishment.[19] Thus the continuous see-sawing among the various professions, and within each profession, demonstrates the complex nature of the professionalisation in health and is evidence that the whole situation is presently in flux.

Quality assurance

We have referred to the need for accountability of health care professionals, both to the governments that fund their services and the clients who use them. One aspect of this accountability is allowing their work to be assessed in order to monitor the quality of the care provided. Such assessment can be done by clinical reviews among medical or nursing peers. It is also achieved by carrying out evaluation trials and research, including surveys of client satisfaction. All these activities help maximise the quality of the clinical or professional care.

Professional accountability is, however, only one aspect of quality assurance; another is *management* accountability. High quality management of health services is achieved, for example, by improving the financial reporting systems and by allocating public funds to health services on a rational basis. This is why diagnosis related groups (DRGs) are currently so topical; DRGs are used to calculate the exact costs of the services needed for specific conditions, so that governments can reimburse hospitals fairly and appropriately.[20] Management accountability means that managers are able to show that their decisions, communication and actions were effective. In the case of hospitals, this includes, for example, making hotel and maintenance operations efficient. It also includes setting up staff training programs and evaluating them, in order to ensure that human resources are used to best advantage. The involvement of consumers in the planning of health care is a way of ensuring that the care is acceptable to the recipients; without such acceptability, the desired outcomes can not be achieved.

When a hospital comes up for accreditation, all these aspects and others, are assessed against standards set down by the Australian Council of Health Care Standards.[21] The recent push for nursing homes, day procedure facilities and community health services, as well as public and private acute hospitals, to become accredited reflects a concern with quality of care and accountability. The strict accreditation of health personnel, through registration boards (see ch. 12), is also an important component of quality assurance.

Quality assurance is, in summary, the umbrella term for any activity that a health service undertakes in order to attain the goal of *high quality* health care delivered *efficiently* and *effectively*[22]. It is widely believed that if these goals are achieved, then Australians will have *better* and more *equitable* health care. Because the achievement of equity is now a key health care policy[23], quality assurance has also become an important objective. Quality assurance and accountability are thus linked and both underlie current health care initiatives such as providing services where they are most needed and eliminating duplications, coordinating hospital and community-based health care, and spending money on prevention in order to save on the costs of cure.

The concept of quality assurance comes from consensus-oriented management theory. This approach says that management should set the goals and strategies for the organisation to achieve its goals efficiently and effectively. All staff will share these goals and work towards them because it is in their own interest as well as for the good of the organisation as a whole. This reflects functionalist views, of organisations as systems of interconnected parts, operating in a stable, co-operative atmosphere.

Moderate pluralists point out that various groups have interests in quality assurance. Professionals want to demonstrate their usefulness while consumers want to stay well or get better, at a reasonable cost. Governments need to allocate scarce resources on the basis of efficiency, effectiveness and equity. However, interests do not always coincide. While a board of management may want clinicians to carry out quality assurance activities, the clinicians may feel it is a threat to their autonomy. Clients may participate in a satisfaction survey, expecting the findings to be published and some changes to occur, but managers may have political reasons for deciding not to act on the findings. In the moderate pluralist view, quality assurance activities must be discussed and negotiated between all the interested parties. The variety and increase in quality assurance activities is proof that differences between groups can be resolved. The policy of the Australian Council of Health Care Standards, that quality of care can be assured by developing a multidisciplinary approach and a variety of methodologies, reflects moderate pluralism.

Radical pluralists emphasise that it is the nursing profession and managers who have led the way with quality assurance, and that the medical profession often merely pays lip service to it. At most, doctors carry out some peer reviews, the findings of which are not accessible to outsiders. Radical pluralists point to the confrontations that occur between managers and the medical profession with respect to account-ability in general and quality assurance in particular. Many examples are given, such as the Chelmsford psychiatric hospital scandal in NSW, where the controversial deep sleep therapy went without investigation for fifteen years because the doctors were immune to accountability.[24] Another example is the how the medical establishment in a university hospital was able to avoid having its cervical screening program scrut-inised and changed, despite the huge amount of evidence that its procedures were known to be dangerous and unacceptable.[25]

14 Conclusion

The focus of this book has been on health issues which are at present taking up a great deal of space in the public media. The widespread concern about these issues is generated by four dominant features of the current Australian health care system: a massive increase in the number of chronic conditions in the community over the last 50 years; the fact that ill-health, whether acute or chronic, is not evenly spread throughout the community; the burgeoning of medical technology; and, as a consequence of these three features, a large rise in health care costs which has caused the community and governments to demand that there be more accountability for the money that is spent on health.

Four main points emerge from the data we have presented in this book. First, while more people than ever before are now living to complete a full life span, certain social groups are not yet achieving this. Second, because successful efforts are made to keep alive the less healthy members of the community at all ages, there are in the community many people who have to live for years with chronic conditions. This puts pressure on the health care system, which is expected by the community to deal with their problems. Third, because of these two factors, scientists and health care professionals have taken the opportunity to search for new ways of improving people's health by developing new technologies. These technologies are changing the practice of medicine, increasing its cost and causing unanticipated social and ethical problems. Fourth, as a consequence of these factors, the community has begun to demand that all this activity and expenditure should be justified. This then has ramifications beyond the health sector into State and Federal politics.

The political nature of the health debate is now very evident and this is because science can do more than society can afford. The major health issues for the next few years will therefore continue to be equity and cost containment, and therefore focus will be on the social and environmental factors that produce illhealth, in an effort to prevent as much as possible of that illhealth. These issues, and each new issue that emerges in the future, must be considered from alternative sociological viewpoints in order to assess them more fully than can be done by economic or political theories alone. In Chapter 1 we mentioned the recent predominance of economics over other social sciences in the debate on health care issues. We have not directly addressed the issue of rising costs of health care. Yet increased costs are mentioned throughout, along with some of the causes and consequences. Our focus on sociology rather than economics results from our belief that sociological thinking has been neglected. This is largely because sociologists have been preoccupied with descriptive studies of health and health care and have failed to relate the *nature*, *timing*, *definition* and *discussion* of health issues to sociological perspectives.

It is our belief that understanding of particular health care issues is enhanced by the realisation that although there are some 'unarguable facts' such as mortality rates, there are a great many ways of seeing and analysing those same facts. Although obviously each sociologist has certain values and biases, one important role of sociologists is to analyse, in as value-free a way as possible, how issues are debated in society, and we have tried to do this.

Many readers of this book will be students training to be health professionals, who are either working in the health system already or expect to work in the health system more or less as it presently exists. Other readers will be people already doing health-related jobs, and some will be people who are interested in the health system not because they work in it, but because they or their relatives have been affected by it. It is therefore important to understand the different ways in which that system can be examined. We hope that, having completed this book, readers will not express views without saying to themselves 'that comes from the X perspective; what would the Y, or Z explanation be instead?' It will no longer be assumed that an opinion is the correct, or best one; only that it is correct as seen from a particular point of view. This means that there will be far less certainty in readers' beliefs and more understanding of disagreements and complexities. There will also undoubtedly be occasional frustration when other people are not aware that they are talking from a particular perspective. We hope that this book has provided readers with an opportunity to examine their own values, as well as an opportunity to see how sociological thinking can be used in relation to health matters.

We have presented here at some length four perspectives on the structure of society. Structural explanations of social behaviour and of social issues are only one side of the sociological coin; on the other side are explanations of individual experiences that also play a part in social issues. We have contrasted structural perspectives with interactionist ones in a number of examples in this book. Even though we feel that structural features of society have a greater impact than do the ideas and actions of individuals, there is no question that interactionist research and explanations complement the structural approach to health care.[1]

Two of the structural perspectives we have dealt with are unitary explanations, which explain issues in terms of a one-and-only-one feature of the social world. To consensus-oriented people, that underlying feature is social stability and order, which is maintained by society adopting patterns of behaviour that reinforce orderliness, while rejecting behaviours which are dysfunctional to that stability. Consensus-oriented people blame social problems on deviant minorities and emphasise the need for these minorities to conform to 'normal society'. To conflict-oriented people, the underlying explanation of all social problems is the two-tiered economic organisation of society and to them, society as a whole needs changing. The disadvantage suffered by migrants, women and the elderly is either *due* to, or *leads* to, their being in the lower social class. Thus inequalities of gender, age and ethnicity amount to class inequality. The conflict perspective has various scenarios which would enable disadvantaged groups to obtain more control of resources. These scenarios range from full revolution to incremental change where disadvantaged groups organise themselves to confront the groups in power. The latter includes both moderate and radical pluralist solutions.[2]

Pluralism, whether moderate or radical, is not unitary but looks for many, diverse explanations of the social world. Pluralists do not look for a one-and-only cause of social patterns or problems, nor do they advocate a single overriding solution to problems.

Pluralism has elements of both other perspectives. Moderate pluralism shares with the consensus perspective an emphasis on the usefulness of social stability, though moderate pluralism has a different explanation of how stability is achieved. Radical pluralism shares with the conflict perspective an awareness of the inequalities of power and the difficulties in achieving change in society. Pluralism is, then, a linking perspective. It was developed in fact, by people who found the other two perspectives too simplistic. Moderate and radical pluralism are distinctive sociological perspectives because they suggest different possible outcomes to issues.

Notes

Chapter 1 Introduction

1 Cuff, E.C. and Payne, G.C.F. *Perspectives in Sociology* London: George Allen & Unwin, second edition, 1984.

2 Burrell, G. and Morgan, G. *Sociological Paradigms and Organisational Analysis* London: Heinemann, 1979; Cuff and Payne *Perspectives in Sociology* p.2.

3 It is important to remember that data on Australian health themselves reflect the perspectives of the researchers. The questions asked and the findings highlighted are influenced by whether the world is seen in consensus, conflict or pluralist terms. However, all structural perspectives assume that social reality exists objectively and is observable. Since interactionists, by contrast, believe only in subjective experiencing of the social world, their research is more intricate and time-consuming. Very little interactionist research of Australian health issues has been done; notable examples are Darroch, D.B. 'Power and Participation: The Dynamics of Medical Encounters' PhD thesis, Australian National University, 1978, and Russell, C. *The Ageing Experience* Sydney: George Allen & Unwin, 1983.

4 Edgar, D. 'Social Class Differences and the Structure of Education', in S. Hiller, (ed.) *Class and Inequality in Australia* Sydney: Harcourt Brace Jovanovich, 1981, Chapter 15.

5 The term 'pluralism' comes from political science and organisational sociology but corresponds to what is known as the neo-Weberian school of sociology. See Wild, R.A. *Social Stratification in Australia* Sydney: George Allen & Unwin, 1970, pp.110–116; Edgar, D. *Introduction to Australian Society* Prentice Hall of Australia, 1980, Chapter 11; Burrell and Morgan *Sociological Paradigms and Organisational Analysis*. See also Gardner, H. *A pluralist democracy? Interest groups and the political process*. In Gardner, H (Ed) *The Politics of Health: The Australian Experience*,

Churchill Livingstone, 1989, pp.178–202. Gardner distinguishes between pluralism, elitism and ruling class theory. This corresponds to our distinction between moderate pluralism, radical pluralism and conflict theory.

6 Cuff and Payne *Perspectives in Sociology* p.86. op cit.

7 For more detailed discussion of sociological perspectives see for example, Cuff and Payne *Perspectives in Sociology*; Burrell and Morgan *Sociological Paradigms and Organisational Analysis*; Edgar *Introduction to Australian Society*; Sargent, M. *Sociology for Australians* Melbourne: Longman Cheshire, 1983; Austin, D.J. *Australian Sociologies* London: George Allen & Unwin, 1954; Russell and Schofield, T. *Where It Hurts* Sydney: George Allen & Unwin, 1985.

8 Abel-Smith, B. *Value for Money in Health Services* London: Heinemenn, 1976.

9 Grant, C. and Lapsley, H. *The Australian Health Care System, 1988.* Australian Studies in Health Services Administration, No. 64, Table 6.2.

10 Abel-Smith, B. *Value for Money in Health Services*. op cit.

11 *Health for All Australians. Report of the Health Targets and Implementation (Health for All) Committee to Australian Ministers, 1988* Canberra: AGPS, 1988, p.75.

12 Commonwealth Department of Health *Annual Report of the Director-General of Health 1983–84* Canberra: AGPS, 1984, p.262, Table 83.

13 *Health for All Australians*. Op cit., p.86.

Chapter 2 Social stratification and health

1 Wild, R. *Social Stratification in Australia* Sydney: George Allen & Unwin, 1978; Cuff, G.C. and Payne, G.C.F. *Perspectives in Sociology*, 2nd edn, London: George Allen & Unwin, 1984.

2 ibid. pp.13–14.

3 This view, called moderate pluralism here, is that called neo-Weberian sociology by Wild (ibid). It is a perspective that often combines a concern with structural determinants of behaviour with individual, subjective determinants.

4 World Health Organisation. *Development of Indicators for Monitoring Progress Towards Health for All by the Year 2000* Geneva: WHO, 1981.

5 See, for example, MacMahon, B. and Pugh, T.F. *Epidemiology: Principles and Methods* Boston: Little, Brown & Co, 1970; Kark, S.L. *Epidemiology and Community Medicine* New York: Appleton-Century-Crofts, 1974.

6 Oberd, R.W. et al. 'Differences and Comparative Declines in Ischematic Heart Disease Mortality Among Subpopulations in Australia, 1960–1978' *International J. Epidemiology* 13, 1, 1984, pp.25–31.

7 Mann, M. *The Macmillan Student Encyclopaedia of Sociology* London: Macmillan, 1983, p.45; Wild *Social Stratification in Australia*.

8 *Inequalities in Health*, Report of a Research Working Group (The Black Report) London: DHSS, 1980, p.13.

9 ibid. p.13.

10 Taylor, R. 'Health and Class in Australia' *New Doctor*, 13, 1979, p.28.

11 Australian Bureau of Statistics, *Social Indicators*, 2, 1978, Table 5.2; Pullan, R. 'The Wealthy Grab More as the Poor Struggle Harder', *National Times* 17 January–2 February 1984, p.8.

12 Stevens, L. 'Social Factors in Low Birthweight' in *Bulletin of the Post-*

graduate Committee in Medicine, Sydney University Special Issue: Workshop in Perinatal Medicine, quoted in Western, *Social Inequality in Australian Society*, p.87.

13 Hobbs, M. 'Data Sources and Requirements of Perinatal Epidemiology in Australia' in *Bulletin of the Postgraduate Committee in Medicine*, Sydney University Special Issue: Workshop in Perinatal medicine, quoted in Western *Social Inequality in Asutralian Society*, p.87.

14 Siskind, V., Najman, J.M., and Copeman, R. *Infant Mortality in Socioeconomically Advantaged and Disadvantaged Areas of Brisbane*, Community Health Studies XI, 1, 1987, pp.24–30, p.24.

15 Harris, M. 'In the West Twice as Many Babies are Born Deformed' *Sydney Morning Herald* 17 December 1984, p.1.

16 McMichael, A.J. 'Social Class (As Estimated by Occupational Prestige) and Mortality in Australian Males in the 1970s' *Community Health Studies* 9, 3, 1985, pp.220–230.

17 Powles, J. 'Socioeconomic Determinants in Working-age Males' in *The Impact of Environment and Lifestyle on Human Health* Canberra: Society for Social Responsibility in Science, p.34; Dasvarma, G. 'Causes of Death Among Males of Various Occupations' in *Environmental Studies Occasional Paper* University of Tasmania, Special Issue: 'Studies in Australian Mortality' ed. N. McGlashan, 4, p.63 (no publication date).

18 Najman, J.M. 'A Social Epidemiology of Australia using Mortality Data 1965–1967' PhD thesis, University of New South Wales, 1978; Najman, J.M. and Congalton, A.A. 'Australian Occupational Mortality, 1964–1967' *Sociology of Health and Illness*, 1, p.158; Dobson, A.J. Gibberd R.W. Leader S.R. and O'Connell D.L. 'Occupational differences in ischaemic heart, disease mortality and risk factors in Australia', *American Journal of Epidemiology*, 122, 2, 1985, pp.283–290.

19 Davis, P. *Health and Health Care in New Zealand* Auckland: Longman Paul, 1984.

20 Broom, D. 'The Social Distribution of Illness: Is Australia More Equal?' *Social Science and Medicine*, 18, 11, 1984, pp.909–917.

21 Shiraev, N. and Armstrong, M. (eds) *Health Care Survey of Gosford-Wyong and Illawarra 1975*, Health Commission of New South Wales, 1978.

22 Broadhead, P. 'Social Status and Morbidity in Australia' *Community Health Studies* 9, 2, 1985, pp.87–98.

23 See Chapter 4 for a discussion of mental health differences between employed women and others.

24 *National Heart Foundation Risk Factor Prevalence Study*, National Heart Foundation, Canberra, 1983.

25 *Health for All Australians*, op cit., p.85.

26 ibid, p.85.

27 Broadhead, P. 'Social Status and Morbidity in Australia' *Community Health Studies* pp.87–88; Krupinski, J. and Mackenzie, A. *The Health and Social Survey of the North-West Region of Melbourne, Victoria* Mental Health Authority, Special Publication No. 7, 1979; Krupinski, J. and Stoller, A. 'Occupational Hierarchy of First Admissions to the Victorian Mental Health Department, 1962–1965', *ANZ J. Sociology* 4, 1968, pp.55–63; Andrews. G. et al. 'The Relation of Social Factors to Physical and Psychiatric Illness' *American J. Epidemiology* 108, 1, 1978, pp.27–35; Bruen, W.J. 'Socio-

economic Status and Mental Health in Canberra' *Australian J. Social Issues* 2, 1974, pp.127–132.
28 Bates, E.M. *Models of Madness* St. Lucia: University of Queensland Press, 1977; Maykovich, M.K. *Medical Sociology* Sherman Oaks, Ca.: Alfred Publishing Co., 1980, Chapter 4.

Chapter 3 Ethnic variations in health status and health care

1 Encel, S. (ed.) *The Ethnic Dimension* Sydney: George Allen & Unwin, 1981; de Lepervanche, M. 'Immigrants and Ethnic Groups' in S. Encel (ed.) *Australian Society* 4th edn, Melbourne: Longman Cheshire, 1984; Martin, J. *The Migrant Presence* Sydney: George Allen & Unwin, 1978.
2 Cuff, E.C. and Payne, G.C.F. (eds), *Perspectives in Sociology*, 2nd edn, London: George Allen & Unwin, 1984.
3 Mann, M. (ed.), *The Macmillan Student Encyclopedia of Sociology* London: Macmillan, 1983.
4 Australian Bureau of Statistics, *Social indicators* 4, 1983, Canberra: AGPS, p.2.
5 ibid. p.2.
6 Martin, J. 'The Development of Multiculturalism' in *Report to the Minister of Immigration and Ethnic Affairs* vol. 2, Canberra: AGPS, 1983.
7 ibid. p.133.
8 ibid. p.135.
9 ibid. p.135.
10 Constantinou C. et al. *The Injured Ethnic—Medical and Social Problems* Melbourne: Australian Greek Welfare Society, 1977, p.16.
11 Committee to Advise on Australia's Immigration Policies: *Immigration: A Commitment to Australia*, Canberra: AGPS, 1988.
12 ibid. p.30.
13 *Health Differentials for Working Age Australians*. Australian Institute of Health, Canberra, 1987.
14 Krupinski, J. 'Changing Patterns of Migration to Australia and Their Influence on the Health of Migrants' *Social Science & Medicine* 18, 11, 1984, pp.927–937.
15 Saint, E.G. 'Medical Problems of Migrants' *Medical J. Australia*, 1, 1963, pp.335–338; Joseph, M.R. 'The Incidence of Tuberculosis', *Medical J. Australia*, 2, 1974, p.142.
16 Reported in Australian Commission of Inquiry into Poverty, Third Main Report, George S. Martin, Commissioner *Social–Medical Aspects of Poverty in Australia* Canberra: AGPS, 1976, p.185.
17 ibid. p.185.
18 Parker, N. 'Accident neurosis', *Medical J. Australia* 2, 1970, pp.362–365.
19 Balla, J.I. and Moraitis, S. 'Knights in Armour—a Follow-up of Injuries after Legal Settlement' *Medical J. Australia*, 2, 1970, p.355.
20 Stenhouse, N.S. and McCall, M.G. 'Differential Mortality from Cardiovascular Disease in Migrants from England and Wales, Scotland and Italy, and Native-born Australians' *J. Chronic Diseases* 23, 1970, pp.423–431; Health Commission of New South Wales *Health Care Surveys in Gosford–Wyong and Illawarra Area of New South Wales*, 1975; *Health for All Australians*, op. cit., p.80

21 McMichael, A.J., et al. 'Patterns of Gastro-intestinal Cancer in European Migrants to Australia: The Role of Dietary Change' *International J. Cancer* 25, 1980, pp.431–437; McMichael, A.J. and Bonett, A: 'Cancer Profiles by British and Southern–European Migrants' *Medical Journal Australia*, 1, 1981, pp. 229–232; Western, J.S. *Social Inequality in Australian Society* Melbourne: Macmillan, 1983, pp.283–286. *Health for All Australians*, Ibid.

22 Moore, C. 'Relationship between country of birth and psychiatric admissions in Western Australia'. *Acta Psychiatrica Scandinavica* 66, 4, 1982, p.322; Davis, A and George, J. *States of Health: Health and Illness in Australia*, Harper and Row, 1988, p.92.

23 Krupinski, J. 'Sociological Aspects of Mental Ill-Health in Migrants' *Social Science & Medicine*, 1967, pp.267–281; Cade, J.F.J. and Krupinski, J. 'Incidence of Psychiatric Disorders in Victoria in Relation to Country of Birth', *Medical. J. Australia*, 1, 1962, p.400.

24 Western *Social Inequality in Australian Society* p.289.

25 Mulock, R.J., Preface to *Review of Ethnic Services in Hospitals* Office of Minister of Health NSW, 1984.

26 NSW Department of Health, 'Report of Ethnic Services Working Party' Circular No. 83/61; 1983, p.2.

27 Keam, R.G. 'If You Can Make My Voice Heard. Satisfaction with Health and Helping Services, and Renewed Health Wefare Needs, in the Inner Suburbs of Melbourne' Melbourne: Health Services Research Group, 1978.

28 Shoebridge, J. 'The Unspeakable in Pursuit: The Australian Health Service and Its Migrants' *Community Health Studies* 4, 3, 1980, p.238.

29 Australian Govenment Commission of Inquiry into Poverty *Social–Medical Aspects of Poverty in Australia* p.183.

30 Australian Government Commission of Inquiry into Poverty, *The Australian Government Rehabilitation Service* Canberra: AGPS, 1977, p.51.

31 Retchford, F. 'Medico-Social Problems in the Greek Population in Melbourne 3. Social Work Experience in Public Hospitals' *Medical J. Australia* 2, 1972, pp.883–885; Moraitis, S. 'Medico-Social Problems in the Greek Population in Melbourne. 2. Paediatric Problems as Seen by the Medical Practitioner' *Medical J. Australia*, 2, 1972, pp.881–883; Judge, S. 'Some Social Aspects of Illness Among Italian Migrants', *The Australian Nurses J.* 6, 12, 1977, pp.41–43.

32 See, for example, Legge, V. 'Migrants and Health' Sydney: Cumberland College of Health Sciences, 1981; Legge, V. (ed.) 'Disability in Cultural Content' Sydney: Cumberland College of Health Sciences, 1982.

33 NSW Health Department 'Guidelines to Improve Migrant Access to Hospitals' Circular 83/60, Sydney, 1983.

34 ibid.

35 NSW Health Department 'Ethnic Affairs Policy Statement', Sydney, 1984.

36 McIlwraith, S. 'Aboriginal Health and Lifestyle' (Monograph) Canberra: Australian Medical Association ACT, 1982, p.9, a quote from 1937 Conference of state representatives in Canberra.

37 Briscoe, G. 'Aboriginal Health and Land Rights' *New Doctor* No. 8, 13–15, 1978, p.14.

38 Australian Parliament House of Representatives Standing Committee on Aboriginal Affairs *Aboriginal Health* Canberra: AGPS, 1979; Australian Government Commission of Inquiry into Poverty *Social–Medical Aspects of*

Poverty in Australia; McIlwraith 'Aboriginal Health and Lifestyle' pp.5–8; Report of National Aboriginal Health Working Party, 1988.

39 Australian Parliament House of Representatives Standing Committee on Aboriginal Affairs *Aboriginal Health* p.129.

40 Thomson, N. 'Australian Aboriginal Health and Health Care', *Social Science & Medicine* 18, 11, 1984, pp.939–948.

41 Australian Institute of Health, *Australia's Health,* 1988, p.113–119; Australian Institute of Health, *Health Differentials for Working Age Australians*, Canberra, 1987, p.140–141; *Health for All Australians.* op. cit pp.86–88; see also Thomson, N. (ed.) *Aboriginal Health Information Bulletin*, published annually by the Australian Institute of Aboriginal Studies and the Australian Institute of Health, Canberra.

42 Australian Parliament House of Representatives Standing Committee on Aboriginal Affairs *Aboriginal Health* p.129.

Chapter 4 Health variations according to gender

1 Nathanson, C.A. 'Illness and the Feminine Role: A Theoretical Review' *Social Science & Medicine* 9, 1975, pp.57–62.

2 *Australia's Health*, Australian Institute of Health, 1988, op. cit. p.25.

3 *Health for all Australians*, op. cit. 1988, p.76.

4 Jeanneret, O. 'Mortality and Morbidity in Adolescence' Paper given at Second National Conference of Australian Association for Adolescent Health Sydney, 10–11 December 1981, p.6.

5 Clarke, J.N. 'Sexism, Feminism and Medicalism: A Decade Review of Literature on Gender and Illness' *Sociology of Health & Illness* 5, 1, 1983, pp.62–82.

6 Gove, W.R. 'Gender Differences in Mental and Physical Illness: The Effects of Fixed Roles and Nuturant Roles' *Social Science & Medicine* 19, 2, 1984, pp.77–91; Grantham, H. 'Are Women Really Most Likely to Suffer from Depression?' *Modern Medicine of Australia* June, 1983, pp.27–34; Verbrugge, L.M. 'Gender and Health: An Update on Hypotheses and Evidence' *Journal of Health and Social Behaviour*, 26, 1985, pp. 156–182.

7 Clarke 'Sexism, Feminism and Medicalism' *Sociology of Health & Illness* pp.62–82.

8 Australian Bureau of Statistics *Handicapped Persons Survey 1981* Catalogue No. 4343.0, Canberra: AGPS, 1982.

9 Australian Bureau of Statistics *Social Indicators* 4, 1984, p.76, Table 3.8.

10 ibid. p.79, Table 3.11.

11 Western, J.S. *Social Inequality in Australian Society*, Sydney: Macmillan, 1982, p.173; Commonwealth Department of Health, *Australian Women—A Health Perspective: A Summary of Statistical Indicators'* Canberra: AGPS, 1985; *Australian Health Survey 1983*, ABS Cat. No. 4311.0.

12 Wyndham, D. 'Sexism as it Affects Women as Consumers of Health Care' *New Doctor* 11, 1979, pp.24–28; Wyndham, D. 'My Doctor Gives Me Pills to Put Him Out of My Misery' *New Doctor* 23, 1982, pp.21–25; 'Women and Psychotropic Drugs' in *Man, Drugs and Society—Current Perspectives* Proceedings of 1st Pan-Pacific Conference on Drugs or Alcohol, Canberra: Australian Foundation on Alcoholism and Drugs Dependence, 1981; Verbrugge, L.M. Gender and Health: 'An Update on Hypotheses and

Evidence'. op. cit. pp.156–182.

13 Lugg, M.M. 'Women's Use of Western Australian Health Services' in Commonwealth Department of Health *'Women's Health in a Changing Society'* Canberra: AGPS, 1978, vol. 3, pp.5–13; Commonwealth Department of Health *Australian Women—A Health Perspective.*

14 Commonwealth Department of Health *Australian Women—A Health Perspective*; Benn, K. 'Psychiatric Industry and Women's Health' in *Women's Health in a Changing Society* vol. 3, pp.3–7.

15 Lugg, M. M. 'Women's Use of Western Australian Health Services' in *Women's Health in a Changing Society* vol. 3; Commonwealth Department of Health *Australian Women—A Health Perspective; Australia's Health,* 1988, op. cit. p.65.

16 Benn, K. 'Psychiatric Industry and Women's Health' in *Women's Health in a Changing Society* vol. 3, pp.3–7.

17 Australian Bureau of Statistics *Australian Health Survey 1983,* Preliminary Findings, Canberra: AGPS, 1984; Hennessy, B.L. et al. 'The Canberra Mental Health Survey: Preliminary Results' *Medical J. Australia* 1, 1973, pp.721–724.

18 Commonwealth Department of Health *Australian Women—A Health Perspective* pp.11–12.

19 ibid. p.12.

20 Western *Social Inequality in Australian Society* p.172; Broadhead, P. 'Social Status and Morbidity in Australia' *Community Health Studies* 9, 1985, p.2.

21 Nathanson 'Illness and the Feminine Role: A Theoretical Review' *Social Science & Medicine* 9, p.57.

22 Gove 'Gender Differences in Mental and Physical Illness' *Social Science & Medicine* pp. 7–91; Brown, G. 'Depression: A Sociological View' in Tuckett, D. and Kaufert, J.M. (eds) *Basic Readings in Medical Sociology* London: Tavistock, 1978.

23 Brown, G. 'Depression: A Sociological View' in *Basic Readings in Medical Sociology.*

24 Gove, 'Gender Differences in Mental and Physical Illness' *Social Science & Medicine,* pp.17–91; Mugford, S. and Lally, J., 'Socioeconomic Status, Gender Inequality and Women's Mental Health: Findings from the Canberra Mental Health Survey', *Australian J. Social Issues* 15, 1, 1980, pp.30–42.

25 Ware, J.E. et al. 'The Measurement and Meaning of Patient Satisfaction', *Health & Medical Care Services Rev.* 1. 1, 1978, pp.1–15.

26 *National Policy on Women's Health: A Framework for Change.* A discussion paper for community comment and response. Issued by the Special Consultant to the Federal Minister for Community Services and Health on Women's Health, Canberra: AGPS, February 1988.

27 Broom, D.H. 'In Sickness and in Health: Social Policy and the Control of Women' in Baldock, C. and Cass, B. (eds) *Women, Social Welfare and the State* Sydney: George Allen & Unwin, 1983, pp.262–278; Broom, D. 'Natural Resources: Health, Reproduction and the Gender Order' in Broom, D. (ed.) *Unfinished Business—Social Justice for Women in Australia* Sydney: George Allen & Unwin, 1984, pp.46–61.

28 Whitlam, E.G., Speech at 'Conference on Women's Health in a Changing Society' Commonwealth Department of Health, Canberra: AGPS, 1978 vol. 1, p.14.

29 Editorial 'Women's Health in a Changing Society' *Medical J. Australia* 2, 14, 1975, pp.539–40.
30 South Australia Health Commission *Report of the Working Party on a Women's Health Policy*. Adelaide: SA Government Printer, 1984; NSW Women's Health Policy Review Committee, *Women's Health Services in New South Wales* Sydney: NSW Government Printer, 1985.
31 Verbrugge, L.M. Gender and Health. 'An Update on Hypotheses and Evidence', op. cit.
32 McKinlay, J.B. (ed.) *Issues in the Political Economy of Health Care* New York: Tavistock, 1984, p.33.

Chapter 5 Chronicity of ill-health

1 Grant, C. and Lapsley, H. *The Australian Health Care System 1985* Australian Studies in Health Service Administration, 55, Table 3.19. Kensington: School of Health Administration, University of New South Wales.
2 Australian Bureau of Statistics *Australian Health Survey 1977–78, Chronic Conditions* Canberra: AGPS (no publication date) p.9.
3 Results of a survey by the Australian Bureau of Statistics, as reported in the *Sydney Morning Herald*, 20 February 1989.
4 Tindall, B. Swanson, C. Whyte, B.M. Perdices, M. and Cooper, D.A. 'Report on Fourth International Conference on the Acquired Immuno-deficiency Syndrome'. *Medical J. of Australia*, 150, January 16, 1989, p.87–92.
5 Data from NHMRC Special Unit in AIDS Epidemiology and Clinical Research, Sydney, April 1989.
6 Curtin, J. 'AIDS may double in year' Report on W.H.O. AIDS Conference, the *Sydney Morning Herald*, 8 June, 1988.
7 Clark, P. 'AIDS Can Stay Latent for 25 Years, says Expert', quoting Professor Ian Gust in the *Sydney Morning Herald*, 12 May 1988.
8 NHMRC data, April 1989. Op. cit.
9 *AIDS: A time to care, a time to act* Policy Discussion Paper, AGPS, 1988, pp.73–82.
10 This was said by Mr Wilson Tuckey, conservative MP and Federal Shadow Minister for Health at the National AIDS Conference, Hobart 1988.
11 Altman, D quoted in the *Sydney Morning Herald* 'AIDS Vaccine before cure seen as disaster', 18 May, 1988.
12 Shepherd, B. 'Test Patients for AIDS', *Australian Doctor*, 6 May, 1988.
13 For example, 'AIDS is here: The 1988 Growth Industry: We have top sites available in Sydney and suburbs for condom vending machines', advertisment which appeared in the *Sydney Morning Herald* in April 1988 and reprinted in the *Financial Review* on 13 May 1988.
14 Ballard, J.P. *The Politics of AIDS in The Politics of Health: The Australian Experience*. Gardner, H. (Ed). *Churchill Livingstone*, 1989, pp.349–375.
15 Carswell, P. 'AIDS: What's it Got to Do with Me?' *Bioethics News*, 7, 4, 1988 pp.13–21.
16 Gerson, E. and Strauss, A. 'Time for Living: Problems in Chronic Illness Care' *Social Policy* Nov.–Dec. 1975, p.12.
17 For a discussion on the concept of social deviance see Erikson, K.T. 'Notes

on the Sociology of Deviance' *Social Problems* 9, 1962, pp.307–314; Edgar, D. *Introduction to Australian Society* Sydney: Prentice Hall, 1980; Cuff, E.C. and Payne, G.C.F. (eds) *Perspectives in Sociology* 2nd edn, London: George Allen & Unwin, 1984, Chapter 2.

18 Kosa, J. et al. (eds) *Poverty and Health: A Sociological Analysis* Cambridge Mass.: Harvard University Press, 1969.

19 Krupinski, J. et al. *A Community Survey of the Rural Town of Heyfield, Victoria, Australia* ·Melbourne: Mental Health Authority, Special Publications L, 1970; Australian Bureau of Statistics *Australian Health Survey 1977–78.*

20 Goffman, E. *Stigma* Ringwood, Vic.: Pelican, 1968.

21 Parsons, T. *The Social System* Glencoe, Ill.: The Free Press, 1951.

22 Freidson, E. 'Client Control and Medical Practice' *American J. Sociology* 65, 1960, pp.374–382; Freidson, E. *Professional Dominance: The Social Structure of Medical Care* New York: Atherton Press, 1970; Maykovich, M. *Medical Sociology* Sherman Oaks, Ca.: Alfred Publishing Co., 1980, Chapter 5, p.151.

23 Gibson, D. and Boreham, P. 'Managing Communication: Appropriate Communication in Medical Consultations' *Australian J. Social Issues* 16, 1, 1981, pp.52–66.

24 ibid. p.63.

25 Najman, J.M. et al. 'Patient Characteristics Negatively Stereotyped by Doctors' *Social Science & Medicine* 16, 20, 1982, pp.1781–1789.

26 Goffman *Stigma.*

27 Sax, S. 'The Challenges of Effective Care for the Disabled' *AMA Gazette* August, 1981, p.30.

28 Blaxter, M. 'Disability and Rehabilitation: Some Questions of Definition' in C. Cox and A. Mead (eds) *A Sociology of Medical Practice* London: Collier–Macmillan, 1975, pp.207–8.

29 Peroni, F. 'The Status of Chronic Illness' *Social Policy & Administration* 15, 1, 1981, pp.43–53.

30 Sleep, N. 'Strategies for Social Change in Australia: Future Directions of the Disabled Person's Movement' *Quad Wrangle* April, 1983, pp.1–4; Alsop, L. 'A New Theory of Social Justice' *Australian Social Welfare Impact* 15, 1, 1985, pp.11–12.

Chapter 6 The Shadow of illness on an ageing population

1 Russell, C., *The Ageing Experience* Sydney: George Allen & Unwin, 1981.

2 Australian Bureau of Statistics *Social Indicators* 4, 1984, Canberra: AGPS, Table 1.6, p.10.

3 Sinnett, P. 'Problems of Geriatric Management in Australia' Paper given at Health Seminar at University of New South Wales, May 1983.

4 Russell *The Ageing Experience.* This is a study of ageing from an interactionist perspective.

5 Australian Bureau of Statistics *Social Indicators* 4, 1984, Table 3.12, p.80.

6 Andersen, N.A. 'The Assessment of Need for Support Services' *Australian Family Physician* 7, 1978, pp.307–312.

7 Sinnett, P. 'Problems of Geriatric Management in Australia'.

8 Opit, L.J. 'Economic Policy and Health Care: The Inverse Care Law in Australia' *New Doctor* 26 1982, pp.9–12.

9 Australian Bureau of Statistics *Social Indicators* 4, 1984 Table 3.25, p.90.

10 Sinnett, P. 'Ageing and Dependency—Myths and Reality' Paper given at Senior Citizens' Week Forum—Accommodation After Retirement, 13 March 1984.

11 Cumming E. and Henry W. *Growing Old* New York: Basic Books, 1961.

12 Prinsley, D.M. 'Does Australia Know How to Cope with Growing Old?' *Medical J. Australia* July 11, 1981, pp.6–10.

13 Wild, R.A. 'Social Stratification and Old Age' *Australian J. Social Issues* 12, 1, 1977, pp.19–31.

14 Department of Social Security, 1985.

15 Grant, C. and Lapsley, H. *The Australian Health Care System 1985* Australian Studies in Health Service Administration, 55, 1986 Table 3.17, Kensington: School of Health Administration, University of New South Wales, 1986.

16 Pollard, A.H. and Pollard, G.N. 'The Demography of Ageing in Australia' in A. Howe (ed.) *Towards an Older Australia* St. Lucia: University of Queensland Press 1981, pp.13–34.

17 Kendig, H. 'Housing and Living Arrangements of the Aged' in A. Howe (ed.) *Towards an Older Australia* pp.85–101.

18 Kinnear, D. and Graycar, A. 'Ageing and Family Dependency' *Australian J. Social Issues* 19, 1, 1984, pp.13–25.

19 Day, A.T. 'Women and the Challenge of Long Life' Report of a Survey 'For women over 60', National Women's Advisory Council, Canberra: AGPS, 1984.

20 Ford, B. *The Elderly Australian* Ringwood, Vic.: Penguin 1977, p.54.

21 Ehrlich, F. 'Health and Illness' in A. Howe (ed.) *Towards an Older Australia*. pp.102–116.

22 Gibson, D.M. and Rowland, D.T. 'Community Vs Institutional Care: The Case of the Australian Aged' *Social Science & Medicine* 18, 11, 1984, pp.997–1004, Table 1.

23 House of Representatives Standing Committee on Expenditure *In a Home or at Home: Accommodation and Home Care for the Aged* Canberra: AGPS, 1982.

24 Gibson and Rowland 'Community Vs Institutional Care: The Case of the Australian Aged' *Social Science & Medicine*.

25 *Report of the Committee on Care of the Aged and Infirm* Canberra: AGPS 1979. With respect to this paragraph, we were not able to find more recent, comparable estimates and ratios.

26 Australia, Report of the Auditor-General on an Efficiency Audit, Commonwealth Administration of Nursing Home Programs, Efficiency Audit Report No. 2, Canberra: AGPS 1981; Australia. Parliament. House of Representatives Standing Committee on Expenditure. Review of the Auditor-General's Efficiency Audit Report; Commonwealth Administration of Nursing Home Programs. February 1982, Canberra: AGPS 1982; Australia, Parliament. House of Representatives Standing Committee on Expenditure: *In A Home Or At Home: Accommodation and Home Care for the Aged*. October 1981 Canberra: AGPS 1982; Advisory Council for Intergovernmental Relations Report 6, *The Provision of Services for the Aged: A*

214 NOTES

Report on Relations Among Governments in Australia. Canberra: AGPS 1983; Commonwealth Department of Community Services. 1 Annual Report 1985–86 Canberra: AGPS P. 20; Commonwealth Department of Community Services Nursing Homes and Hostels Review AGPS 1986.

27 Australia 1987–88 Budget Paper No. 1, Canberra: AGPS, pp.131 and 134.

28 Grant and Lapsely *The Australian Health Care System, 1987* Australian Studies of Health Service Administration No 62, 1988, p.167.

29 Warren, W.G. and Chopra, P.N. 'An Australian Survey of Attitudes to Death' *Australian J. Social Issues* 14, 2, 1981, pp.134–142.

30 Strauss, A. and Glaser B. 'Patterns of Dying' in C. Cox and A. Mead *A Sociology of Medical Practice* London: Collier Macmillan, 1985, p.247.

31 Najman, J. 'Death and Dying: Towards a Sociological Understanding' *Hospital & Health Care Administration* May, 1973, pp.7–9; Kellehear, A. 'Are We a "Death-Denying" Society? A Sociological Review' *Social Science & Medicine* 18, 9, 1984, pp.713–723.

Chapter 7 Health disregarded: drugs and chronic conditions

1 Senate Standing Committee on Social Welfare *Drug Problems in Australia— an Intoxicated Society* Canberra: AGPS, 1977, p.15.

2 Senate Standing Committee on Social Welfare *Drug Problems in Australia* p.15.; Parliament South Australia *Report of the Royal Commission into the Non-Medical Use of Drugs* Adelaide: South Australian State Information Centre.

3 Senate Standing Committee on Social Welfare *Drug Problems in Australia* p.22.

4 Sargent, M. *Drinking and Alcoholism in Australia: A Power Relations Theory* Melbourne: Longman Cheshire, 1979.

5 Hawks, D. 'The proposal to make heroin available legally to intravenous drug users' *Medical J. Australia*, 149, 7, 1988, pp.455–456.

6 The Royal College of Physicians, London *Smoking or Health* London: HMSO, 1962.

7 US Department of Health, Education and Welfare *The Health Consequences of Smoking* Washington DC: US Govt Printer, 1964.

8 Armstrong, B.K., Daube, M.M. and Shean, R.E. 'A Smoke-free Australia —our Bicentenary resolution?' *Medical J. Australia* 149, July 4, 1988, pp.1–2.

9 Stapleton, J. 'Men lead in giving up smokers' *Sydney Morning Herald*, 8 April 1988, quoting findings from the Quit for Life campaigns in Sydney and Melbourne.

10 Hetzel, B. *Health and Australian Society* Ringwood, Vic.: Penguin, 1980.

11 National Cancer Institute, USA, reported in *Boston Globe* 3 December 1985, p.1; Woodward, A. 'Commentary: Current Smoking Issues: Risks to Women and the Promotion of Tobacco' *Community Health Studies* 8, 3, 1984, pp.335–7.

12 Hetzel *Health and Australian Society* pp.171–2.

13 Hill, D. 'Australian Patterns of Tobacco Smoking in 1986' *Medical J. Australia* 149, July 4, 1988, pp.6–10.

14 Royal College of Physicians *Smoking and Health Now* p.29. Reported in Senate Standing Committee on Social Welfare Report *Drug Problems in*

Australia p.89.

15 Taylor, P. 'Smoke Ring: The Politics of Tobacco' London: The Bodley Head, 1984, p.280. Cited by A. Woodward 'Commentary: Current Smoking Issues: Risks to Women and the Promotion of Tobacco' *Community Health Studies* p.337.

16 ibid. p.337.

17 Sargent *Drinking and Alcoholism in Australia* p.3.

18 Commonwealth Department of Community Services and Health. *Statistics on Drug Abuse in Australia*, 1988. An information document for use in association with the National Campaign Against Drug Abuse. Canberra: AGPS, 1988, p.49.

19 Senate Standing Committee on Social Welfare *Drug Problems in Australia* p.65.

20 ibid. p.27.

21 Drew, L. 'Public Health and Alcohol' *New Doctor* 3, 1977 pp.29–31.

22 Diehm, P. 'Alcohol: What's the Problem?' *New Doctor* 3, 1977 pp.32–33.

23 World Health Organisation, Technical Report Series 478, cited by Sargent *Drinking and Alcoholism in Australia* p.99.

24 Commonwealth Department of Community Services and Health. Statistics on Drug Abuse in Australia, 1988. op. cit. p.14.

25 Sargent *Drinking and Alcoholism in Australia* p.2, and Senate Standing Committee on Social Welfare *Drug Problems in Australia p.31.*

26 Commonwealth Department of Community Services and Health. Statistics on Drug Abuse in Australia, 1988. op. cit. p.14.

27 Senate Standing Committee on Social Welfare *Drug Problems in Australia* p.31 (quote from evidence given by J. Rankin).

28 Sargent *Drinking and Alcoholism in Australia passim*, e.g. p.88.

29 Senate Standing Committee on Social Welfare *Drug Problems in Australia* p.30, citing Egger et al. at Senate's footnote 16, p.73.

30 Pierce, J.P. and Levy, S.J. 'Smoking and Drinking problems in Young Australians' *Medical J. of Australia* 146, Feb 2, 1987, p.121.

31 Senate Standing Committee on Social Welfare *Drug Problems in Australia* p.25.

32 *Health for All Australians*. op. cit., p.61.

33 ibid, p.60.

34 Commonwealth Department of Community Services and Health. *Statistics on Drug Abuse in Australia*, 1988. op. cit., p.33.

35 ibid, p.35.

36 For example, Whitlock, F. *Drugs: Drinking and Recreational Drug Use in Australia* Sydney: Cassell, 1980.

37 For example, I. Reyolds et al. 'Drinking and Drug Taking Patterns of 8516 Adults in Sydney' *Medical J. Australia* 20 November 1976, pp.782–5.

38 Senate Standing Committee on Social Welfare *Drug Problems in Australia* p.114.

39 See Chapter 5, 'Social Rejection of Illness and Handicap: the Idea of Deviance'.

40 Pokorny, B. 'The Quest for an 'At Risk' Marker' *Boston Globe* 11 November, 1985, pp.63–4.

41 Sargent *Drinking and Alcoholism in Australia*.

42 Inglis, B. *The Forbidden Game: A Social History of Drugs* Kent, UK:

Hodder & Stoughton, 1975, p.226.

43 Duckett, S.J. 'Structural Interests and Australian Health Policy' *Social Science & Medicine* 18, 11, 1984, pp.959–66.

Chapter 8 Changing delivery of health care: old faiths renewed

1 Sinnett, P. *Problems of Geriatric Medicine in Australia* Proceedings of a Health Seminar at University of New South Wales, Kensington: University of New South Wales, 1983; Department of Community Services. *Nursing Homes and Hostels Review* Canberra: AGPS, 1986.

2 For example NSW Department of Health *The Richmond Report* 1983; Hoult, J., Rosen, A. and Reynolds, I. 'Community Oriented Treatment Compared to Psychiatric Hospital Oriented Treatment' *Social Science & Medicine* 18, 11, 1984, pp.1005–10; Crouch, M. and Colton, C. *The Course of Community Health in New South Wales* Australian Studies in Health Administration No. 48, Kensington: University of New South Wales, 1983.

3 Bennett, C. and Wallace, R. 'At the Margin or on the Average: Some Issues and Evidence in Planning the Balance of Care for the Aged in Australia' *Community Health Studies* 7, 1, 1983, pp.35–41.

4 Graycar, A. 'Ageing in Australia: A Pointer to Political Dilemmas' *Australian Quarterly* Spring 1981, pp.280–300.

5 Kinnear, D. and Graycar, A. 'Ageing and Family Dependency' *Australian J. Social Issues* 19, 1, 1984, pp.13–25.

6 Willis, E. 'Alternative Medicine and the Struggle for Legitimacy: Consequences for the Consumer' *New Doctor* 9, 1978, pp.15–18.

7 Parker, G and Tupling, P. 'The Chiropractic Patient: Psychosocial Aspects' *Medical J. Australia* September 4, 1976, pp.373–378.

8 Committee of Inquiry into Chiropractic, Osteopathy, Homeopathy and Naturopathy *Report* (the Webb Report) Canberra: AGPS, 1977; Sheehan, M. *Report to the National Chiropractic Consultative Committee on a Review of Chiropractic Services—1985*. Uniquest Ltd, University of Queensland, 1985.

9 Parker G. and Tupling N. 'Consumer Evaluation of Natural Therapists and General Practitioners' *Medical J. Australia* 23 April 1977, pp.619–22.

10 Sweeney, J.A. *Extrapolations based on data from the Report to the National Chiropractic Consultative Committee on a Review of Chiropractic Services— 1985*, op. cit. Australian Chiropractors' Association, 1989.

11 Willis, E. Alternative Medicine and the Struggle for Legitimacy: Consequences for the Consumer' *New Doctor* pp.15–18; Sweeney, J.A. 'Submission to the Better Health Commission', prepared on behalf of the *National Chiropractic Consultative Committee*, 1985.

12 For example in Maddocks, I. 'Alternative Medicine' *Medical J. Australia* 142, 13 May 1985, pp.547–51.

13 See chapter 13 (Autonomy of the professions) for a discussion of how the medical profession dominates other health professions.

14 Davidson, L., *Health Promotion in Australia in 1978/79* Sydney: AGPS, 1979.

15 Reiser, S.J. 'Responsibility for Personal Health: A Historical Perspective' *J. Medicine & Philosophy* 10, 1985, pp.7–17.

16 Illich, I. *Medical Nemesis: The Expropriation of Health* London: Calder &

Boyars, 1975; Darby, D. 'Self-help and Self-medication in Health Care—A Supplement to Professional Domination' *Australian J. Social Issues* 12, 3, 1977, pp.208–23.

17 Borman, L. (ed.) *Explorations in Self-Help and Mutual Aid* Chicago: Center for Urban Affairs, North Western University, 1975. p.4.

18 *Health for All Australians.* op. cit. p.66.

19 Lawson, J.S. *Health and Health Care*, lecture notes for students, School of Health Administration, University of New South Wales, 1988; *Health for All Australians.* op. cit. p.66.

20 NSW Department of Health *Diet, Nutrition and Health* New South Wales State Health Department, Publication No. (ASU) 84–110, p.5.

21 Lawson J.S. op.cit.

22 Baghurst K.I., Crawford, D.A., Worsley, A. and Record S.J. 'The Victorian nutrition survey—intakes and sources of dietary fats and cholesterol in the Victorian population' *Medical J. Australia*, 149, 1, July 1988, pp.12–20.

23 Webster, I.W. and Rawson, G.K. 'Health Status of Seventh Day Adventists' *Medical J. Australia* 19 May 1979, pp.417–20.

24 Davidson *Health Promotion in Australia in 1978/79.*

25 Russell, L.B. *Is Prevention Better Than Cure?* Washington DC: The Brookings Institution, 1986, p.109.

26 ibid. p.111.

27 Policy Discussion Paper. *AIDS: A time to care, a time to act. Towards a strategy for Australians* Canberra: AGPS, 1988.

28 Russell, L.B. *Is Prevention Better than Cure?* op.cit. p.112.

29 ibid.

30 Fry, D. 'Health for All: Thinking Socially, Acting Locally' *New Doctor* 37, 1985, pp.3–4; Taylor, R. 'The Four Phases of Prevention' *New Doctor* 12, 1979, pp.41–6; Chapman, S. 'Health Eduction and Social Class' *New Doctor* 13, 1979, pp.35–8. Goldstein, G. 'Nutrition in Australia: The Role of Advertising' *New Doctor* 12, 1979, pp.9–12.

31 Wise, M. 'Health Promotion' Lecture delivered at School of Health Administration, University of New South Wales, May 1985.

32 *Health for All Australians.* op. cit.

33 Fry 'Health for All: Thinking Socially, Acting Locally' *New Doctor* pp.3–4.

Chapter 9 The diverse effects of medical technology

1 Bates, E. and Lapsley, H. *The Health Machine* Ringwood, Vic.: Penguin, 1987.

2 Helman, T. 'Lessons from Abroad', *Australian Doctor* 4 April 1985, p.28.

3 Jennett, B. *High Technology: Benefits and Burdens* London: Nuffield Provincial Hospitals Trust, 1984, p.25.

4 Taylor, R. *'Medicine Out of Control'* Melbourne: Sun Books, 1979. See also McKinlay, J.B. 'From "Promising Report" to "Standard Procedure": Seven Stages in the Career of a Medical Innovation' *Health & Society* Milbank Memorial Fund Quarterly, 59, 3, 1981, pp.374–411.

5 Jennett *High Technology: Benefits and Burdens* p.10.

6 ibid. p.27.

7 Brewer, A. 'Traditional Versus Technological Care: Future Issues for

Nursing' *Australian Health Rev.* 6, 5, 1983, p.110.
 8 Brewer, A. 'Nurses, Nursing and New Technology: Implications of a Dynamic Technological Environment' *Australian Studies in Health Service Administration* No. 47, Kensington: University of New South Wales, 1983, p.15, quoting a medical administrator.
 9 Ibid. p.41, quoting a nurse educator.
10 Taylor, R *Medicine Out of Control.*
11 Jennett *High Technology: Benefits and Burdens* p.2.
12 Wildavsky A. 'Doing Better and Feeling Worse: The Political Pathology of Health Policy' in J. Knowles (ed.) *Doing Better and Feeling Worse* New York: W.W. Norton & Co., 1977, p.107.
13 Cuff, E.C. and Payne, G.C.E. *Perspectives in Sociology* 2nd edn, London: George Allen & Unwin, 1984, pp.141–2.
14 Gorman, A. and Gormly, J. *Technology and Society: Partnerships for the Future* Sydney: Social Impacts Management Consultants, 1984, p.6.

Chapter 10 The ethics of rationing health care

1 The questions raised in this paragraph are typical of those asked by people with an interactionist prespective. They concern the meanings, values and interpretations of technologies held by individuals in health care settings. While interactionists often study individuals' subjective experiences against the backdrop of historical and societal processes, they are primarily interested in the individuality of those experiences; they are less concerned with the patterns that emerge or the consequences for the wider society.
 2 Williams, A. 'The Role of Economics in the Evaluation of Health Care Technologies' in A.J. Culyer and B. Horisberger (eds) *Economic and Medical Evaluation of Health Care Technologies* Berlin: Springer-Verlag, 1983, p.40.
 3 Learoyd, B. A. 'The Unnecessary Surgery Debate' *New Doctor* 36, 1985, p.16.
 4 For example, see Taylor, R. *Medicine Out of Control* Melbourne: Sun Books, 1979; Bates, E.L. and Lapsley, H. *The Health Machine* Ringwood, Vic.: Penguin, 1985; Jennett, B., *High Technology: Benefits and Burdens* London: Nuffield Provincial Hospitals Trust, 1984.
 5 McKinlay, J. B. 'From "Promising Report" to "Standard Procedure": Seven Stages in the Career of a Medical Innovation' *Milbank Memorial Fund Quarterly* 59, 3, 1981, pp.374–411; Whitted, G.S. 'Medical Technology Diffusion and Its Effects on the Modern Hospital' *Health Care Management Rev.* 3, 1981, pp.45–54; Neuhauser, D. 'International Workshop on the Evaluation of Medical Technology' Stockholm 18–19 September 1981.
 6 Relman, A. 'The New Medical Industrial Complex' *New England J. Medicine* 303, 17, 1980, pp.968–70.
 7 Schwartz, W.B. and Joskow, P.L. 'Medical Efficacy Versus Economic Efficiency: A Conflict in Values' *New England J. Medicine* 299, 26, 1978, p.463.
 8 Editorial comment 'The Big Business of NMR Scanners' *The Lancet* 17 November 1984, p.1169.
 9 McLean, J. 'Australia Deprived of NRI Conference Told' *Australian Doctor* 21 March 1985, pp.1, 22, quoting a general practitioner who is importing a scanner.

10 ibid. p.22.
11 Brummer, A. 'Scissors, Scalpel—and Record Profits' *Guardian Weekly*, 9 December, 1984 p.7.
12 *The Macquarie Dictionary* Sydney: Macquarie Library, 1981.
13 *Roget's Thesaurus of English Words and Phrases* Nos 636, 816, Middlesex: Penguin, 1984.
14 *The Macquarie Dictionary* Sydney: Macquarie Library, 1981.
15 *Roget's Thesaurus of English Words and Phases* No. 783, Middlesex: Penguin, 1984.
16 Hardin, G. 'The Tragedy of the Commons' *Science* 162, 1968, pp. 1243–48.
17 Hiatt, H. 'Protecting the Medical Commons: Who is Responsible?' *New England J. Medicine* 293, 5, 1975, pp.235–41.
18 Levinsky, N. G. 'The Doctor's Master' *New England J. Medicine* 311, 24, 1984, pp.1573–75.
19 Thurow, L. 'Medicine Vs Economics' *New England J. Medicine* 313, 10, 1985, pp.611–14.
20 Helman, T. 'Lessons from Abroad' *Australian Doctor* 4 April 1985, pp.28–31.
21 Brooks, P. 'Surgery Runs Amok' *Medical J. Australia* 10 November 1984, p.679.
22 Parsons, A. 'Allocating Health Care Resources: A Moral Dilemma' *Canadian Medical Association J.* 132, 15 February 1985, pp.466–9.
23 Thurow 'Medicine Vs Economics' *New England J. Medicine* p.611.
24 *AIDS: A time to care, a time to act.` Towards a strategy for Australians.* op. cit. Section 1.5.
25 Piven, F. F. and Cloward, R. A. *The New Class War* New York: Pantheon Books, 1985, p.53, in R.M. Fisher 'What is Social Justice: *Aust Social Welfare Impact,* pp.2–5.
26 Rawls, J. *A Theory of Justice* Cambridge, Mass.: Harvard University Press, 1971.
27 Ryan, A. 'Reinventing Ethics: Why John Rawls is the most argued-about philosopher of the century' *Australian Society* April, 1985, pp.15–17.
28 Engelhardt, T. Jnr 'Health Care Allocations: Responses to the Unjust, the Unfortunate and the Undesirable' in E.E. Shelp (ed.) *Justice and Health Care* vol 12: 'Philosophy and Medicine' ed. E.E. Shelp, Dordrecht Holland: D. Reidel Publishing Co.
29 Thurow, L. 'Learning to Say "No"' *New England J. Medicine* 311, 24, p.1570.
30 Mechanic, D. 'Ethics, Justice and Medical Care Systems' *Annals of the American Association of Political & Social Science* 437, 1978, p.74.

Chapter 11 Occupational health

1 Parliament of NSW *Report of Commission of Inquiry into Occupational Health and Safety* (T.G. Williams, Commissioner) Sydney: NSW Govt Printer, 1981, Clause 2.15.
2 World Health Organisation *Joint ILO–WHO Committee on Occupational Health, Second and Third Reports* Geneva: WHO, 1951, 1957.
3 Navarro, V. 'The Determinants of Health Policy, A Case Study: Regulating Safety and Health at the Workplace in Sweden' *J. Health Politics, Policy & Law* 9, 1, 1984.

4 Health Commission of NSW *Occupational Health and Safety Services—Draft Health Policies for Discussion Only* Sydney: 1980, p.1
5 Brooks, A. 'Rethinking Occupational Health and Safety Legislation' *The Journal of Industrial Relations*, September 1988, pp.347–362.
6 NSW Department of Industrial Relations and Employment. Central Planning and Research Unit. 'Employment Injuries 1982–1985 Overview and Summary. A Statistical Analysis.' Information Paper 18 in *Employment In New South Wales Series.*
7 *Worksafe Australia*, National Occupational Health and Safety Council. Annual Report, 1986–87. Canberra: AGPS.
8 NSW Department of Industrial Relations and Employment. Central Planning and Research Unit. 'Employment Injuries 1982–1985 Overview and Summary. A Statistical Analysis'. op. cit.
9 Hunter, D. 'Health in Industry' cited in L.E. Kerr 'Black Lung' *American J. Public Health Policy* 1, 1, 1980, p.52.
10 For example, Workers' Compensation Commission of New South Wales *Workers' Compensation Statistics* NSW Annual reports.
11 National Data Set for Compensation-based Statistics *Worksafe Australia*, National Occupational Health and Safety Council, AGPS 1987.
12 Christie, D. and Kelman, G.R. 'Epidemiology in Occupational Health' *Medical J. Australia* 142, 21 January 1985, pp.135–7.
13 ibid. *passim.*
14 NSW Department of Industrial Relations and Employment. Central Planning and Research Unit. 'Employment Injuries 1982–1985 Overview and Summary. A Statistical Analysis'. op. cit. p.9.
15 Ferguson, D. 'The "new" industrial epidemic' *Medical J. Australia* 17 March 1984, pp.318–9; Stone, W.E. 'Repetitive Strain Injuries' *Medical J. Australia* 10 December 1983, pp.616–8.
16 NSW Department of Industrial Relations and Employment. Central Planning and Research Unit. 'Employment Injuries 1982–1985. Overview and Summary. A Statistical Analysis' op.cit. pp.36 and 41.
17 ibid. pp.27–28.
18 Taylor, R. 'Repetition Injury in Process Workers' *Community Health Studies* 6, 1, 1982, pp.7–13.
19 Taylor, R. and Pitcher, M. 'Medical and Ergonomic Aspects of an Industrial Dispute Covering Occupational-Related Conditions in Data Process Operators' *Community Health Studies* 8, 2, 1984, pp.172–80.
20 Hocking, B. 'An Anthropological View of Stress Diseases' *Community Health Studies* 6, 1, 1982, pp.14–17.
21 Wyatt, A. 'Occupational Stress' *J. Occupational Health & Safety* 1, 1, 1985, pp.6–8.
22 Selye, H. *Stress Without Distress* London: Teach Yourself Books, 1977.
23 Spillane, R. 'Stress at Work: A Review of Australian Research' *International J. Health Services* 14, 4, 1984, pp.589–604.
24 ibid. *passim.*
25 Otto, R. 'Health Damage through Work Stress: Is Stress Management the Answer?' *New Doctor* 35, 1985, pp.13–15.
26 Spillane 'Stress at Work' *Int J. Health Services* pp.589–604.
27 ibid; also Singer et al. 'Report on Automated Work in a Clothing Factory' Unpublished Report, Brain Behaviour Research Institute, La Trobe

University, Bundoora, Vic. Also Bassett, J.R., Marshall P.M. and Spillane R. 'The Physiological Measurement of Acute Stress (public speaking) in Bank Employees'. *International J. Psychophysiology* 5, 1987, pp.265–273.
28 Otto, R. 'Health Damage through Work Stress' *New Doctor* pp.13–15.
29 Layman, L. 'Occupational Health at Wittenoom 1943–1960' Paper presented at ANZ/APHA, University of Adelaide, May 1984.
30 Jacubovicz, A. and Meekosha, H. 'Some Social Implications of the Medical Effects of the Introduction of New Technology—Repetition Strain Injury—A Case Study' Paper presented at Behavioural Medicine Conference, Sydney, 1985.
31 Otto, R 'Health Damage through Work Stress' *New Doctor* pp.13–15.
32 Stagoll, B. 'Work-injuries and Invalidism in Migrant Families: A System View' *Australian J. Family Therapy* 2, 2, 1981, p.66.
33 'But I Wouldn't Want My Wife to Work Here' Melbourne: Centre for Urban Research & Action, 1979.
34 McDonald, G. 'Defining the Objectives: Immediate and Future' Occupational Health and Safety Symposium *UNSW Occasional Papers* No. 10, Kensington: University of New South Wales, 1984, p.18.
35 ibid. pp.17–20.
36 Workcover legislation, NSW government, 1987.

Chapter 12 Public participation in health care

1 Pitkin, H.F. *The Concept of Representation* Berkeley: University of California Press, 1967.
2 Arnstein, S. 'A Ladder of Participation' *J American Institute of Planners* July 1969, pp.216–24; Langton S. (ed.) *Citizen Participation in America* Lexington, Mass.: Lexington Books, 1978.
3 *Medical Letter*, No. 697, January 19, 1989, p.1.
4 Checkoway, B. and Van Til J. 'What do we Know About Citizen Participation' in Langton *Citizen Participation in America*.
5 Schattschneider, E.E. *The Semisovereign People* Hensdale, Ill: Dryden Press, 1960, p.35.
6 Deery, S. and Plowman, D. *Australian Industrial Relations* Sydney: McGraw-Hill, 1980.
7 Hirschman, A.O. *Exit Voice and Loyalty* Cambridge, Mass.: Harvard University Press, 1970.
8 Commonwealth Department of Health. *Health Care and the Consumer*, Canberra: AGPS, 1985.
9 Bates, E. *Health Systems and Public Scrutiny: Australia, Britain and the USA* London: Croom Helm, 1983.
10 Smith, P. Interview 'A Government Watchdog' *Australian Doctor* 20 February 1985, pp.16–19.
11 ibid. p.19.
12 *Review of the Community Health Program* Canberra: AGPS, 1976.
13 Bates, E. *The Western Health Involvement Project* Sydney: NSW Govt Printer 1983.
14 ibid. p.22.
15 ibid. p.27.

16 Gibson, D.M. 'How Community Oriented is Community Health?' *Regional J. Social Issues* 8/9, 1981, pp.35–51.
17 Victorian Health Commission, Discussion Paper, Regionalisation of Health Services In Victoria, 1980.
18 See Chapter 5 (Social rejection of illness and handicap) and Chapter 13 (The changing roles of doctors) on the changing doctor–patient relationship.
19 Kirby, M. 'Accountability and Regulation of the Professional' Paper given at Rotary Club of Sydney Symposium, June 1978.
20 Deery, S. and Plowman, D. *Australian Industrial Relations* Sydney: McGraw-Hill, 1980.
21 Richardson, A. 'Thinking About Participation' *Policy & Politics* 7, 3, 1979, pp.227–44.
22 The following discussion comes from Bates *The Western Health Involvement Project* pp.36–55.
23 Palmer, G.R. 'The Regionalisation of Health Services: Objectives, Models and Recent NSW Experience' *Australian Health Rev.* 4, 1, 1981, pp.16–21.
24 The principle of devolving power is stated in paragraphs 2.4 and 2.5 of the Victorian Health Commission's discussion paper *Regionalisation of Health Services in Victoria* Melbourne, 1980.
25 Bates *Health Systems and Public Scrutiny.* Op. cit.
26 Pateman, C. *Participation and Democratic Theory* Cambridge: Cambridge University Press, 1980, *passim.*

Chapter 13 Professional accountability

1 Hughes, E. *Men and Their Work* Glencoe, Ill: Free Press, 1958.
2 Turner, B.S. 'Knowledge, Skill and Occupational Stragegy: The Professionalisation of Paramedical Groups, *Community Health Studies* 9, 1, 1985, pp.38–47.
3 Refer to Chapter 5 ('Social rejection of illness and handicap') for alternative sociological perspectives on the medical profession.
4 Willis, E. 'Alternative Medicine and the Struggle for Legitimacy: Consequences for the Consumer' *New Doctor* 15, 1978, pp.15–18.
5 In a detailed study of the division of labour in Australian health care, Willis argues against the role of knowledge and technological expertise in explaining the division of labour (the consensus view) and sees instead a continuing struggle over occupational territories based on the class structure of Australian society (the conflict view). See Willis, E. *Medical Dominance* Sydney: George Allen & Unwin, 1984.
6 Freidson, E. *Profession of Medicine* New York: Dodd Mead & Co., 1970; Willis, E. 'Work Settings in the Professions, Doctors and the Autonomy/Bureaucracy Debate' Paper presented at ANZAAS Conference, Perth, 1978.
7 Easdown, R. 'If the Socialists Don't Get You, the Capitalists Might', *Australian Dr* 8 July 1985, p.45.
8 See Chapter 8 ('Alternative medicine: holism', and 'The self-help movement.'
9 Maxmen, J.S. 'Goodbye, Dr Welby' *Social Policy 3, 4 & 5* 1972, pp.97–106, quoted in J.B. McKinlay and J. Archer, 'Towards the Proletarianisation of Physicians' *International J. Health Services* 15, 2, 1985, pp.161–95.
10 ibid. p.178.

11 Kirby, S. *Administration of Nursing Services* School of Health Administration, Kensington: University of New South Wales, 1985, Unit 4, p.16.
12 Cuthbert, M. *Structure and Controls in Nursing Administration* School of Health Administration, Kensington: University of New South Wales, 1985, Units 4 and 5.
13 Fagin, C.M. 'The Shortage of Nurses in the United States' *J. Public Health Policy* 1, 1, 1980, pp.293–311.
14 Kirby, S. *Administration of Nursing Services* Units 1 and 8.
15 Gardner, H and McCoppin, B. 'The Politicisation of Australian Nurses 1984–1986'. *Politics* 22, 1, pp.19–34, 1987; White, D. 'The Challenges of Industrial Relations'. *Australian Health Review* 8, 4, pp.221–223, 1985; Haines, J. 38 Hour week Campaign. The Lamp, pp.6–9, 1984.
16 Willis, E 'Alternative Medicine and the Struggle for Legitimacy: Consequences for the Consumer' *New Doctor* p.17.
17 Ehrenreich, B. and English, D. *Witches, Midwives and Nurses* London: Compendium, 1974, pp.34–8.
18 Fett, I. 'The Monash University Survey of Australian Women Medical Graduates' *Medical J. Australia* 24 April 1971, pp.920–2; Fett, I. 'Australian Medical Graduates in 1972' *Medical J. Australia* 4 May 1974, pp.689–97; Wyndham, D. 'Women in Health Occupations: Prospects for Doctors and Other Health Workers' *Healthright* 2, 4, 1983, pp.22–7.
19 Australian Women in Medicine *Sensible Women: Not all Doctors Want to be Men* Marrickville: Southwood Press, 1978.
20 Palmer, G. 'Hospital output and the use of diagnosis-related groups for purposes of economic and financial analysis' in Butler, R.J. and Doessel, D.P. (eds.) *Economics and Health 1985* Australian Studies in Health Service Administration, No. 56, University of NSW, 1986.
21 Australian Council of Healthcare Standards. *Review 1988, Preview 1989.* ACHS, Sydney.
22 Australian Council of Healthcare Standards *Quality Assurance, 1987; and Quality Assurance Program Implementation* ACHS Education and Resource Unit, Sydney, 1989.
23 *Health for All Australians.* op. cit. 1988; Leeder, S. *Sydney Morning Herald* 23 July, 1987;
24 The Royal Commission of Inquiry into Deep Sleep therapy carried out at Chelmsford Hospital, as reported almost daily in the *Sydney Morning Herald*, 1988 and 1989.
25 Cartwright, S.R. The Committee of inquiry into allegations converning the treatment of cervical cancer at National Women's Hospital and into other related matter. The report of the cervical cancer inquiry. Auckland, Government Printing Office, 1988.

Chapter 14 Conclusion

1 Cuff, E.C. and Payne, G.C.F. *Perspectives in Sociology* London: George Allen & Unwin, 1984; Maykovich, M. *Medical Sociology* Sherman Oaks, Ca.: Alfred Publishing Co., 1980.
2 Russell, C. and Schofield, T. *Where it Hurts* Sydney: George Allen & Unwin, 1985, pp.203–207.

Index

Studies in Society

Titles include: